Food and Agriculture in a Market Economy

FOOD AND AGRICULTURE
IN A
MARKET ECONOMY

An introduction to theory, practice and policy

by

MICHAEL TRACY

APS
Agricultural Policy Studies

First published 1993 by
APS—AGRICULTURAL POLICY STUDIES
20 rue Emile François
1474 La Hutte (Genappe)
Belgium

Printed and bound in Prague by
V. KRIGL, POLYGRAFICKÁ A NAKLADATELSKÁ ČINNOST
Saratovská 37, 100 00 Praha 10
Czech Republic

Distributed by:

CBS—COMBINED BOOK SERVICES LTD.

406 Vale Road, Tonbridge, Kent TN9 1XR, England

tel. (0)732 357755   fax (0)732 770219

ISBN 2–9600047–0–1

CONTENTS

This book is dedicated to all those men and women who despite decades of oppression under totalitarian regimes have had the courage to preserve their intellectual integrity.

INTRODUCTION

Public opinion in the West is very conscious of major issues of agricultural policy: the surpluses, the costs of farm subsidies, the trade conflicts. The main *benefit* of the food and agriculture system is often taken for granted: the availability, at prices most people can afford, of a wide range of foodstuffs.

Yet this success of the market economies in terms of food supply contrasts with the mediocre results of socialised agriculture. The achievement within the European Community (EC) of a common market in agricultural products compares very favourably with the planned management of trade under the now defunct Council for Mutual Economic Assistance (CMEA).

The new democracies of Central and Eastern Europe, in the general process of dismantling their planned economies, are moving their food and agriculture sectors towards a market system, by removing price controls and consumer subsidies, privatising State farms and collectives, and reforming the food processing and distribution channels.

However, the nature of the food and agriculture system in the market economies is not always well understood. The market does operate: farmers are, as a rule, free to produce what they want, in the ways they decide, and to sell for the best price they can get. The entrepreneurship of several million individual farmers in Western Europe and North America, together with the dynamism of "agribusiness"—the industries that supply inputs to agriculture as well as those which process and distribute the food—have made possible the ample supplies from which consumers benefit.

What is not always realised is the extent of public *intervention* in agriculture: to support prices, to control production in cases of overproduction, or to promote structural change. Very large sums of money have been pumped into the system in this way: and this too has been responsible for the growth in output, sometimes excessive growth. There is intervention too as regards agribusiness, which—like any other form of business—is subject to various State controls aiming to curb restrictive practices and monopolistic tendencies.

The aim of this book is to explain how the food and agriculture system works in the developed market economies. Part A combines an explanation of basic economic theory with description of the agri-food sector in Western Europe, and to some extent in North America. There is more attention to agribusiness than is normally found in textbooks on agricultural economics—an essential feature, in view of the importance of all the activities both "upstream" from the farm sector (the agricultural input industries) and "downstream" (marketing, processing, distribution).

Part B gives an account of agricultural and food policies, with emphasis on the European Community: after explaining the historical development, it describes and discusses current measures, including trade issues. Chapter 14 on "decision-making" seeks to explain the underlying political forces, at the EC level and in various countries.

In Part C, the final chapter assesses some implications for the countries undergoing transition from socialised agriculture.

The book does not necessarily have to be read in the order in which it is written. Those who are mainly interested in theory, for example, could begin with Chapter 4 on demand, or even with Chapter 5 on price determination, and go on to Chapter 2 on supply. In Part B, the various aspects of policy—market organisation, structural and regional measures, food policy, trade issues—can to some extent be studied separately. Readers particularly interested in the politics of the subject may even choose to start with Chapter 14.

The book takes particular account of the needs of readers in the Central and Eastern European countries (CEECs for short). In general, no prior knowledge is assumed. The introduction to economic theory as it is understood in the West may be helpful, since textbooks on the subject are only beginning to circulate in the CEECs: vital differences between Western and Marxist economics are pointed out (see also section below). In the description of the Western agricultural and food system, there are explanations of features which may be of special interest to countries seeking to transform their own systems. Particular attention has been given to trade relations between the EC and the CEECs.

Western readers will find that basic economic theory, which is set out in many more specialised textbooks, is here illustrated by material relating not to any particular country but to Western Europe, as a rule to the countries of the EC. Chapter 3 on agribusiness contains material which has not been put together before. The explanations in Part B of the various aspects of EC policy take into account the various common market organisations following the 1992 "MacSharry" reforms, and the emerging agreement on agriculture in the GATT "Uruguay Round". The relatively brief discussion of policies in the US, Canada and other developed market economies aims to provide parallels and contrasts.

The book has been sub-titled an "Introduction": on each topic, much more could be said. The Appendices aim to guide those who want to know more, by indicating relevant sources, particularly on-going sources which will help further studies. The Appendices also include technical material which need concern only specialised readers.

The subject-matter of agricultural economics

Agricultural economics is not distinct from economics in general. In fact, a study of the main elements of agricultural economics can serve as an introduction to general economic theory. The examples given in general economics textbooks to illustrate the working of the market often relate to foodstuffs and agricultural production. Through farm accounts surveys, more is known about costs and returns in agriculture than in most other economic sectors. Certain important aspects of general economics (or "macro-economics") are outside the field of agricultural economics. These include the "business cycle", the causes of unemployment and inflation, fiscal and monetary policy. However, the *consequences* of these can be vital for agriculture: in Chapter 7 there is brief discussion of the main issues.

The agri-food sector has some special characteristics, which may be briefly mentioned here (they will be more fully discussed in Part A):

* **The production structure.** In Western Europe and in North America, "family farms" predominate. Some of these can be quite large, but no one of them can on its own alter the market conditions: the farm sector is generally cited as the main example of "perfect competition".
* **The influence of nature.** Changes in the weather, outbreaks of disease, infestation by pests, make agricultural production to some extent uncontrollable and unpredictable: fluctuations in output can be substantial.
* **The "inelastic" character of demand for food.** People cannot do without food: for several foodstuffs, the quantity demanded is not much influenced by price. Hence, supply shortages may provoke large price increases; if there are surpluses, large price cuts may be needed to clear the market.
* **The falling *share* of food in consumer expenditure, as incomes rise.** This observation, true on average for individuals or households, is also applicable at the national level: agriculture accounts for a declining share of national income. It follows that, unless the share of the farm work force in total employment also declines (but see next point), individual returns from farming will tend to fall.
* **The relative immobility of farm labour.** For the farm family—and sometimes for hired workers as well—the farm is a home as well as a place of work: farm labour is not very mobile.

The combination of these factors gives rise to the basic problems of the farm sector in a market economy. These are: short-term fluctuations in product prices; and over time, a tendency for product prices to decline relatively to other prices and costs, and for farm incomes to fall relatively to other incomes. Such problems have motivated government action on behalf of the farm population: protection against imports, promotion of exports, intervention to stabilise markets, subsidies of various kinds, "structural" programmes to accelerate the move from farming to other sectors, and so on. Moreover, as technological progress has continued to promote expansion of output despite the difficulties of farmers, and surpluses have grown, increasingly complex measures have been devised to control supply, but these have proved costly to governments and not very successful.

Marxism and economic science

The economic failure of the socialised economies can be attributed in large part to the doctrinal application of Marxist economics. The denial of legitimate returns to private capital, the suppression of private enterprise and its replacement by centralised planning have led to the misuse of resources and diminished the incentives for productivity and innovation.

In the West, economic science has evolved enormously since the days of Karl Marx. In the history of economic thought, Marx is regarded as the last of the "classical" economists, following Adam Smith, Ricardo, Malthus and others: the pioneers who sought to explain the factors responsible for "the wealth of nations", for the allocation of that wealth between the main classes of the population, for the formation of prices and rents to land, and so on. Subsequently, well after the first volume of *Das Kapital* had been published in 1867, and after Marx's death in 1881, came the "neo-classical" revolution, led by Stanley Jevons in England, Carl Menger in Austria, Léon Walras in France, and others. The *Principles of Economics* of the Cambridge economist, Alfred Marshall, first published in 1890, established the "marginalist" explanation of the determination of prices and returns to the various factors of production, providing a far more satisfactory explanation than Marx's "labour theory of value". (See Appendix, item 3, on the history of economic thought.)

Following the economic depression of the 1930s, another Cambridge economist, John Maynard Keynes, tackled the problems of business cycles and unemployment, and laid the theoretical basis for government action to mitigate such crises. In recent decades, there has been much argument over the respective roles of monetary policy, fiscal policy and other measures in guiding the economy. Now, controversy aroused by the "supply-siders" and "monetarists" seems to have abated, though this may be due to a common recognition that the problem of ensuring stable economic growth without either inflationary overheating or excessive unemployment has not been satisfactorily solved. (See the discussion in Chapter 7.)

In fact, there is much common ground among Western economists. Most would agree that economics should strive to be *scientific*. It is recognised that, unlike the physical sciences, economics is limited in the extent to which it can conduct experiments to verify its hypotheses. Nevertheless, the tools of statistical analysis can be used to test the validity of economic "laws". Above all, as in any science, the hypotheses must be abandoned if they are contradicted by facts, and better ones must be honestly sought: *dogma* is incompatible with the scientific approach. Some writers thus refer to the "positive" as opposed to the "normative" approach: terms derived from philosophy, distinguishing statements describing what happens from those prescribing what one might *like* to happen—the latter necessarily involving "value judgements". (See Appendix, item 5.)

It can be argued that genuine objectivity is impossible: we are all influenced by the context in which we live. That is a risk of which we must be aware. Is Western economic science in fact serving the cause, and rationalising the existence, of the capitalist system—in particular, by justifying the attribution to capital and land, as well as to labour, of a share in profits? To that question there are three main answers.

The first must be that the value judgements involved in Marxism are far more evident than those in "neo-classical" economics and its modern variants. Marx's justified concern with the conditions of his time led to the use of subjective terms—"capitalist accumulation", "surplus value", "exploitation", "pauperisation (*Verelendung*) of the workers", and so on—which have appealed to many people with a genuine social conscience, but have not facilitated objective analysis. Indeed, with Marx, economics and political theory are intertwined: his "labour theory of value" leads directly to the theme of capitalist exploitation.

A second answer is empirical: while economies based on Western economics have shown that they can "deliver the goods", Marxist-based economies have failed.

The more fundamental answer is that Western economic science often tries to evaluate the consequences of alternative policy measures, but should not—properly used—become the arbiter of policy. Considerations other than economic enter into most political choices: the final decision must be reached through the appropriate policy-making process. Most of the exponents of "neo-classical" economics are careful to avoid political statements (standard textbooks can seem quite arid as a result).

However, a major contribution of modern economics, deriving from the "Welfare Economics" pioneered in the 1920s by yet another Cambridge economist, Arthur Pigou, is the analysis of "externalities": the recognition that the "social" costs of a transaction may diverge from the "private" costs. Some externalities are beneficial; others—notably environmental damage—are harmful. This approach provides a basis for governmental intervention, through regulation or through subsidies or taxes, aiming to bring social and private costs into line (the "polluter pays principle" is a major example): it has considerable relevance to major issues of agricultural policy, as will be seen at various points in this book.

It is also recognised that the real economy does not conform to all the theoretical conditions of "perfect competition". Business firms may become powerful enough to control their markets; successive mergers may lead to monopoly. Policy measures are required to prevent or limit such developments. This issue is very relevant to agribusiness, and is discussed under "competition policy" in Chapter 11.

Further, it is understood that economic efficiency does not necessarily produce *equity*, and that measures of income redistribution may be justified. This is a key point in agricultural policy.

So economic science by no means provides unqualified support for the capitalist system, or even for the market economy. On the contrary, it offers a rationale for a degree of public intervention. How far that justifies the support granted under agricultural policy is one of the topics of this book.

Acknowledgements

The author owes a very great debt to Professor Chris Ritson at the University of Newcastle and to Professor Allan Buckwell at London University's Wye College for comments on the theoretical sections in Part A. Allan Buckwell in particular spent many hours discussing these matters with the author: his own involvement with agricultural policy reform in Bulgaria also led him to make many constructive suggestions as to how the work could be made more relevant to the needs of the CEECs. Professor Wayne Moyer, of Grinnell College, Iowa, has made helpful comments on the US policy process. The author is of course responsible for any errors which remain.

As regards Part B, many officials in the EC Commission and Council Secretariat have commented helpfully on the various chapters or sections in their respective fields of competence. These are too numerous to cite individually, but there must be special mention of the officials in DG VI (Agriculture) responsible for relations with the CEECs, who have helped the author to understand the complexities of the recent "Europe Agreements".

No author could produce a book of this kind, in a short space of time, without the backing of a good library. The staff of the Commission's DG VI library—in particular Mary Brown, Maria Korsch and Ann Maher, have been unfailingly helpful, often bringing to the author's attention works which he might otherwise have missed.

The author is grateful to his wife, Rosalind, for her continued support.

This work has been finalised in early January 1993, and takes account of major events up to the end of 1992. These include:
* The 1992 reform of the CAP.
* The bilateral US–EC trade agreement of November 1992, which enabled the multilateral "Uruguay Round" negotiations to be re-opened.
* The trade agreements between the EC and the CSFR, Hungary and Poland which came into force during 1992.
* The EC "Summit" in Edinburgh in December 1992, which found a solution to assist Danish ratification of the Maastricht Treaty and reached agreements on the future EC budget (including finance for the CAP), on the outlines of an economic growth package and other matters; and which permitted negotiations to begin with EFTA countries on their accession to the EC.

APPENDIX

1. **Textbooks on general economics.** Widely-used textbooks include:
* P. Samuelson and W. Nordhaus, *Economics*. The latest edition at the time of writing is the 13th (McGraw-Hill, New York etc.: 1989).
* R. Lipsey, P. Steiner and D. Purvis, *Economics*: latest current edition is 1987 (Harper & Row, New York etc.).

Both these are designed for an American audience and illustrations are taken from US experience. The following cover similar ground, but without the US references:
* R. Lipsey, *An Introduction to Positive Economics*. Latest edition is the 7th (Weidenfeld and Nicolson, London: 1989).
* D. Begg, S. Fisher and R. Dornbusch, *Economics*, 3rd edn. (McGraw Hill, London etc.: 1991).

2. Textbooks on agricultural economics. Earl Heady's *Economics of Agricultural Production and Resource Use* (Prentice-Hall, New Jersey: 1952), though itself somewhat unwieldy, has been a basis for many subsequent works. The following in particular have been used in preparing the present work:
* C. Ritson, *Agricultural Economics: Principles and Policy* (Granada, London: 1977). Very thorough. The chapters on policy are somewhat out-of-date.
* H. Halcrow, *Economics of Agriculture* (McGraw-Hill, New York etc.: 1980). Very clear explanations.
* G. Cramer and C. Jensen, *Agricultural Economics and Agribusiness* (Wiley, New York, etc.: 2nd edn., 1982). Designed for American students.
* B. Hill, *An Introduction to Economics for Students of Agriculture* (Pergamon, Oxford etc.: 1990). Designed for British students.
* D. Colman and T. Young, *Principles of Agricultural Economics* (Cambridge University Press: 1989). Concentrates on issues for less-developed countries, but contains a clear exposition of basic principles.

In German, a convenient textbook is E. Wöhlken, *Einführung in die landwirtschaftliche Marktlehre* (Ulmer, Stuttgart: 3rd edn., 1990).

In French, there was no good textbook on agricultural economics until J.-M. Boussard's *Economie de l'Agriculture* (Economica, Paris: 1987); this, however, is rather difficult.

A review of current theoretical and policy issues—definitely for the professional economist and not the general reader—is contained in K. Burger *et al.*, *Agricultural Economics and Policy: International Challenges for the Nineties* (Elsevier, Amsterdam etc.: 1991).

3. History of economic thought. A useful short account is to be found in the *Encyclopaedia Britannica* under "Social Sciences—Economics". J. Schumpeter's classic *Capitalism, Socialism and Democracy*, which was first published in 1943 by Allen & Unwin (London) and has gone through many editions, is still a helpful introduction to the subject.

4. "Positive" and "normative" approaches. These philosophical terms are confusing, since in this case "positive" does *not* mean the opposite of negative. Illustrations of the "normative" approach can be found weekly in the *Economist*, many of its articles being specifically aimed at prescribing policy (the word "should", or its equivalent, appears frequently in their conclusions).

5. Marxist thought in France. The impact of Marxist economists in Western countries too has generally been marginal, except in France. Particularly during the 1970s, many French agricultural economists—probably the majority—had Marxist leanings. This led them to concentrate on structural and social problems in the rural sector, where they did useful work: on the other hand, they made little contribution to study of market problems, and seemed to have a conceptual difficulty in dealing with surplus problems.

The present author has discussed these matters in more detail in "Les économistes et la politique agricole", pp. 21–24 in "L'économie rurale depuis 1945: les faits et les idées", *Economie Rurale* no. 200, nov.–déc. 1990. See also item 2 in the Appendix to Chapter 1.

SYMBOLS AND CONVENTIONS

Crop years are shown with a slash, thus: 1991/92.

>....< indicates a three-year average: e.g. >1990< is an average of 1989, 1990 and 1991.

"Tonnes" are metric tonnes.

One billion equals 1,000 million.

In tables:
- .. indicates not available.
- * indicates an estimate.
- - indicates nil or negligible.
- 0 indicates less than half the relevant unit.

As data in most tables have been rounded, minor discrepancies may appear between totals and their parts.

The expression "European Community" (EC) will be used as a general rule. Strictly speaking, we are here concerned with the "European *Economic* Community", which together with the "European Coal and Steel Community" and the "European Atomic Energy Community" make up the "European Communities". The plural form is however inconvenient in non-legal usage.

References to the EC are to the post-1986 twelve-nation Community, unless otherwise specified. The countries in question (with the abbreviations used in tables and diagrams) are:

—1958–1972: "EC 6", i.e. Belgium (B), France (F), Germany (D), Italy (IT), Luxembourg (L), Netherlands (NL).

—1973–1980: "EC 9", i.e. the above plus Denmark (DK), Ireland (IR) and the United Kingdom (UK).

—1980–1985: "EC 10", i.e. the above plus Greece (GR).

—from 1986: "EC 12", i.e. the above plus Portugal (P) and Spain (SP).

References to "Germany"—unless otherwise stated—are to the Federal Republic in its pre-1990 boundaries.

In tables, countries have usually been arranged in an approximate geographical order, starting from the north-west (Ireland) and ending in the south-east (Greece).

Following the accession of new Member States, Eurostat has generally tried to extend backwards the main statistical series. Thus, most series for "EC 12", particularly those related to national accounts, are available at least from 1980.

The "ECU" is the "basket" of currencies used by the EC for its budget and increasingly for various other purposes. It is the basis for determining agricultural prices: in this case, however, a "co-efficient" may be applied—see Chapter 9.

In 1992, the ECU was worth approximately 2.1 DM. Its relationship to non-EC currencies is subject to fluctuations. Its dollar value in recent years was as follows:

1985: $0.76;	1989: $1.10;
1986: $0.98;	1990: $1.27;
1987: $1.15;	1991: $1.15;
1988: $1.18;	1992: $1.19–1.45.

It is convenient to refer to the countries of Central and Eastern Europe as the "CEECs", although this of course does not correspond to any formal entity.

See also list of abbreviations and acronyms at the end of the book.

PART A

THEORY AND PRACTICE

CHAPTER 1

FARM STRUCTURES AND RESOURCES

This chapter aims to give a general view of farm sizes and types in Western Europe, particularly in the European Community, with some reference to the United States. It also discusses the roles of the various factors of production used in farming, and describes institutional provisions relating to land tenure. finance for farming and other matters.

(a) Farm structures

Farms in Western Europe and North America, though they vary considerably in size, are still mostly "family farms". The land they work is often their own: if this is not the case, it is usually rented from private landlords (forest land, but not farmland, is often in public ownership). Capital is obtained from the financial markets, sometimes through special agricultural credit institutions. Co-operation in production is rare, small-scale and usually not very successful (as opposed to co-operation in marketing which, as will be seen, plays an important role in several countries). Although some of the larger farms, particularly in the UK and the US, may take the legal form of companies (mainly for fiscal reasons), only a few farms are *owned* by companies: these tend to be specialised, intensive units, mainly producing eggs, poultrymeat and pigmeat: they are often "vertically integrated" with subsequent processing and marketing. State farms, or other publicly-owned enterprises, are virtually non-existent apart from research units.

But what constitutes a "family farm"? Opinions and definitions vary: sometimes it is held to mean a farm that employs only family labour. The more general and useful definition is that of a unit *managed* by the farm family, even though hired labour may also be employed. In most Western European countries, *small* family farms are numerous, though they account for a relatively small part of total output. On the other hand, some family farms are big in terms of area, employment and/or size of business.

In the twelve-nation European Community (EC) in 1987, out of a total of nearly 7 million farms (holdings under 1 ha. are not counted), about half had less than 5 ha. But most of these very small farms are in Southern European countries. In the United Kingdom, which has the largest farms in terms of area, only 13% were under 5 ha., while 59% were over 20 ha.

Area is not a good basis for comparing farm size, in view of the varying quality of land. In the EC, size of business on farms is measured in terms of "European size units" (ESU), and the results for seven key countries are shown in Table 1.1. On this basis, the Netherlands has the most substantial farms, followed by the UK and Denmark. In Germany and France, farms are fairly evenly distributed across all the size groups. At the other extreme, Italy and Spain have high percentages of small farms.

Table 1.1—Distribution of farms by ESU classes, 1987 (percentages)

ESU classes:	<2	2–4	4–8	8–16	16–40	>40	Total
EC 12	40	17	15	11	11	5	100
of which:							
UK	23	8	10	11	20	27	100
Denmark	1	6	15	19	31	29	100
Netherlands	0	4	11	13	27	44	100
Germany	19	12	15	18	26	10	100
France	15	9	13	18	30	15	100
Italy	46	20	15	9	7	3	100
Spain	51	19	15	9	5	1	100

Note: In the 1987 survey, a farm was counted as having an economic size of 1 ESU if its total standard gross margin (value of production minus certain variable costs) was 1,200 ECU.
Source: Eurostat, *Farm Structures, 1987 Survey* (pp. 246–7).

Although the larger farms are in the minority, their economic importance is relatively significant. Thus in the twelve Member States of the EC, farms above 20 ha. are only one-fifth of the total number but they account for three-quarters of the farmland. In terms of business size, only 17% of farms are above 16 ESU but these account for 73% of total ESU; the relative weight of the bigger farms is particularly marked in North-Western Europe. The proportionate contribution of the larger farms to total sales of farm produce is probably even greater, since the smaller farms have to keep a relatively large part of their output for domestic use and livestock feed.

Figure 1.1 shows, for the same seven countries, the distribution of labour on farms. In the UK, hired labour accounts for a third of the total labour force, and it is quite important also in Denmark, the Netherlands and France (mostly in northern France): still, the farm family accounts for the greater part of the labour force. In Spain and especially in Italy, hired labour is not significant.

These figures reflect the importance in North-Western Europe of relatively big, market-oriented farm enterprises. However, these remain in most cases

Figure 1.1—Distribution of labour on farms (percentages)

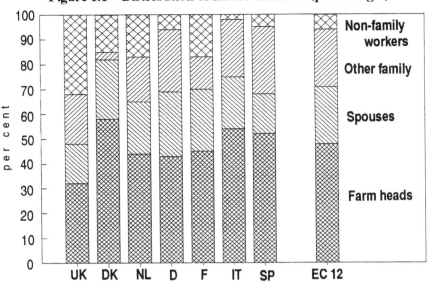

Source: Commission, *The Agricultural Situation in the Community—1991 Report* (Table 3.5.1.5).

"family farms": they employ large amounts of capital and current inputs, and some hired labour, and account for most sales of farm produce. In most of Southern Europe—and in less-favoured regions in North- Western Europe too—there remain numerous small holdings, many of which cannot provide enough employment and income for the farm family (and therefore sometimes worked on a part-time basis).

In Western Europe, farm structures result from a long process dating back to feudal times in the 8th century onwards: the feudal pattern was characterised by open fields, owned by hereditary landlords and farmed by the peasantry. In England, in the 15th and 16th centuries, landlords "enclosed" the open fields with fences and hedges, creating relatively large unified farms which they farmed themselves or let out to a reduced number of tenants; further enclosures occurred in the 18th and 19th centuries. In Scandinavian countries, enclosures creating medium-sized farms occurred mostly in the 19th century. In France under the Revolution of 1789, and subsequently in the vast areas conquered by Napoleon, feudal privileges were abolished and, in many cases, peasants became owners of the land they farmed: their possessions, however, remained small and fragmented. (See Appendix, items 1 and 2.)

In Italy, large estates (*latifundia*) remained until land reforms were carried out after the Second World War, which caused new problems by creating many small holdings on poor land. In Greece too, successive land reforms led to many small farms (average farm size under 4 ha.). In Spain and in Portugal, large estates persist in southern parts, though elsewhere farms are mostly small; attempts by

Table 1.2—United States: farm sizes by economic class, 1990

Gross value of sales dollars	% of all farms	% of all farmland	average size of farms	
			acres	ha.
1,000–2,499	22	3	62	25
2,500–4,999	14	3	104	42
5,000–9,999	12	4	162	66
10,000–19,999	11	6	262	106
20,000–39,999	12	11	411	166
40,000–99,999	14	23	743	301
100,000–249,999	10	26	1198	485
250,000 and over	5	24	2256	913
All farms	100	100	461	187

Source: US Department of Agriculture, *Agricultural Statistics 1990* (Table 5.3.4).

Portuguese workers to form collectives on estate land were mostly frustrated. (Appendix, item 3).

In North America, where farm structures have been formed by relatively recent colonisation, farms are much larger on average in terms of area, and on the whole larger in terms of size of business. Table 1.2 shows data for the US, where the average farm size is 187 ha. Note that the two largest economic classes, with value of sales exceeding $100,000, account for 15% of all farms but for 50% of farmland, and certainly for an even higher share of all sales of farm produce.

Even in North America, most farms are family farms. Out of a total farm work-force averaging some 2.8 million in 1989 (there are seasonal variations), about 1.9 were "unpaid"— i.e. farm operators and other unpaid workers, presumably family members. Some farms have a "corporate" legal form, for reasons related to taxation and inheritance, without this fundamentally changing their manner of operation.

Inheritance systems have a big influence on farm structures over time. In the United Kingdom and in Scandinavia, and in North America, legislation permits owner-occupied farms to be handed down intact to a single heir: customarily, other arrangements are made for other heirs. On the continent of Europe, legal provisions vary, but in countries where "Napoleonic" law predominates, the principle is that of equal division between the heirs. This has caused farms to be divided at each generation, and is largely responsible for the predominance of small—and often fragmented—holdings. Such an outcome clearly runs counter to the need to maintain farms of a viable size: the modern tendency therefore is to seek ways around this difficulty, sometimes assisted by legislative changes, more often through arrangements within the family. The problem is not fully solved. (Appendix, item 4).

(b) Factors of production

While the Marxist approach recognises only one basic factor of production, i.e. labour, neo-classical economic analysis customarily distinguishes between three factors: land, labour and capital. "Management" is commonly held to be a fourth factor. These various factors will be considered more closely.

i) Land

Agricultural production is characterised by its dependence on land (except for some highly-intensive enterprises, particularly eggs and poultry production, which still depend on purchased feed).

For the agricultural sector as a whole, the *quantity* of land is more or less fixed in Western Europe. There is little or no scope for expanding the area—only the Netherlands, by reclamation from the sea, has obtained more land in recent times. On the other hand, there is a gradual loss for the building of houses, roads, etc. Even in North America, there is no longer much land that could be taken into cultivation: some land has been lost through erosion, particularly in the "Dust Bowl" phenomenon of the 1930s.

Also for individual farms, at least in the short term, the quantity of land is fixed. As some farmers give up or retire, others can buy or rent their land, but such opportunities do not often arise when wanted: on the whole, dynamic farmers in Western European conditions feel themselves constrained by shortage of land.

The *quality* of land can of course be improved over time by good management—or worsened by neglect. Decisions on such matters as drainage (or irrigation), on liming and to some extent on fertilising, on crop rotation, are essentially the same as the investment decisions that will be considered below in relation to capital.

Land values and rents

The *value* of agricultural land is influenced by the quality of the soil, and by the climate of the region in question, which in turn determine its productivity. Distance from centres of consumption has traditionally been regarded as a major factor determining land value (see Appendix, item 5, on Von Thünen's theory) and still plays a role, although modern methods of transport—including refrigerated vehicles—have diminished its importance while other cost elements have become more significant.

Marginal farmland is that land which, under given price and cost relationships, it only just pays the farmer to cultivate. This concept, though apparently clear-cut, is in fact somewhat imprecise when alternative farming uses are considered: uplands, for example, may be unable to produce any crop profitably, but may have some value for rough grazing. It plays a role, however, in the theory of "*economic rent*"· this refers to any payment to a factor of production which exceeds that which is necessary to keep it in its present use. If, at a certain level of prices and costs, some farmland is "marginal", it follows that better-located and/or higher-quality land must be earning more than is needed to keep it in use. The expression "economic rent" to describe such excess (derived from a preoccupation by Ricardo with land prices) is unfortunate, as it creates confusion with the monetary rent paid by a tenant to a landlord (which may reflect, but is not identical with, this concept of *economic* rent). Moreover, the concept is applicable to factors of production other than land. It can be contrasted with *transfer earnings*, i.e. what the factor in question would receive in the most profitable alternative use, any excess over this amount being economic rent.

The land market is basically free, in the sense that governments place no restriction on the right of citizens to buy or sell or influence price (except in some cases—particularly France—where a public body may have right of pre-emption in order to improve farm structures). However, as the number of transactions is limited, prices at individual sales can vary widely depending on particular circumstances. Farmland prices in the EC reflect big differences in quality and in location, but also in the pressure of demand for non-agricultural purposes. Thus prices are highest in the densely-populated regions of north-western Europe: for example, around 15,000 ECU per hectare for arable land in Germany and the Netherlands, while the average for arable land in France is only some 3,200 ECU.

Rents also vary widely (sometimes being kept down by rent controls—cf. next section): they average over 200 ECU/ha. for arable land in Germany and the Netherlands, but only about 90 ECU/ha. in Wales and Scotland. Such rents correspond generally to a range of 1–3% of land values: this is a low current return on capital, but landowners generally hope for an increase in land values over time.

Over time, land prices, and to some extent rents, reflect the general prosperity of the farming sector. The difficulties the sector has been experiencing since the early 1980s have generally been reflected in a fall in prices: thus in Belgium, the price of arable land reached a peak in 1979, but by 1991 had dropped by 10% below this level (i.e. in current prices: this represents a substantial fall in "real" terms when the general price rise is taken into account).

Land tenure

The pattern of land tenure varies between countries, and has altered significantly over time. In the EC as a whole in 1987, owner-occupancy accounted for two-thirds of the farmland. Tenancy is important in Belgium (68% of the land) and in France (53%). Many farms have some rented land in addition to the land they own, and such "mixed" tenure appears to be increasing since renting extra land is often a way to expand the total farm area. Share-cropping, whereby the user of the land provides the owner with some part of the produce, survives only in some Southern European countries.

Tenancy is often held to have, in principle, several advantages over owner-occupancy. The tenant does not have to find money to purchase the land and buildings: he can concentrate his available funds on equipment and current inputs. Tenancy makes entry into farming easier for young people who are well qualified but have limited capital (in the case of owner-occupied farms, most transfers take place through succession within the family). It is sometimes considered that the need to pay a regular rent ensures more efficient farming, though this point can be disputed.

On the other hand, ownership of the land provides security; access to credit is easier when the land can be offered as "collateral". Most farmers in fact prefer to own at least their farm buildings and the greater part of their land, in spite of the financial burden which this may entail.

Attitudes to land tenure vary considerably, mainly as a result of historical and social factors. Thus there is a striking contrast between Ireland, where tenancy became deeply unpopular following centuries of oppression by absentee English landlords and has now virtually disappeared; and England itself, where the hereditary aristocracy generally took a responsible attitude to the management of their estates. At the beginning of the 20th century, tenancy still accounted for about 90% of the land in England, but heavy "death duties" led to the break-up of most of the big English estates, with the land being sold, often to the "sitting tenants", while institutions such as insurance companies and pension funds have become a new type of landowner. Legislation aimed at protecting tenants has had the result of discouraging the letting of land, so that by 1985 only some 39% of the land was still rented.

Although custom plays a part in determining tenancy arrangements, all Western European countries have introduced legislation which, to varying degrees, regulates the relations between tenants and landowners. In some cases, regulation is minimal: thus in Germany, conditions as to the length of lease and level of rent are freely negotiated between the partners. In other cases, these and other provisions are subject to legal constraints. It is difficult to achieve the right balance between the interests of owners and tenants. Excessive protection of tenants can have the result that owners become unwilling to let out their land, and either farm it themselves or look for other arrangements—as has happened in the British case.

The case of Belgium may be cited as a country where tenancy remains important. Taking account of amendments to the law made in 1988 (see Appendix, item 6), the main provisions are as follows:
* Leases run for at least nine years; if not terminated by either party after each nine-year period, a further term of nine years begins.
* During each nine-year period, the landowner can take back the land only if it is classified as building-land (with a minimum of three months notice, plus sufficient time for crops to be harvested). At the end of each period, he can take it back only for his own use (or that of his spouse or heirs), or for certain other purposes defined in the law (minimum notice two years).
* Leases can also be concluded for 27 years, or until the tenant reaches age 65 with a minimum of 27 years ("bail de carrière"). The latter was the principal innovation of the 1988 law: it gives security to the tenant, and the landowner is sure of getting the land back at the end of the period.

* Either landlord or tenant can ask for the rent to be adjusted by an official body, which determines maximum levels by reference to "cadastral values", multiplied by certain "co-efficients" fixed for each region for three years at a time. For the long-term leases, higher rents can be authorised.
* The tenant is generally free to make any improvements he wishes; on termination of the lease, he is entitled to compensation for the value added by such improvements, subject to certain conditions.
* If the owner sells the land, the tenant has a "right of pre-emption" (he can buy the land at the market price).
* If the tenant dies, his heirs can continue the lease.

Particularly in the UK, but to some extent in other countries as well, alternatives to tenancy can be found. Thus under a partnership or share-farming contract, the owner may provide the land, possibly on an annual basis, but still be able to get it back when he wants; the farming partner may get a chance to begin farming, or to expand, without having to find so much money. However, since the farmer has no long-term security, such contracts are more appropriate to particular enterprises than to whole farms.

Farming companies may be formed, even within families, as a means of facilitating succession and avoiding inheritance duties (a company does not die...). As has already been observed, many of the larger British farms, and many farms in North America, are constituted as companies, although this does not fundamentally change their mode of operation nor their essentially family-based character.

Different types of **group farming** have been developed in various countries, to meet different needs. The most significant is the *Groupement agricole d'exploitation en commun* (GAEC) in France. This enables two or more farmers (the legal maximum is ten) to pool their means of production, including their land, and their work. Some GAEC result from combining farms that were previously separate. Most involve members of the same family, and many consist just of a father and son: but when the father retires or dies, another relative or non-relative can be brought in. Most are livestock enterprises, and a major advantage is the possibility for a participant to take time off while others look after the animals. At the end of 1991, there were 48,000 GAEC, with 116,000 members: with an average size of 73 ha. (well above the average for France), they occupied 3.5 million ha., i.e. 11% of the agricultural area.

Other arrangements in France are the *Groupement foncier agricole* (GFA), whereby non-farming partners can provide land and share in the profits (this helps to avoid division of a farm between heirs); and the *Entreprise agricole à responsabilité limitée* (EARL), whereby non-farming partners provide not land but working capital.

In Southern Italy, there are cases of integrated joint management (*gestioni associate* or GEA), whereby small farmers bring their land together into units of economic size, with the aim of improving production on a common basis: income is divided according to the work and land contributed. (See Appendix, item 7.)

In Spain, some group farms have been formed following land consolidation (putting together scattered plots) as a means of permitting some of the owners to leave the area in order to work elsewhere, putting their land into the group in return for a share in the profits: these appear to have been a transitional phase. In Portugal, there are legal provisions relating to group farming, but with little practical result.

Their appeal is limited to regions where individual farms are small: even there, they do not make up a large proportion of farms. Generally, the strong preference of farmers is for individual management and, where possible, owner-ship, even at the sacrifice of efficiency.

ii) Labour

As has been seen above, most of the labour on Western farms is family labour. On the whole, this is not very "mobile". Obviously, it cannot be quickly expanded: having more children to increase the farm work force is a very long-term process, and no longer a significant motive in developed countries. On the other hand, if there is not enough work because the farm is too small and/or because it is undercapitalised, the farmer and maybe members of his family are quite likely to be underemployed (this is the situation on many "subsistence" farms in remote, backward regions).

Nevertheless, adjustments are possible. Sons or daughters, and sometimes the farmer's wife or even the farmer himself, may find part-time or even full-time employment off the farm; or additional money-earning activities may be developed on the farm, such as renting rooms or caravan sites. Both these developments have become important: the former particularly in areas where employment in manufacturing or services can be found near to farming areas (such as Bavaria), the second in rural areas with tourist attractions. Although the extent of income earned from such activities is not precisely known, it appears that in most EC countries about a third of "farm heads" have employment off the farm. (See also Chapter 7.)

The amount of hired labour is somewhat more variable: sometimes, casual workers are engaged for a particular seasonal task, such as the grape harvest or the picking of hops. Other workers may be engaged for a year or more. The bigger farms which regularly employ skilled workers—tractor- drivers, cowmen, etc.— tend to keep them over the years.

Minimum wages and other terms of employment of full-time agricultural workers are usually laid down in agreements concluded between agricultural workers unions and farmers' unions at the national level: the actual wages paid depend on individual contracts, and by no means all workers are union members. Agricultural wages tend to be lower than those in other sectors: in the United Kingdom, where hired labour is relatively important, the wages of farm workers are on average about three-quarters of those of industrial workers. This may reflect a lack of mobility on the part of the former, and their exposure to redundancy through mechanisation. On the other hand, farm workers may be willing to accept lower wages because of non-monetary rewards in terms of job interest, diversity, challenge and responsibility; the availability of farm produce, and above all cheaper housing, sometimes provided with the job, are also considerations.

iii) Capital

The meaning of capital

In popular usage, "capital" can have several meanings: it can refer to assets such as buildings, machinery, livestock, stocks of fertiliser, feedingstuffs and unsold produce; or it can refer to the finance needed to acquire those items; or even—more loosely—to the amount of money a person or enterprise has in bank accounts and other financial assets.

Capital consists in the first place of physical assets, produced in the past and intended to be used in producing something else in the future: capital is both an output and an input. To produce capital, someone has foregone current consumption, in the expectation of a higher reward later on. Looking at the economy as a whole, we can say that resources are being diverted from producing consumption goods to producing capital goods: a future gain should occur in so far as in the long run production will be higher with the new capital than without it.

A certain *stock* of capital is needed in the production process in order to obtain a *flow* of services. The acquisition of this stock of capital is *financed* by savers who lend funds for the purpose, getting interest in return (if it is "self-financed" by the user, an allowance for return on this "own capital" should be deducted in calculating net profit.)

The entire process can be broadly described as "investment". "Gross" investment represents the total addition to the capital stock; "net" investment is this amount less necessary replacements. This too can be regarded either as the physical process of replacing worn-out equipment at the end of its life, or the corresponding financial allowance, usually on an annual basis, for depreciation of the equipment. (Net investment can be negative, when gross investment is insufficient to allow for replacement.)

Non-Marxist economics thus sees investment as desirable, indeed essential for economic growth: and investment will not occur without a return. (For Marx, capital accumulation arose from the appropriation by the capitalist class of the "surplus value" of labour.) Another matter is whether profits from capital may sometimes be excessive: this leads into the analysis of imperfect competition (see Chapter 3), since competition provides the main assurance against such excesses.

Yet another question is whether capital should be owned by the individual or by the State. That is an issue which in general terms lies beyond the scope of the present book: Western economists (not to mention politicians) are divided as to where the frontier between public and private ownership should lie. However, it is manifest that the economies of countries which have excluded or severely restricted private capital have performed very badly: the *prima facie* evidence is strong that in all sectors where there is not a strong "public utility" case for nationalisation, private ownership is a far better way of ensuring that capital equipment is efficiently used and maintained.

Though this issue has vital implications for the transition from socialised agriculture in Central and Eastern Europe, such questions hardly arise as regards the farm sector in the West. The Western farmer is, in a sense, a "capitalist": he owns various productive assets, and he must take investment decisions, trying to assess the cost of such investment in relation to the future return he can expect. This is a very important element in the relative success of agriculture in the market economies.

Financial institutions

The sources of credit to farmers in the Western market economies include the banking system, co-operative organisations, agricultural merchants and private persons.

In the UK and the US, farming credit is provided mainly by general commercial banks which are only partly concerned with agriculture. In several continental European countries, the greater part of credit to farmers comes from co-operative banks, although the share of agricultural credit in the total operations of these banks has greatly diminished.

The first co-operative loan societies were founded in Germany in the 1860s by F.W. Raiffeisen, in response to the problems of agriculture, crafts and small industries in rural areas at a time of rapid industrialisation together with severe pressures on farm product prices arising from low-priced imports, while commercial interest rates were high. They were based on the principles of self-help, self-responsibility and self-administration (*Selbsthilfe, Selbstverantwortung und Selbstverwaltung*): deposits by members formed the basis for loans to members, and profits were re-invested or distributed. As individual societies would be too weak on their own, Raiffeisen formed in 1872 a Union at national level, combining a "vertical" with a "horizontal" structure.

These basic Raiffeisen principles have continued to guide the formation of credit co-operatives throughout the world, subject to national differences depending on the existing credit structure, legal provisions and social conditions. The Raiffeisen network also extends to supply and marketing co-operatives, which will be discussed in the next chapter.

In several Western European countries, co-operative banks—whether or not affiliated to the Raiffeisen system—are widespread in rural areas. In Germany, the DG Bank (*Deutsche Genossenschaftsbank*) provides over 40% of loans to farming, although this accounts for only some 13% of its total medium- and long-term lending. In the Netherlands, the Rabobank (for *Raiffeisen-Boerenleenbank*) provides over 70% of farm credit, but this is only some 22% of its total lending. In Belgium and Luxembourg, the CERA banks (for *Centrale Raiffeisen*) also account for most banking activity in rural areas. In France, the local branches of the *Crédit Agricole* are co-operatives, although until 1987 its central office was a public body and it acted as the main channel for government subsidies: it is not the only rural credit co-operative, but it accounts for much the greater part of lending to farmers. However, the *Crédit Agricole* has developed its activities far beyond agriculture to become not only the biggest French bank but the biggest non-Japanese bank in the world. (See Appendix, item 8.)

The universal tendency of such institutions to diversify beyond the rural sector underlines the inherent limitations of a purely agricultural base: deposits by the farming community will not suffice to finance the borrowing needs of the farm sector. Moreover, the restrictions placed by policy measures on expansion of agricultural output make the farming sector a less attractive and indeed riskier outlet for the banks concerned.

Private credit—often between members of the same family—is often important in facilitating the passage of farms from one generation to another, particularly in countries and regions where otherwise the principle of equal division between heirs would cause farms to be split up.

Terms of credit

It is customary to distinguish:

* **Short-term credit**, which serves mainly to finance current inputs such as seeds and fertiliser: this may be provided by any of the institutions just described (other than mortgage banks), or sometimes by the merchants selling the items in question.
* **Medium-term credit**, for the purchase of machinery, livestock, etc.: this is particularly the domain of the banks and of the co-operative organisations, where these exist. Ownership of the land is particularly helpful here since it provides the "collateral" usually required by the lender for substantial amounts of credit.
* **Long-term credit**, for the purchase of land: from banks, particularly mortgage banks where these exist. Under mortgage contracts, the land itself provides security for the lender (provided land prices do not fall...).

Medium-term interest rates (5–10 years) by the co-operative banks in 1989 were, for example, 8.50% in Germany, 10.10% in the Netherlands, 9.75% in Belgium, 9.90% in France. Allowing for inflation, these would correspond to "real" rates in the range 5–8%. In Southern European countries, interest rates were higher, but so were rates of inflation.

Except where governments intervene to subsidise agricultural credit—a large exception, which will be discussed in Part B—interest rates tend to correspond to the general conditions of the credit market in the country concerned. Increases in the general interest rate, such as those widely experienced during the late 1980s, thus have a direct effect on the farm sector: farmers who, in times of relatively low interest rates, have incurred large debts by investing heavily in land, buildings or equipment can then find themselves in difficulty. The "marginal farms" in this respect, at risk of bankruptcy if farm product prices fall, may thus be not the holdings on unproductive land, but relatively dynamic and productive farms: this issue is further discussed in Chapter 7.

Data on the use of farm credit are not easily available, but in Germany, the annual report of the Ministry of Agriculture includes useful information on borrowings by farmers. In 1989/90, net investments amounted on average to 3,460 DM per farm for land, 3,099 DM for machinery, 1,594 DM for buildings; 411 DM for livestock, and 1,832 DM for other purposes. Short-term debt amounted to 22,772 DM per farm, medium-term debt to 15,022 DM, and long-term debt to 76,701 DM.

One way for farmers to limit their investments in machinery and thus to avoid excessive debt is to contract out for specific tasks, especially field operations such as harvesting where large and expensive equipment is required. (This can also be regarded as a way of coping with seasonal peaks in the work-load, without keeping so many workers throughout the year.) Particularly in arable regions with large farms, contracting enterprises have grown up to meet these needs.

iv) Management

The typical private farmer has many decisions to make. Some of these occur daily: looking at the weather, and the state of the crops, to assess what field operations should be carried out on that particular day; or watching his animals for signs of trouble and deciding whether treatment is needed. Some decisions are seasonal: how much to sow of each crop; which fields to rotate; how much fertiliser or other chemicals to use. Some are longer-term: what machinery to purchase, or what new buildings to put up—and where to get the money? The farmer must also know how best to market his produce; and increasingly in the modern world, he must pick his way through a maze of administrative complications, involving tax declarations, applications for a variety of subsidies, and so on. Indeed, the list is endless: the modern farmer has to be an expert in many subjects.

Simply to classify these activities under the general heading "labour" is to obscure a vital aspect of farming: the title "management" is justified. (It is of course a simplification to refer just to "the farmer" or "the farm head" in this connection: depending on circumstances, the farmer's spouse and other members of the family may play a role in the decision-making.)

Since this management factor has played a key role in the development of Western agriculture, it is worth while considering further how it is constituted. Agricultural colleges providing full-time courses and various other short-term courses are important in some countries, particularly where farms are large; so are public advisory services (called "extension" services in the US). Still, many farmers have never had any formal training, and many do not make use of the advisory services.

Most farmers are farmers' sons: experience handed down over the generations is the basis of their farming practice—but of course, this can also be a handicap when adaptation to new methods is required. Weekly or monthly farming journals provide much of the technical information and market data which farmers need; so do radio and, occasionally, television programmes.

Information comes also from the agricultural supply industries: although some of their publicity consists of competitive advertising, they also provide technical information about their products. Banks and other credit institutions may give advice, particularly when the farmer gets into financial difficulties. Agricultural shows give farmers an opportunity to compare rival machinery and other items, to inspect the most productive livestock breeds, and so on.

There is in fact no lack of information available to the modern farmer; and although his scale of operation may be less than in most manufacturing enterprises, the management task is probably just as complex.

On the larger farms, farmers may make use of private consultancy services: this has become significant particularly in planning and accounting, and in adjusting to policy measures. While the private family farm remains the most prevalent type of organisation, some big farms, owned by institutions or corporations, are run by hired professional managers: these tend to be intensive and productive, and to specialise in particular crops. The class of career managers has thus become significant in some countries, particularly the UK and the US.

APPENDIX

1. Structural change. Developments over a long historical period, as well as the evolution of agricultural policy, are more fully described in the author's *Government and Agriculture in Western Europe, 1880–1988* (Harvester-Wheatsheaf, London etc.: 3rd edn., 1989).

2. Farm structures and the Marxist view. The fact that concentration of farms into large-size capitalist units has *not* occurred as Marx predicted has been a theoretical problem for Western Marxist economists, particularly in France (cf. Appendix to Introduction, item 5); the French Communist Party, in spite of doctrinal hesitations, has given some support to small-farmer movements. See P. Coulomb *et al.*, *Les Agriculteurs et la Politique* (Presses de la Fondation Nationale des Sciences Politiques, Paris: 1990), particularly the contribution by Rose-Marie Lagrave (pp. 355–369); or the English translation by the present author of the main papers of this volume, *Farmers and Politics in France* (The Arkleton Trust, Enstone, Oxford: 1991).

The last significant attempt to resolve the problem was by J. Cavailhès, *Les réponses des marxistes à la question agraire* (Document de recherche no. 16, Institut national de la recherche agronomique, Dijon: mars 1981). His thesis was to the effect that while the expected decomposition of the peasantry and development of capitalist enterprise had not happened in the agricultural sector *per se*, a similar process *had* happened in so far as large-scale capitalism had developed in related sectors—the agricultural supply, distribution and processing industries—so that the peasant had in fact lost much of his independence.

This is partly true—Chapter 3 will discuss the role of "agribusiness"—but does not adequately fit all the facts. To a large extent, farmers—even peasants on small holdings—remain their own masters. It also neglects the role of supply and marketing co-operatives—quite important even in France in some sectors such as dairying, and very important in Denmark and the Netherlands, as will also be seen in Chapter 3.

3. Land reform. Political as well as economic factors have influenced such reforms. In Italy after the Second World War, a major aim was to counter the spread of Communism in the countryside by giving land to the peasants. In Greece, after the exchange of population between Greece and Turkey in 1922, land was redistributed from big estates, followed after the civil war of 1949–52 (in which Communists were defeated) by further compulsory redistribution aimed largely at reinforcing support for the victorious regime. In Portugal in 1975 (after the Salazar dictatorship), Communist-led workers on the big estates of the Alentejo took over much of the land, initially supported by legislation which authorised expropriations, creating for a while the only farming collectives in Western Europe ("new production units" or NUP): but from 1977 onwards, successive Socialist and Centre-Right governments, afraid of this Communist influence, forced the abandonment of most of these collectives, partly by cutting off credit, and returned most of the land to the former owners, though some small farmers who previously rented their land obtained freehold. See J.P. Carrière, *Les transformations agraires au Portugal* (Economica, Paris: 1989).

4. Succession to farms. The EC Commission has published a study (prepared by a team of French researchers: the English text is barely comprehensible) on *Farm take-over and farm entrance within the EEC* (1992). This explains how in most cases farms are taken over by farmers' sons, though the processes and problems vary between countries: it includes a description of the system of taxation on farm inheritance in each EC Member State.

5. Location of production. A pioneer work, in 1826, was J.H. von Thünen's *Der Isolierte Staat*, available in English as *The Isolated State* (Pergamon, Oxford: 1966). Von Thünen showed that around a market centre, zones of production would develop, the inner zones being devoted to crops that have a high value per hectare but are expensive to transport, either because they are bulky or because they are perishable: the outer zones would produce items that are easier and cheaper to transport. Rents for land would be higher in the inner zones. At the time, animal transport was the only means available and there was no refrigeration: subsequent technological developments have altered the cost pattern, though distance from markets is still a handicap.
This simple theory underlines the point that State intervention can lead to inefficient location of production. Differential rents or land prices help to bring about optimal location: the suppression of a land market, as in most countries with socialised agriculture, prevents this factor from operating. So do production or transport subsidies for distant or otherwise less-favoured areas: such subsidies have been widely practised in market economies. There may of course be good non-economic reasons for wanting to support the population in such areas.

6. Land tenure. The relevant legislation in each EC Member State is described in *Les baux ruraux dans la CEE*, published by CEPFAR (Centre Européen pour la promotion et la formation en milieu agricole, Brussels: 1990). See also *Pachten, Kooperieren, Bewirtschaften* (DLG-Verlag, Frankfurt a/M: 1987). An earlier but useful study was "Factors influencing ownership, tenancy, mobility and use of farmland in the member states of the European Community", in the series *Information on agriculture*, no. 86 (Commission: 1982). Developments in the UK are well described by J. Nix, P. Hill and N. Williams in *Land and Estate Management*, (Packard, Chichester: 2nd edn., 1989).

The Belgian tenancy law, as amended in 1988 (*Loi sur le bail à ferme*), can be obtained from the Ministère de l'Agriculture, Service Information, 1 rue Marie-Thérèse, 1040 Bruxelles.

7. Group farming. Information on France is available from the ANSGAEC (Association nationale des sociétés et groupements agricoles pour l'exploitation en commun), 11 rue de la Baume, 75008 Paris. This publishes a monthly bulletin, *Agriculture de groupe*. See also G. Cesarini, "Rural production cooperatives in Southern Italy" (Arkleton Trust, UK: 1979).

8. Financial institutions. Some of the information in this section has been supplied by the Association of Cooperative Banks of the EC, 23–25 rue de la Science, 1000 Brussels.

CHAPTER 2

THEORY OF SUPPLY

This chapter provides an introduction to the theory of supply. It seeks to answer the questions: how can a "firm" best combine its inputs and outputs to maximise profits? and what determines the amounts of produce supplied by individual firms and by their "industry" as a whole?

The basic theory is general, applicable to any branch of the economy: but a "firm" can be a farm, and the "industry" can be the agricultural sector. Indeed, the farm sector is the main case where conditions close to the theoretical definition of **"perfect competition"** apply. These require, in the first place, that there should be so many sellers that none of them can individually alter the market price: firms in perfect competition are "price-takers". With numerous farms, this condition is largely fulfilled in agricultural produce markets. Also on the input side, individual farms can reasonably be held to have no significant influence over their price of their purchases.

Other conditions for perfect competition are that the produce offered by different sellers should be essentially the same and should thus obtain the same price. Most agricultural products, or grades thereof (such as milk with a specified fat content, or wheat of a particular variety and specified moisture content), broadly fulfil this condition of homogeneity. It is also required that markets should be sufficiently transparent and buyers well enough informed so that they do not pay more than the going price to a particular seller: these are also conditions that hold good for most if not all agricultural products in a developed market economy.

A perfectly competitive *industry* is characterised by free entry and exit: existing firms cannot stop new ones from setting up, and there are no legal prohibitions on entry or exit. Then, even if existing firms manage to organise themselves to restrict supply and drive up the market price, the consequent increase in profits will attract new firms into the industry, thereby increasing total supply again and driving the price back down. Conversely, when firms in an industry with free exit are losing money, some will close down, total supply will be reduced and the price can recover. In farming, there is in fact little scope for new entrants to farming (otherwise than by replacing existing farmers), but in general it is difficult for farmers to combine to push up prices: marketing boards or similar institutions with effective market control are the exception. The converse condition can be said to apply to agriculture only with a considerable time-lag: farmers tend to hold on as long as they can in the face of declining prices (which, as will be seen in Chapter 7, is one reason for the tendency of agricultural prices to fall relatively to other prices).

Despite such limitations, the theory of perfect competition is a useful approach to analysing the behaviour of farm "firms" and the farm sector or "industry".

(a) Theory of the farm firm

The general theory of the firm is based on the assumption that the entrepreneur aims to maximise profit. The theoretical literature also tends to make statements as to what the firm "will" do to this end. This can be misleading, since it is doubtful whether even business firms make the kind of calculations found in economics textbooks: it is even more unlikely that farmers use the sort of approach that will be explained below, even assuming that profit maximisation is their goal. Such statements have to be read as a kind of shorthand for a more complex sentence, to the effect that *if* firms are successful in maximising profits, by whatever decision-making process they actually employ, then certain fundamental relationships will apply between their costs and their revenue: the purpose of the theory is to identify and explain these relationships.

Further, in relation to the economy as a whole, it can be shown that, under the theoretical conditions of perfect competition, if all firms are successful in maximising profits, this is consistent with economic efficiency in that it maximises the total value of output that can be produced from a given set of resources.

The distinction between *economic* efficiency and *technical* efficiency is very important and should be made clear at this point. Technical efficiency is usually a measure of the *physical* output per unit of input (e.g. milk yields per cow, or crop yields per hectare). Economic efficiency is a measure of the success of the *choices* that are made between the methods of production and the commodities that are produced: these choices must relate to costs of production and to the values of the final products. Maximum yield may be economically *in*efficient if it is obtained at a cost in resources that outweighs the additional value of output.

As to whether *farmers* actually seek to maximise profits, this seems a reasonable approximation to reality for the larger "commercial" farmers, who account for the bulk of marketed output. It is much more doubtful whether small "subsistence" farms operate in this way: this point will be further considered under section (f) below.

Like any other entrepreneur, the profit-maximising farmer has several types of decision to take: *resource-product* decisions, i.e. how much of a given input to use in the production of a commodity; *resource-resource* decisions, relating to the most profitable combination of resources; and *product-product* decisions, as to the most profitable mix of products. These will be considered in turn below.

The technical relationship between factors of production and output is described as a **"production function"**, which can be written algebraically as:

$$Y = f (X_1, X_2 ..., X_n)$$

where Y is the quantity of output and $X_1 ... X_n$ are the quantities of n different factors of production, all expressed as rates per unit of time.

The use of each of these factors involves a cost, which is also the return to the factor concerned. In some cases, this appears clearly as a monetary transaction—the rent of land, or the hiring of labour, or the purchase of inputs such as seed, fertiliser or equipment. Sometimes, however, no money passes hands, as in the case of land or capital which the farm family owns and on which it has no debt, or the labour of the farmer himself and unpaid members of his family. For the economist, however, *all* factors of production have an **"opportunity cost"**, which is *the amount they could earn in an alternative occupation*, or (which is the same thing) *the amount needed to keep them in their present occupation*. Thus own capital is valued by reference to the current rate of interest, and family labour by reference to wages in "comparable" occupations.

The economist's concept of costs is thus different from that of the accountant and serves a different purpose: opportunity costs are the relevant consideration in a firm's decisions as to how to allocate its productive resources and, ultimately, whether or not to stay in business.

"Normal profit", as will be seen below, implies a situation where all factors of production are earning just their opportunity costs: **"supernormal profit"** implies something extra.

In the case of the farm sector, it must be recognised that labour—particularly farmers themselves—may have very little opportunity to move to other employment, especially in conditions of widespread unemployment, and since farmers cannot work without some land and capital, all factors of production in farming are relatively immobile. Farmers' "opportunity costs" are low, and they may be forced to accept a level of earnings which, though it corresponds to the theoretical concept of "normal profit", represents a low income by comparison with other sectors. The policy implications of this situation will recur at several points throughout this book.

Production factors need different periods of time to adjust their quantities up or down. Buildings, machinery, land, and livestock involve planning and investment decisions, and take quite a long time; applications of fertiliser, feed and other current inputs are day-to-day management decisions. (Labour may be hired on a long-term basis or for relatively short periods.) On this basis, different time periods are defined for analytical purposes.

* **The short run** is a period of time over which the amounts of some factors *cannot* be varied. For the farmer, this may be, for example, the period from sowing the crop until harvest: his input of land is fixed, as are his "overhead" charges for buildings and equipment, but he can still decide how much labour, fertiliser and other treatments to apply.

* **The long run** is a period long enough for the amounts of *all* factors to be varied. The farmer may decide to buy or rent more or less land, to have more or less machinery or livestock, or to employ more or less permanent labour.

It is also necessary to take into account situations in which *technology* is subject to change, leading to new and improved methods of production. Production may then increase even without an increase in the quantity of the factors employed (in other words, the "production function" changes), although usually improved technology and increased capital go together (sometimes with reduced labour, as new technology is often labour-saving). Such situations are sometimes described as the **"very long run"**, although the actual duration may not be any longer than the "long run" as defined above.

Some authors also refer to the "very short run" (or "momentary" or "immediate" run), during which production is *fixed*: in farming, this could be the time between harvest and marketing of a crop. The expression "medium term", often used in popular discussion, does not have precise economic meaning according to the definitions given above.

i) Resource-product relationships in the short run

In the short run, as defined above, some factors are fixed. Then the **law of diminishing returns** is applicable. It can be stated thus:

If the input of one factor is increased by equal increments while the input of other factors is held constant, total product will increase, but beyond some point the resulting increments in output will get smaller and smaller.

In this case the foregoing equation can be rewritten:

$$Y = f(X_1 \mid X_2 ..., X_n)$$

X_1 being the variable factor.

This "law" is often illustrated—even in general economics textbooks—by reference to the application of fertiliser to a given area of land. Empirical evidence here supports the hypothesis: the extra output obtained from equal increments of fertiliser tends to diminish, and indeed, beyond a certain point, over-application of fertiliser can result in reduced crop yields (toxicity in the soil, or too fast growth of crops causing them to be toppled (or "lodged") by wind and rain, for example). A similar argument applies to labour: there may be *increasing* increments in output initially, since two men working together can often achieve more than twice as much as one on his own (by using a cross-cut saw, for example), but too many workers trying to do the same job get in each other's way.

Diagrams are useful to demonstrate these relationships. In the following discussion, hypothetical data will be presented as well as graphs, since this helps to make the relationships clear for those unused to "marginal" analysis.

Table 2.1 and Figure 2.1 illustrate the case of diminishing returns with one variable input. (It is not important to know what sort of input and product are concerned—in this example, the input might be labour, or land, but is unlikely to be fertiliser, since even without fertiliser some product is obtained.)

Table 2.1—Physical product with one variable input

Units of input (X):	0	1	2	3	4	5	6	7
Total product (Y)	0	5	13	20.3	26.3	30.3	31.7	30.2
Marginal product ($\Delta Y / \Delta X$)		5	8	7.3	6	4	1.4	-1.5
Average product (Y/X)	0	5	6.5	6.8	6.6	6.1	5.3	4.3

The input-output relationship shown in Figure 2.1 can be divided into three stages, of which only one would be "rational". Thus in **stage 1**, up to an input of three units, each additional unit of input increases total output by more than the previous unit of input: in other words, *marginal* product exceeds *average* product. There is no point in stopping before the point where marginal product equals average product—which is also the point where average product (or yield) is highest.

In **stage 3**, additional units of input cause a *decrease* in total product: i.e. marginal product becomes *negative*. This too would be irrational: inputs could be reduced with the effect of increasing total output.

So the best level of resource use must lie somewhere in **stage 2**, between three and six units in this example.

This much can be deduced just by looking at the *physical* relationships. To determine the point of greatest *profit* or least loss (total revenue minus total cost), the cost of the input and the price of the product must be brought into the calculation. This is done in Table 2.2 and the corresponding Figure 2.2.

NOTE: In Figure 2.1, which illustrates the data given in Table 2.1, the curve representing marginal product cuts the average product curve at the highest point on the latter: so long as average product is rising, each increment of output is greater than the previous one, i.e. marginal product is higher than average product. When average product starts falling, marginal product must be less than average product. When *total* product starts falling, marginal product is negative.

Note also that *marginal* data, since they represent the increment between one unit and another, are placed *between* the units in all tables and diagrams.

Figure 2.1—Physical product with one variable input

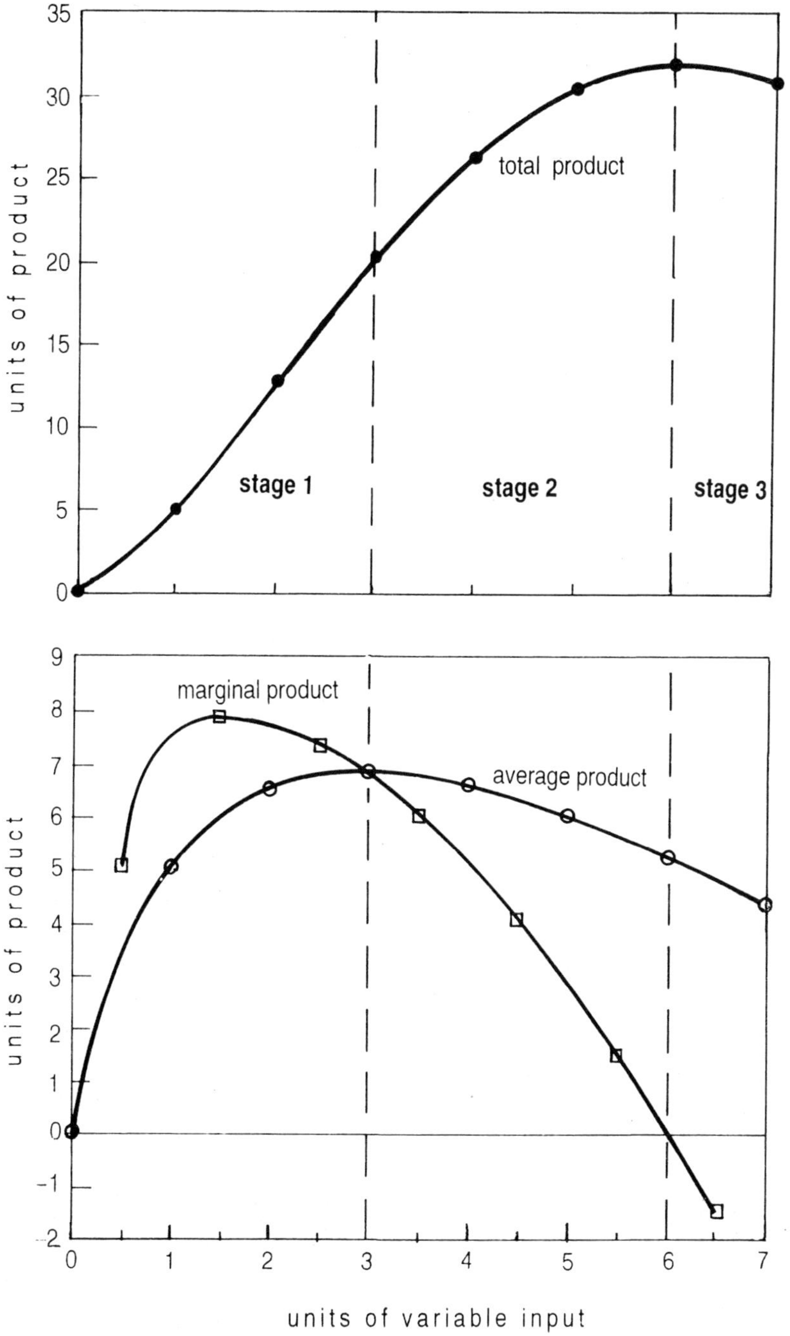

In Table 2.2 and Figure 2.2, it is assumed that the cost of the variable input is 8 ECU per unit (fixed costs can be ignored for the time being), that the product price is 2 ECU per unit, and that these remain unchanged since the farmer is held to be operating in conditions of perfect competition. (No farmer actually receives or pays ECU, as yet, but it is convenient to use this European currency unit rather than any national one.)

Table 2.2—Maximum profit with one variable input

Units of input (X):	0	1	2	3	4	5	6	7
Variable input cost (C) (= X x 8)	0	8	16	24	32	40	48	56
Total physical product (Y)	0	5	13	20.3	26.3	30.3	31.7	30.2
Total product value (R) (= Y x 2)	0	10	26	40.6	52.6	60.6	63.4	60.4
Marginal physical product ($\Delta Y / \Delta X$)		5	8	7.3	6	4	1.4	-1.5
Marginal product value ($\Delta Y / \Delta X$ x 2)		10	16	14.6	12	8	2.8	-3

There are two ways of determining precisely the point of maximum profit. In the upper part of Figure 2.2, this is found where total product value exceeds total input cost by the greatest amount. This situation, i.e. where the line and the curve are furthest apart, occurs where both are increasing *at the same rate*, or where a line drawn *tangential* to the curve of total product value is *parallel* to the total input cost line (i.e. rising at the same rate).

In the lower part of the diagram, the line representing the input cost of 8 ECU per unit intersects the curve representing the marginal value of the product. Up to this point of intersection, there is extra profit to be made by increasing the variable input: the addition to product value (marginal product value) exceeds the price of the extra input (marginal input cost). Beyond this point, the extra value obtained from additional inputs does not cover the extra costs. *Maximum profit is found where marginal input (or "factor") cost equals marginal product value.*

NOTE: In Figure 2.2, since the same physical data have been used as in Figure 2.1, the *shapes* of the total product value curve and the marginal product value curve are the same as the physical product curves previously shown, though on a different vertical scale. As the unit cost of the variable input remains the same however many units are used, the total variable input cost (disregarding for the moment the cost of other inputs) appears as a straight line. In the lower part of the diagram, a horizontal line represents the price of the input: average and marginal input cost are identical.
Some textbooks refer to "total value product" and "marginal value product" or "marginal revenue product"; and to "factor cost" rather than "input cost".

Figure 2.2—Maximum profit with one variable input

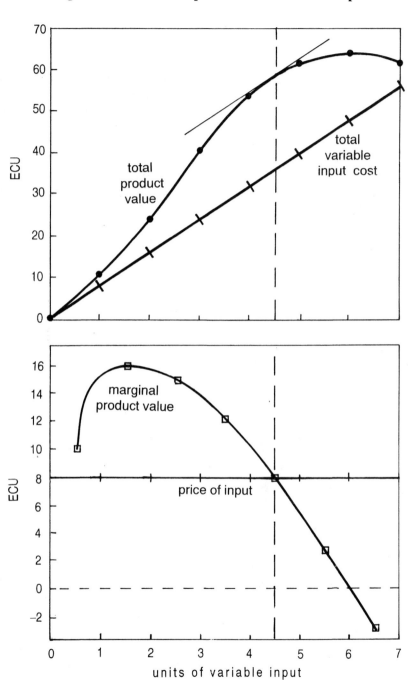

ii) Resource-resource relationships in the short run

The previous discussion simplified the issue by considering only one variable input. In practice, the farmer can probably vary more than one input, even in the short run: indeed, one of his essential tasks as entrepreneur is to *combine* his productive resources as efficiently as possible.

The least-cost combination can be explained by pursuing numerical and graphical illustrations as in the previous section, but it is easier to introduce another type of diagram which is widely used by economists. In Figure 2.3, the vertical axis measures expenditure on fertiliser and the horizontal axis expenditure on land (best considered as rent). The straight lines are *isocost* lines, each showing all the combinations of fertiliser and land that can be employed at a given cost (as in the previous example, we continue to assume that the price of inputs is not affected by the amount purchased by an individual farmer). Three such lines are drawn, representing total outlays of 700, 1000 and 1400 ECU, but any other level of expenditure could be shown.

The curves are *isoproduct* lines or *isoquants*, showing the *maximum* physical output which can be obtained with different combinations of the two inputs.

Figure 2.3—Least-cost production with two variable inputs

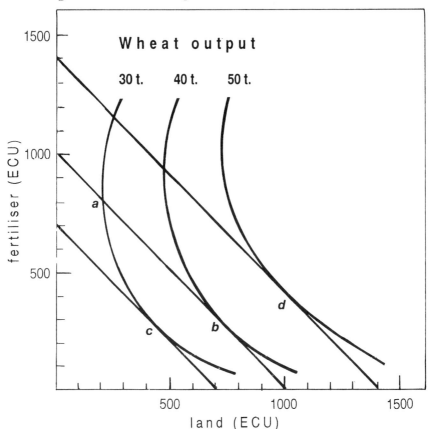

The slope of the isoquants at any point measures the amount of fertiliser that can be substituted for land (or *vice versa*) while maintaining the same output: it is described as the *marginal rate of transformation* of the two inputs.

In principle, there is an infinite number of isoproduct curves, but here again only three are shown, representing outputs of 30, 40 and 50 tonnes of wheat. It is assumed that these inputs are perfectly "divisible" into small units (a fairly realistic assumption for fertiliser, less so, in practice, for land or many other inputs). It is also implicitly assumed that there are adequate technical data upon which to base these curves, which is questionable: but reasonable suppositions as to their general shape can be made.

The isoproduct curves have been drawn *convex to the origin*. This reflects diminishing returns to each factor: as fertiliser is substituted for land, increasing increments are needed to compensate for each unit of land that is lost. In this particular example, it is possible to produce wheat with land and no fertiliser, so the isoproduct curves tend towards the horizontal axis, but the reverse is clearly not possible. Indeed, as additional quantities of fertiliser are added, production will eventually fall unless more land is also used, so the upper end of the isoproduct curve is shown as sloping back to the right: it would be technically as well as financially irrational to operate in this area where more of both inputs are being used to produce the same output.

The *least-cost* combination at any level of total expenditure can be found as follows. If the farmer's total outlay on the two inputs is, for example, 1000 ECU, he would not maximise output by combining them at point *a*, where only 30 tonnes can be achieved. On the other hand, an output of 50 tonnes is beyond his reach: the 50-tonne isoproduct curve does not anywhere touch the 1000 ECU isocost line. A combination at point *b*, however, permits production of 40 tonnes: here, the 1000 ECU isocost line just touches (is tangential to) the 40-tonne isoproduct curve. As this is the *lowest* possible isocost line that can touch the 40-tonne curve, it represents the least-cost solution for that level of output.

Points *c* and *d* represent the least-cost solutions for expenditures of 700 or 1400 ECU respectively.

Looked at in other way, the least-cost combination is found at the only point on the isoproduct curve where this curve has the same slope as the isocost lines: in other words, where *the ratio of the prices of land and fertiliser (the slope of the isocost line) is equal to their marginal rate of transformation (the slope of the isoproduct curve).*

As the diagram is drawn, there are diminishing returns to scale, since a doubling of expenditure on the two factors together, from 700 to 1400 ECU, produces a less-than-proportionate increase in production, from 30 to 50 tonnes. This might occur, for example, if the labour input was not increased sufficiently to cope with the extra land and fertiliser.

Finally, it can be noted that a farm producing a given amount would be technically inefficient if it is spending more on inputs than is indicated by the isoquant (i.e. if it is situated above the isoquant for that amount of output).

iii) Product-product relationships in the short run

Some products are "complementary", i.e. the output of one is positively linked to the output of the other (as with mutton and wool); in some cases there is partial complementarity, as with milk and beef. Often, however, products are "competitive" in the use of resources: land cannot be used for two crops at the same time.

Here the issue concerns the allocation of *fixed* inputs: if all inputs are variable, so that there is no limit to the amount that can be used, an increase in output of one product does not imply a reduction in output of another. But when the quantity of one or more inputs is limited—as is the case for "fixed" costs in the short run—a choice has to be made (supposing that the fixed inputs can be used for different products).

An approach similar to that of the previous section is useful for demonstrating profit maximisation in the two-product case. Figure 2.4 considers two products—wheat and potatoes—which compete in the use of land and other inputs. The *"production possibility curve"* (or *"frontier"*) represents at each level of output of one product the maximum that can be produced of the other: this is determined by technical factors. The production possibility curve is drawn *concave to the origin*, indicating that as, say, wheat is substituted for potatoes, increasing amounts of potatoes have to be given up for each extra unit of wheat: this could reflect increasing use for wheat of land that is more suitable for potatoes. In this diagram, it is possible, with the resources available, to produce *either* 70 units of barley *or* 70 units of wheat, or various combinations of the two. With the given resources, production *below* the production possibility curve—e.g. at point *x*—would be technically inefficient; production *above* the production possibility curve would, by definition, be impossible.

Given the prices of the two products, *"isorevenue"* lines can also be drawn (for convenience, it is here assumed that the price is 1 ECU per unit for both wheat and barley, so that we can use the same scale to represent revenue). As always under perfect competition, we assume that the price is unaffected by the output of this individual farm. If it is possible, with the given resources, by producing only potatoes, to obtain a revenue of 95 ECU, and likewise by producing only wheat, a straight line drawn between these points represents all the alternative combinations of the two products which will produce this same revenue. In principle, there is an infinite number of isorevenue lines, but this is the *highest* one that can be achieved given the available resources: it touches the production possibility curve at point *a*, which corresponds approximately to an output of 40 units of wheat and 55 units of potatoes.

The production possibility curve is here at a tangent with the isorevenue line: i.e. the two have the same slope, or in other words *the marginal rate of substitution between the two products equals the ratio of their prices.* A change in the price ratios, hence in the slope of the curve, will shift the optimum along the production possibility curve.

Figure 2.4—Maximum profit with two products

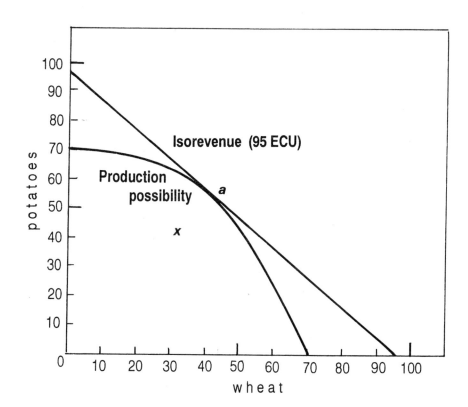

iv) Short-run supply of the individual firm and of the "industry"

It has already been established, in section i) above, that maximum profit is obtained from the use of a given input when the marginal factor cost of that input equals its marginal product value. Further, if the firm is combining all its factors of production *and* determining their allocation between products in the most economically efficient ways, as outlined in the two last sections, the firm (or farm) will maximise its profit *when the marginal cost of production for each product (all inputs combined) equals the marginal revenue obtained from that product.*

This principle can be used to determine the level of output at which the firm can maximise profits *depending on the price of its product*, i.e. its "supply schedule" or "supply curve". Illustrations are given in Table 2.3 and Figure 2.5 respectively.

Table 2.3—The supply schedule of the individual firm (in ECU)

Units of output:	0	1	2	3	4	5	6	7
Fixed cost	25	25	25	25	25	25	25	25
Variable cost	0	10.5	21.5	33.5	47.5	65	88.5	122.5
Total cost	25	35.5	46.5	58.5	72.5	90	113.5	147.5
Av. variable cost		10.5	10.8	11.2	11.9	13	14.8	17.5
Av. total cost		35.5	23.3	19.5	18.1	18	18.9	21.1
Marginal cost	10.5	11	12	14	17.5	23.5	34	
Marginal revenue (= product price)	30	30	30	30	30	30	30	

In the short-run situation, as originally defined, some costs are fixed: then increases in *variable* costs determine the marginal cost for each unit of output. Assuming, as always in perfect competition, that product price is fixed for the individual firm, marginal revenue per unit of product equals price (and also equals average revenue at each level of output). If the product price is, for example, 30 ECU, reference to the marginal cost data in the supply schedule shows that maximum profit will be found at an output around 6 units: below that level of output, each unit adds more to revenue than to costs, and above it, each unit brings in less than the extra cost of production. In the diagram, this point is identified at *a*, where price (or marginal revenue) equals marginal cost, at a level of 25 ECU. An increase in price would cause the point of maximum profit to move up the marginal cost curve, or *vice versa*, with corresponding changes in output.

At *a*, the firm is receiving a price exceeding average total cost (including both fixed and variable costs): it is therefore making a profit to the extent of this difference. Since costs have been defined (at the beginning of section (a)) to include remuneration for each factor of production on the basis of its "opportunity costs"—i.e. the amount needed to keep that factor in its current use—this extra amount can be regarded as **"supernormal" profit**. In perfect competition, this situation will not last: other firms will enter the market, pushing down the price. If price falls to 17.5 ECU, at point *b* the average total cost of production is only just covered. This is the situation already described as **"normal" profit**, where each factor is earning just its "opportunity cost".

Below 17.5 ECU in this example, the firm makes a loss. However, so long as the price remains above 10.5 ECU, the average *variable* cost (AVC) is still covered, so it is worthwhile to continue production (the firm is now minimising losses rather than maximising profits). But a fall in price below 10.5 ECU (point *c*) will make production uneconomic, since even *variable* costs are no longer being covered: this is the "shutdown point". (As the diagram is drawn, this point

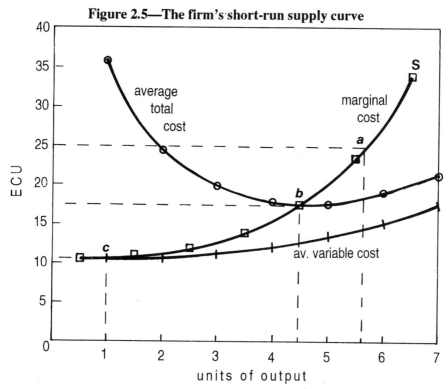

Figure 2.5—The firm's short-run supply curve

occurs at the minimum output level of 1 unit, but it could of course occur at a higher level.)

The firm's marginal cost curve thus indicates the level of output at which profit can be maximised for each level of price: *the marginal cost curve is therefore also the supply curve.* For the farm sector as a whole (the "industry"), the short-term supply schedule is simply the addition of the supply schedules of all the individual farm firms, or in graphical terms, the horizontal addition of the individual supply curves.

v) Long-run supply of the individual firm, and returns to scale

The long run has been defined as a period during which output can be changed by varying *all* inputs. We shall suppose for the moment that technology remains the same. Effects on production costs will then depend on "returns to scale":

* **Constant returns to scale** denote a case where a proportionate increase in all inputs leads to the same proportionate increase in output.
* **Increasing returns to scale** imply a more-than-proportionate increase in output.
* **Decreasing returns to scale** imply that a proportionate increase of all inputs leads to a less-than-proportionate increase in total output.

Figure 2.6—Short-run and long-run cost curves

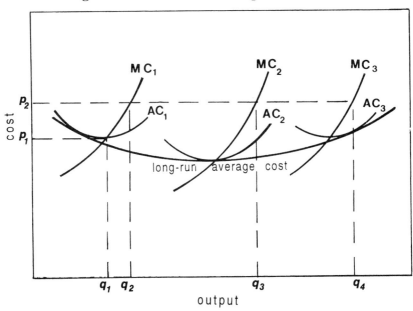

In graphical terms (Figure 2.6), if output can be increased over time, there will be a series of short-term cost curves corresponding to the level of output that can be obtained with the factors available at each point in time: over the whole period, a long-run average cost curve can be derived from the lowest points of each short-term curve (only three of the latter have been shown, but in principle there is an infinite number, permitting a smooth long-run curve to be drawn).

The long-run curve is generally envisaged as U-shaped, reflecting initially a fall in costs (increasing returns to scale), but subsequently an increase in costs (decreasing returns to scale.

In the initial short-term situation, a rise in price from p_1 to p_2 brings about a smallish increase in the quantity supplied from q_1 to q_2. If after some time the firm can employ more of the factors that were initially fixed, supply might rise to q_3. A further increase in output, to q_4 is possible but in this illustration involves rising costs (diminishing returns to scale). The outcome can be regarded either as a series of shifts in the short-run supply curves or as a movement along a long-run curve.

In the manufacturing sector, the expectation of increasing returns to scale— justified or not—is a motive for expansion, concentration and take-overs. Costs which are relatively fixed—research and development, marketing, etc.— can be spread over a bigger volume of activity. If falling returns to scale are encountered, it may make sense to split up the enterprise.

How far does this sort of argument apply in farming? Individual farmers, if they are dynamic, are usually keen to take on more land so as to by-pass the diminishing returns that arise from having land as a fixed factor: but this does not necessarily imply *increasing* returns to scale. Increasing returns may however be obtained if the extra land permits more efficient use of existing machinery: large machines such as combine harvesters are "indivisible" and may be underemployed on a smallish farm. Increasing returns to scale can also be obtained through *specialisation*: a larger size of business may, for example, permit skilled employees or even managers to be hired for specific parts of the farm enterprise.

The issue is important, because in countries with socialised agriculture and large State farms or collectives, there has been an implicit assumption of increasing returns to scale. The results, however, show that the possible technical advantages of large size and specialisation are not the only consideration. One vital factor remains fixed, i.e. the overall management of the farm; and even if the supervision of different activities within the farm is delegated, technical inefficiencies are liable to arise. While a large factory, or even a group of factories, can perhaps be efficiently managed, the nature of farming is such that beyond a certain point the necessary individual supervision can no longer be properly carried out.

This would suggest that the rising section of the U-shaped long-run cost curve is likely to be encountered in most farming conditions. But at what point? While many big collectives under socialised agriculture were probably well beyond the point of lowest-cost production, there is not much empirical evidence as regards Western farms. Such data as exist suggest an L-shaped rather than a U-shaped curve: costs per unit of output fall steeply at first, but then flatten out over a considerable range. This may be because few farms, even in North America, are so big as to encounter rising long-run costs. (See Appendix, item 2).

"Optimal size", then, cannot be precisely defined: farms with different sizes, provided they are not too small, can do equally well. On the other hand, there can be very big variations in costs as between different farms with the same size of business. The important implication is that it is more important to be technically efficient and to maximise profit, at whatever size beyond a certain minimum, than to pursue economies of scale through overall expansion.

The foregoing discussion considered the long-term effect of a rise in price. The response to a price *fall*, however, may be much slower than that to a price increase. It is easier to invest than to disinvest. A farmer who, in response to a price increase, has built a new milking-parlour is unlikely to leave it unused (let alone demolish it); or if he has bought a new tractor, he will be reluctant to sell it and may make a substantial loss if he does so—especially in a context where all farmers are facing the same difficulties. This is the problem of **"asset fixity"**. Capital assets used in farming often have little or no alternative use. The supply curve, in effect, may be *asymmetrical*—much steeper (less "elastic"— see section (d) below) in the initial downward stages than it was on the way up. Ultimately, as was observed at the beginning of this chapter, aggregate supply by the agricultural sector may not respond much to price reductions because much of the farm labour force has nowhere else to go: the conditions of perfect competition, in this respect, are not fulfilled.

Finally, the important role of *expectations* should be underlined. Farmers' behaviour may be determined as much by how they *expect* prices to move as by actual price movements. This is an important consideration for policy: a price cut in a single year, for example, may not have much effect unless farmers are led to expect a further price cut in subsequent years. As will be seen in Part B, Ministers of Agriculture and other politicians are unwilling to tell farmers unpleasant truths. The theory of "rational expectations" might imply, in this case, that farmers would not be misled; "naïve expectations", on the other hand, implies that people believe what they are told (especially if it is what they *want* to believe). Experience suggests that, in the field of agricultural price policy, naïve expectations predominate.

(b) Long-run supply of the "industry"

In the long term, it becomes difficult to analyse the individual farm in isolation. As production by the farm sector increases (or decreases), the market price is likely (other things being equal) to fall (or rise). In the general theory of perfect competition, it is usually supposed that if existing firms in an industry have increasing returns to scale in the industry, and hence a chance to increase their profits through expansion, then new firms will enter, raising supply, restricting the outlet for each existing firm and pushing down the price once again. If Figure 2.6 is now considered to represent the "industry" (this only requires an increase in the horizontal scale), the move from q_3 to q_4 might be obtained by an increase in the number of firms: but then price is likely to fall and profits will turn out less than expected.

For the farm sector, this is not a very realistic scenario: the constraint as regards land acquisition makes it difficult to set up new farms except when existing farms are taken over. In fact, the number of farms in all the Western market economies has been falling steadily, with particularly rapid reductions among the smaller size groups (this issue will be further considered in Chapter 7. However, this has not reduced supply, since the land released is usually taken over by other farms.

For farmers, raising output over time usually means, in practice, investing in extra land or capital. Although this may be done in the expectation of greater profit, and although the first to do so may indeed benefit, the profit margin is likely to be squeezed as more and more farmers follow suit, further raising output and pushing down the market price of the produce. In fact, many farmers may feel *obliged* to make additional investments since otherwise they will fall behind in the race—a process frequently referred to (following the term used by the American economist Willard Cochrane) as the "treadmill".

Indeed, farms which have *overinvested* can find themselves in trouble: this has been particularly the case when a period of expansion under relatively low interest rates (as in the 1970s) is followed by a period of falling prices and rising interest rates (as in the 1980s).

On the other hand, farms that are "marginal"—which in the initial situation are only just covering their costs—and which cannot make the necessary investments are likely in this process to fall by the wayside.

(c) Supply with changing technology

For the farm sector as a whole, one factor remains virtually fixed in quantity: land. It was this consideration which led Thomas Malthus (1766–1834) to predict that food supply could not keep pace with population growth: but he did not foresee the significance of *productivity* growth.

It is therefore very important to consider the situation where *technology* can change. This implies that *production functions* change, in the direction of greater physical productivity (output per unit of input). In graphical terms, this means a *shift* of the supply curve to the right.

Clearly, this has been a very important motor of growth in agricultural production in Western market economies. Improvements in crop production through better varieties, more effective agro-chemicals and better knowledge of their use; improvements in livestock production through better breeds, more effective feeding techniques, disease control, etc.; better machinery; better techniques of farm management—all these developments and others have played a vital role. Although improved productivity *can* mean reduced inputs for the same volume of production, in practice it has almost always led to increased output.

In most cases, this process goes with increased investment. What has been said above about the "treadmill" phenomenon, and about the difficulties of "marginal" farms, is thus highly relevant in this context too.

(d) Elasticity of supply

The concept of elasticity will appear frequently from now on, in connection here with supply and later with demand. This is a measure of the response of supply (or demand) to a change in price, assuming that all other things remain equal (*ceteris paribus*): it can also be used in reverse, to estimate by how much price may alter when quantities supplied or demanded change: in which case it is known as "price flexibility".

Elasticity of supply is defined as the proportionate change in the quantity supplied of a product or service in response to a given proportionate change in price, or:

$$E_s = \frac{\Delta Q_s / Q_s}{\Delta P / P}$$

Elasticity may vary at different levels of supply, therefore the co-efficient E_s is related to a small—1%—change in price.

The following situations may arise (note that "increase in quantity supplied" implies a movement *along* the supply curve, and is *not* synonymous with "increase in supply", which implies a *shift* in the whole supply curve to the right):

* Below a certain price, nothing is supplied, but a small increase in price is sufficient to cause the quantity supplied to rise to an infinite level. The co-efficient is infinity, and supply is said to be **"perfectly elastic"**. This serves mainly as a theoretical reference point: however, in "partial-equilibrium" trade theory, as will be seen in Chapter 6, it is common to assume that the supply of imports is perfectly elastic.

* A change in price is related to a *more* than proportionate change in the quantity supplied: i.e. the co-efficient is more than 1. Supply is said to be **"elastic"**. Not a common situation, but not impossible. In agricultural production, the ability to switch land and labour between crops means that the supply of, say, barley could be elastic, but probably not that of all cereals.

* A change in price is related to a *less* than proportionate change in quantity supplied: i.e. a co-efficient between 0 and 1. Supply is said to be **"inelastic"**. This is the most usual situation in farm production.

* A change in price produces *no* change in quantity supplied: the co-efficient is 0. Supply is said to be **"perfectly inelastic"**. Mainly another theoretical reference point, but could occur in the "very short run" when the quantity supplied is fixed, for example between harvest and marketing of a crop, if no storage is possible.

* An change in price causes a change in the *opposite direction* in the quantity supplied: the co-efficient has a *minus* sign and this is called **"negative elasticity"**. An unusual situation, but not impossible: it will be further discussed below under the heading "backward-sloping supply curve".

On the customary diagram with price on the vertical axis and quantity on the horizontal axis, a "perfectly elastic" supply "curve" would appear as a horizontal straight line; one that is "perfectly inelastic" would be a vertical straight line. "Elastic" and "inelastic" supply curves would both slope upwards throughout their range (provided elasticity is positive). (Note that although one curve may be said to be "more elastic" than another if it is steeper *in the same area* in the diagram, the *slope* of the curve alone does not determine elasticity: since elasticity refers to the *proportionate* change in quantity, and thus relates to the absolute amount in the initial period, the co-efficient of elasticity depends also on the distance from the axes.)

Supply elasticity is largely determined by the *time* available for adjustment to the new price: the shorter the period, the more inelastic supply is likely to be. The various possibilities will be considered more fully in Chapter 5 on price determination, after the characteristics of demand have been studied.

The concept of elasticity is in principle a very valuable tool of economic analysis. In practice, there are many difficulties in measuring and applying co-efficients of supply elasticity. Empirical evidence can be gathered from past time-series, relating price changes to quantity changes. However, even assuming that data are adequate, it is not easy to isolate the effect of price changes from other factors, such as structural and technical change, or climatic influences.

Account must also be taken of the fact, already discussed, that producers react not just to *actual* price changes but also according to their *expectations* of future price levels, and in this respect, individual attitudes to *risk-taking* play a key role. Changes in the recent past are therefore bound to have been influenced by the price support policies practised in the Western "market" economies. Under these policies, moreover, price fluctuations have been limited, so that time series may be an inadequate guide if the effect of a substantial price change has to be assessed.

The increasing complexity of agricultural policies also makes it difficult to project the effect of price changes in isolation. Thus, although large price cuts are due to take place in EC price supports under the "reform" of the CAP (see Chapter 9), these are offset by compensatory payments conditional on "set-aside"; the existence of production quotas for certain commodities and other measures of supply control are a further complication. (See Appendix, item 3, on issues arising from some recent studies involving supply elasticities.)

(e) Profit maximisation and the economic optimum

This completes the basic theory of the profit-maximising "farm firm", or indeed of any firm operating under "perfect competition", and of the determinants of supply. It is useful to pause to consider the significance of the ground just covered. In general, the development of *marginal analysis* is an intellectual step of the greatest importance. Though the exposition of the theory in schedules and diagrams may seem abstract and even arid, it formulates in a more precise way the common-sense calculation as to whether extra spending on an input is worthwhile in terms of the extra revenue it will provide. Marginal analysis of supply also constitutes an essential building-block in the general theory of "value", or of price determination, as will be seen in subsequent chapters.

Technical data are rarely sufficient to enable complete and accurate supply schedules to be worked out. Further, even if plans are well-based, they do not necessarily work out. So it is possible that few farmers actually operate at the point of maximum profit.

Even so, if profit *is* the aim of most of those producers who account for most of the supplies that come on the market, and provided there is not a strong overall bias to overshoot or undershoot the optimum, the traditional economists' model might be a reasonable description of the *average* behaviour of the farm sector. One reason to think that the tendency may be to remain short of the optimum is related to *risk*, a topic that has been much debated in recent academic literature: it can be argued that uncertainty on the part of farmers tends to reduce supply.

Analysis of profit-maximisation along the lines described above plays a key role in the definition of "general equilibrium", or of an economic "optimum" for the economy as a whole. The **"Pareto optimum"**, so-called after the Italian economist (1848–1923) who first tried to define it precisely (see Chapter 5), requires *inter alia* that all enterprises within the economy should be maximising their returns by equating marginal costs and marginal revenue. Although this optimal state can never be quite attained, an economy in which many individual enterprises—including farms—are operating far from their points of profit maximisation is likely to be an economically inefficient economy: inefficient, that is, in maximising the output of goods from the available productive resources.

Consequently, the economists' tools here play a potentially useful role in evaluating *distortions* in the economy: as regards agriculture, this applies particularly to the effects of protection and price support, as will be seen in Part B. Such evaluation, however, tends to be static: some degree of distortion at a given point of time may be outweighed by dynamic benefits—a point which will be discussed in the next chapter. Moreover, it relates to the *current* distribution of income, which is quite likely to involve undesirable inequalities. "Normative" judgements become difficult to avoid at this stage.

Equilibrium analysis, however, is a useful basis for dealing with "externalities": cases where "private costs" (those internal to the firm, of the kind so far discussed) may diverge from "social costs" (the effect on others). Farming activities may give rise to *benefits* for others, for example in the conservation of the countryside: but an important contemporary issue is the extent to which modern intensive farming *damages* the rural environment in ways which do not show up in the costs of production (through pollution from agro-chemicals, for example). We shall return to this issue too in Part B.

(f) Farm household strategies

Finally, we must take into account the fact that many farm households have aims other than profit maximisation.

The Russian economist A.V. Chayanov, in the 1920s, analysed the operation of "peasant farms", stressing significant differences from capitalist enterprises. Pointing out that for a peasant family farm, employing no labour, there are neither wages nor net profits, he suggested that there is an element of "self-exploitation", the "drudgery" (*tyagostnost*) of extra work being balanced against the satisfaction of needs. This could cause a peasant farm to intensify *beyond* the point of maximum profit, in order to gain enough income to meet current family needs. On the other hand, once an equilibrium between work and needs has been reached, further work becomes pointless even if profit has *not* been maximised. (This may imply a "backward-sloping supply curve"—see below.) In difficult times, moreover, peasant farms can survive because their lower limit is the means of existence of the family, and they can work at what to a capitalist enterprise would be a *negative* profit.

Chayanov's work ran counter to Stalinist collectivisation policy and led to his arrest in 1930, but it remains relevant to part at least of the farming sector even in Western Europe, particularly in Southern Europe. It provides a basis for more recent work on "peasant economics", which tends to stress "utility maximisation" as an aim incorporating leisure and other goals as well as profit max-imisation. (See Appendix, item 4.)

Currently, valuable light is being thrown on farm household strategies by research conducted by the Arkleton Trust, covering several countries in Western Europe and North America. This analyses ways in which farm households are adapting to changing economic and social circumstances, and distinguishes three main patterns:

* **Professionalisation**—i.e. both a market-oriented and a commercial approach to farming, with clear signs of a "growth" mentality with a tendency towards expansion, and often specialisation, of farming activities. This category may include younger farmers on large farms, and older farmers on large farms where there is a successor and where dependence on farm incomes is high; it may also include small farms where off-farm opportunities are weak.
* **Stable reproduction**—i.e. little change in the importance of farming activities; traditional attitudes are often apparent, causing resistance to change. This is characteristic of less-favoured areas and small farms; often associated with off-farm "pluriactivity".
* **Disengagement**—i.e. an increasingly residual role being attributed to farming: there is a lowering of commitment to farm activities, accompanied in some cases by increasing commitment to non-agricultural activities either on or off the farm. This is characteristic of older farmers on small farms, especially when there is no successor: retirement may then mean the disappearance of the farm.

The assumption of profit maximisation—and the theory of the firm which follows from that assumption—is most relevant to the "professional" category. It is likely that the farms concerned mostly fall into the larger farm groups described at the beginning of this chapter, and which account for by far the greater part of farm sales. Consequently, if we are concerned with the determinants of agricultural *supply*, the foregoing analysis remains relevant.

On the other hand, the behaviour of the other two categories may correspond more closely to the Chayanov model, and it cannot be assumed that their supplies to the market will be determined exclusively or even mainly by market forces. This may not greatly affect the overall supply behaviour by the farm sector: on the other hand, since farms in these categories are probably numerous, they are socially important. They must be particularly taken into account in the context of the "socio-structural" policies that will be described in Chapter 10.

(g) The backward-sloping supply curve

The case of the backward-sloping supply curve can illustrate the relevance of foregoing analysis to a major issue of agricultural policy.

As has been seen in discussing the Chayanov approach, it is theoretically conceivable that an increase in price of a product may, beyond a certain point, cause supply to *fall*. This is due to the "income effect". If the farm household is aiming not to maximise its profit but to reach a certain level of income, and if the product in question provides a large share of its income, a backward-sloping

Figure 2.7—The backward-sloping supply curve

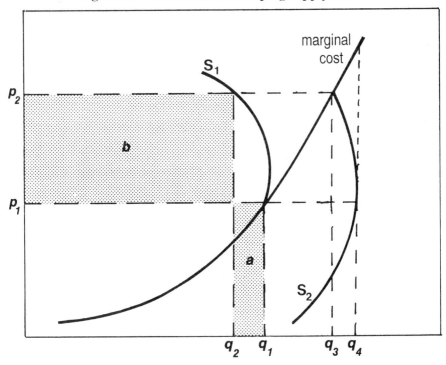

supply curve such as that illustrated in Figure 2.7 (S_1) could arise: price goes up from p_1 to p_2 but supply, instead of moving up the marginal cost curve, *falls* from q_1 to q_2. Although profit is not maximised (as it would be with output q_3, where marginal cost equals price), total revenue from sales—price times quantity has risen (the area of box y, which has been gained, exceeds that of box x which has been given up).

Such behaviour is more likely to characterise the type of peasant holdings which Chayanov had in mind than the larger commercial farms of the West, but it may occur in less-developed countries, and perhaps in Western Europe too among smaller farms in less-favoured regions.

Even in such cases, however, it is questionable how durable this type of reaction is. After a while, in an economy where consumer goods are widely available, the household is quite likely to develop new wants, and may then expand production towards the point of profit maximisation.

Further, for the reasons set out in the previous section, it is unlikely, in developed market economies, that such behaviour is so widespread as to dominate the aggregate response of the farm sector to an increase in price: the supply curve of the *individual* farm firm may sometimes be backward-sloping, but probably not that of the "industry" as a whole. Indeed, there is no empirical evidence to this effect: price increases have always been associated with rising supply (though over time it is not easy to distinguish movements along the supply curve from shifts due to increased use of factors or improved technology).

The backward-sloping supply curve has more often been invoked in the reverse direction. Farmers' organisations, faced with the threat of cuts in government-supported prices in order to reduce surpluses and support costs, often claim that the result will be the opposite of that intended: that output will *rise* following the price cut.

Policy-makers sometimes respond by observing that farmers' representatives raised no objections when prices were being *raised* to encourage more output—as during the Second World War or the early post-war period. Yet this is in fact not a very good answer. It is possible that movements up and down the supply curve are not symmetric: for instance, that a price rise causes output to move up following the marginal cost curve, but that subsequently, farm households having got used to a new, higher, level of income, a price cut will indeed cause a further rise in output as they try to keep their income at the new level to which they have become accustomed.

In Figure 2.5, for example, having initially responded to a price rise in the profit-maximising way by raising output to q_3, they might respond to a price cut back to p_1 by further *raising* output to q_4, implying a backward-sloping supply curve (S_2) in the downwards direction. This is irrational in terms of profit maximisation: marginal cost exceeds price at this level of supply, and a cut in output would save more in costs than it would lose in revenue. It is therefore questionable whether this position would be maintained for very long. Moreover, while some farms might act in this way, it is by no means certain that a sufficient number would do so for the *aggregate* response to be of this kind.

Farmers' organisations often try to prove their point by observing that price cuts in the past have been followed by further increases in output. This neglects the probability that production has increased for other reasons: the supply curves may have *shifted* to the right because of reduced input costs, maybe resulting from technological improvement, or because of changes in other product prices. It may well be that without the price cut, production would have been even higher.

Another—and probably more general—reason why the response to a price cut is limited arises from the problem of "asset fixity" described above: it takes time to "disinvest", and so long as capital assets are present, they are likely to be used.

Yet another reasons is related to the issue of "expectations", already discussed. Ministers of Agriculture have often sent confused messages, cutting prices in one year while giving reassurances to farmers as to their future.

Thus public debate on this issue tends to confuse the individual supply response with that of the sector as a whole, the short-run response with the long-run; it overlooks the possibility of an asymmetric response to price increases and price cuts; and it neglects the role of expectations. Yet the policy implications are significant, and underline the need for precise analysis.

The economist, if asked for advice on an impending price cut, cannot say that this *will* reduce production in a short period of time, or even that it will certainly reduce production in the longer term. What he *can* say with reasonable certainty is that, after a period of adjustment (the length of which can probably be estimated, depending on the production characteristics), production will be *lower than it would otherwise have been*. He still should not say, in his capacity as an economist, that the price cut *should* be made, since that is a "normative" judgement, where benefits to consumers and taxpayers have to be weighed against adverse effects on farm incomes. This leads us into a controversial area of welfare economics, which will be considered in Chapter 5.

APPENDIX

1. Sources. See the Appendix to the Introduction for references to basic textbooks on agricultural economics.

2. Economies of scale. Although there are numerous studies showing that costs are usually much higher on very small farms than on those somewhat larger, the evidence concerning very large farms is not so clear, mainly because of lack of observations. A study by P.J. Dawson and L.J. Hubbard, "Management and size economies in the England and Wales dairy sector", in *Journal of Agricultural Economics*, XXXVIII:1 of January 1987 (pp. 27–37) concluded that the long-run average cost curve was "U-shaped though skewed to exhibit greater economies than diseconomies of size... Better-managed farms are shown to produce any given level of output at lower average cost". Their results showed cost curves falling steeply up to levels of about 300,000 litres per year (the equivalent of 60 cows at the average UK yield of about 5,000 litres per cow), but then remaining quite flat, especially on the best-managed farms, up to 2 million litres per year (or some 400 cows). On the other hand, farms with the lowest level of management (feed costs per litre being taken as the criterion) had costs at least twice as high as those of the best-managed farms, at most levels of output. Further research, reported by S.M. Mukhtar and P.J. Dawson in "Herd size and unit costs of production in the England and Wales dairy sector", in JAE 41:1 of January 1990, produced similar results.

3. Supply elasticities. To estimate the supply response to price changes, a knowledge of the supply function is essential. For the reasons given in the text, it is in practice difficult to calculate from empirical data the supply elasticity at a particular price level, and even more difficult to derive the supply function over a wide range of prices.

Numerous econometric studies have tried to estimate the effect of price changes, particularly in the context of agricultural policy reform and GATT trade negotiations. In all cases, the supply elasticities used involve a large element of judgement, although this is not always made clear. Sometimes the results of alternative assumptions as to elasticities are indicated, as a "sensitivity test".

The choice of elasticity co-efficients should reflect the purpose and nature of the econometric model. Two key considerations are the following:

a) What time period is under consideration? As has been made clear in this chapter, long-term supply adjustments may be quite different from short-term ones. Besides changes in the supply functions due to changes in factor inputs, in the "very long run" (a period which has to be determined), technological change cannot be assumed to be "exogenous" to the model: price developments can influence the adoption and even the rate of development of technology. In other words, how "static" or how "dynamic" is the model?

b) How many commodities are under consideration? A price change limited to one commodity is likely to produce a bigger reaction than if several or all commodities are affected by a similar price change, because of possibilities of substitution. Ambitious models may try to take into account interactions between agriculture and other economic sectors, particularly in terms of resource use. In other words, does the model refer to "partial equilibrium" or to some degree of "general equilibrium"? (full "general equilibrium" is probably unattainable).

Among relevant recent work, the following may be cited:

* R.W. Fraser, in "Price-support effects on EC producers", *Journal of Agricultural Economics*, 42:1 of January 1991, pp. 1–10) made estimates of supply elasticities for wheat, cattle and milk in the EC by *simulating* the effect of price changes on a producer's "optimal" production decision. Each producer was assumed to produce only one product, and the study was of the "comparative static" kind: it did not consider how long it might take for producers to move from one "optimal" position to another. This study concluded that for these commodities— all subject to price support—producer responses were likely to be very much affected by their attitude to *risk*, "risk- averse" producers being unwilling to change output levels in response to a change in support prices. On the whole, supply response seemed "inelastic".

* The Australian economists Kym Anderson and Rod Tyers have published numerous papers giving results of their econometric model on the effects of trade liberalisation: the most recent was in *European Review* no. 19 of 1992. Fuller explanations are given in their book *Disarray in World Food Markets—A Quantitative Assessment* (Cambridge University Press, 1992). This work, related to major world regions, treats the EC as a whole: the elasticities used, largely based on judgement, include the following "short-run" (one year, but two years for coarse grain) and "long-run" co-efficients (these are "own-price" elasticities—"cross-price" elasticities with respect to other commodities are also used in the model):

	Short-run	Long-run
Rice	0.20	0.40
Wheat	0.30	0.90
Coarse grain	0.40	0.92
Sugar	0.10	0.50
Dairy	0.07	0.51
Ruminant meat	0.12	1.02
Non-ruminant meat	0.76	1.14

* The Economic Research Service of the US Department of Agriculture has included elasticity estimates, on a world-wide basis, in *A 1989 global database for the Static World Policy Simulation (SWOPSIM) Modeling framework* (May 1992): more detailed explanations concerning the elasticities were given in *Elasticities in the trade liberalization database* (May 1989). This material has been used by USDA itself in highly- publicised studies of the effect of trade liberalisation, and is made available for use by others. The co-efficients are not the result of original research but have been selected from other studies. Though estimates are given for each EC Member State, they are all nearly identical

for each commodity (an improbable result, given the different production structures). The SWOPSIM model is "static": it aims to show the outcome of "full model adjustment" to policy changes or other "economic shocks", but does not give the "time path" of adjustment. The co-efficients are quite significantly different from those of Tyers and Anderson. Neither of these studies appear to take account of constraints arising from milk and sugar quotas, and other supply controls.

4. Farm household strategies. The main works of A.V. Chayanov have been published in English under the title *The Theory of Peasant Economy* (Manchester University Press: 1966). This includes a bibliography of his works in Russian. See also F. Ellis, *Peasant Economics— Farm Households and Agrarian Development* (Cambridge University Press: 1988).
The references to the Arkleton Trust study are based on the Trust's report to the Commission (publication awaited). Arkleton Trust publications can be obtained from its office at Enstone, Oxford OX7 4HH, England.

CHAPTER 3

AGRIBUSINESS

This chapter will consider the various stages in the supply of food, from the producer to the consumer. "Agribusiness" is defined here very broadly: it covers the agricultural supply industries "upstream" from the farmer which supply agricultural inputs, as well as the "downstream" activities of marketing, processing and distribution. In many of these activities, large commercial enterprises are involved: the biggest operate across national borders.

As will be seen below, the cost of farm inputs may amount to half or more of the value of farm output, while the various "downstream" activities account for the greater part of the value of most foodstuffs by the time they reach the consumer. The efficiency of agribusiness is therefore a vital element in the entire food system, if food is to be supplied to consumers in sufficient quantities, in adequate variety, and at reasonable prices.

In the former socialised economies, where most food distribution has so far taken place through State channels, the role of the various stages of the food chain in a free market is not always appreciated: indeed, in situations of shortage, and when the private channels of distribution are still underdeveloped, the "black market" and the "mafia" can be a serious problem.

Where supplies are abundant, and competition operates, such malpractices are less likely. Further, the successive stages add value to the product. An efficient *market system* ensures that produce moves swiftly from the producer to first-stage buyers, and further down the chain, with minimum loss; sorting and grading may take place at this stage. *Processing* makes the product more useful by changing its form (from grain to bread, for instance). *Transporting* the produce from where it is produced to the centres of consumption involves cost and performs a valuable function. *Storage*, particularly of perishable produce, is necessary but entails cost and also an element of risk, which will not be undertaken without an appropriate financial return.

This is not to deny that, when competition is insufficient, excess profits may be gained, or that the social value of some commercial activities is doubtful: for instance, there is high expenditure by food processors on advertising and promotion campaigns, often linked to artificial differentiation between items which are in fact similar. Moreover, farmers often feel that they are in a weak bargaining position as compared with the power of big enterprises. It is therefore important, in examining those parts of the food chain where a few enterprises are dominant, to consider whether competitive forces remain sufficiently strong.

In discussing agribusiness, where many firms are large, the basic conditions of perfect competition outlined at the beginning of the last chapter do not apply. It is therefore necessary to consider how the theory needs to be adapted.

(a) The theory of imperfect competition

At the opposite end of the spectrum from "perfect competition" lies the case of "monopoly"—literally, one seller. The extreme case where one seller has absolute control over the market is difficult to conceive: it would imply that customers could not shift to any alternative product. Except perhaps in some very localised and temporary contexts, such a situation cannot be said to exist in agribusiness (or in other sectors, except in the case of State monopolies). There has indeed been considerable "concentration" of firms, as will be seen, but the constitution of outright monopoly has been prevented by anti-merger legislation (which will be discussed in Chapter 11).

The more relevant situation is the intermediate one, where a limited number of firms operate in the same or similar business area. The term "monopolistic competition" has been used to describe a situation where firms are quite numerous: "oligopoly" implies that relatively few firms control the market. Agribusiness in general cannot be classified as falling within one or other of these categories, but is characterised by a continuum of situations: some sectors of activity have a greater number of competing firms than others. The term "imperfect competition" will be used to cover this continuum.

Imperfect competition differs from perfect competition primarily in that the product price is *not* independent of the actions of each individual producer: each firm is big enough in relation to the total market for its volume of sales to influence the market price. If it sells more, it will find the price declining. On the other hand, imperfect competition is distinguished from monopoly by the fact that other firms exist, or can enter the industry: so if profits are high, other producers will step in, bringing down the price. There may be some degree of collusion between firms (which is more difficult for the controlling authorities to detect than open mergers); or the biggest firm may act as a price "leader". But in a free enterprise system with good information, the lure of high profits is likely in the end to attract competitors.

An important consequence of imperfect competition is "product differentiation", whereby each firm tries to create a separate market for its own product (contrast the assumption of homogeneous products under perfect competition). The advertising of "brand names" and other forms of sales promotion play an essential role in this respect. The aim is to convince the potential customer that this firm's product is different from (and supposedly better than) that of its rivals. This may represent useful innovation, and it can be defended as adding variety and thus in some sense contributing to consumer welfare; on the other hand it may be a waste of resources, with close substitutes being produced and marketed with considerable expense in competitive advertising.

There have been two main approaches to these issues under economic theory. The following sections will be a very brief and simplified account of subject-matter which at times has been extremely complex and also highly controversial (see Appendix, item 1).

i) Profit maximisation under imperfect competition

As in the previous chapter, graphical illustration is the easiest way to make clear certain fundamental relationships (again, this is not intended as a description of how firms actually make their plans.) Under imperfect competition, the product price cannot be assumed to remain constant: on the contrary, it is assumed to decline steadily as the firm expands its output. Figure 3.1a is similar to Figure 2.5 which illustrated the supply curve of a firm in perfect competition, but now the revenue situation is different. As the price obtainable at each level of output is applicable not just to the last item produced but to the whole range of output, it is equivalent to *average* revenue (AR). And as this is declining, marginal revenue (MR)—the extra value resulting from each increment of output—is necessarily less than average revenue at each level of output.

NOTE: Units of output, as well as the price scale, have been kept the same in Tables 3.1a and 3.1b as in Table 2.5, to facilitate comparison: in fact, a firm under imperfect competition is likely to be operating on a larger scale.

Figure 3.1—Maximum profit in imperfect competition
a. before entry of other firms

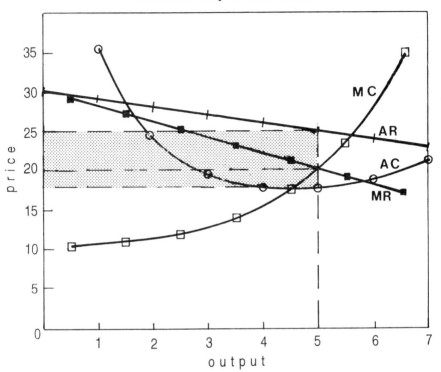

For the reasons explained in the last chapter, maximum profit is always found where marginal revenue equals marginal cost (MC): at lower levels of output, extra production brings in more revenue than it costs, and at higher levels, the cost of extra output is not covered by extra revenue. In Figure 3.1a, this point of maximum profit lies at an output of 5 units, where a price of 25 ECU can be obtained. Here, *average* cost (AC) is 18 ECU, while average revenue (price) is 25 ECU, giving a profit margin of 7 ECU, or a total profit of 5 x 7, i.e. 35 ECU (the shaded area in the diagram). If the firm is a monopoly and can prevent competitors from entering the field, it can hold on to this "supernormal" profit (cf. discussion in the previous chapter).

On the other hand, if other firms can enter, they are now likely to do so, pushing down the price: i.e. shifting the average revenue curve for each existing firm downwards as its market share is reduced. This could go on until price equals average cost, and marginal revenue again equals marginal cost with only "normal" profit being earned, but at a lower level of output (Figure 3.1b).

Figure 3.1—Maximum profit in imperfect competition
b. after entry of other firms

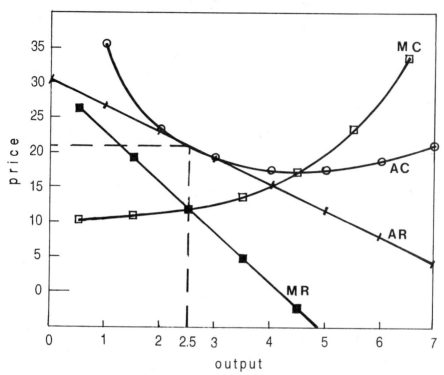

But the firm is not operating at the lowest point on its average cost curve. So long as an element of product differentiation remains, the price which each firm can obtain for its products declines the more it sells. The firm's maximises profit at a point where *output is lower and price higher* than under perfect competition: in the latter case, average revenue (price) and marginal revenue are a single horizontal straight line so that equilibrium is found where marginal cost equals marginal revenue at the lowest point on the average cost curve (compare this diagram with Figure 2.5).

Thus imperfect competition implies an inefficient use of resources, and this is the theoretical basis for a critique of imperfect competition.

ii) Innovation

An alternative view of monopolistic practices, particularly associated with the Austrian-American economist Joseph A. Schumpeter (1883–1950), takes account of *dynamic* factors. It is argued, first, that innovations which bring about lower costs of production have a much greater long-term effect on living standards than any "misallocation" of productive resources at a particular point in time: the traditional analysis outlined above ignores the importance of technological change. Secondly, innovation is held to be much more likely in conditions of monopoly and oligopoly than under more competitive situations: only the incentive of profit leads firms to take the risks of innovation, so they need some assurance that the benefit of their research and development of new technology and new products will not go to other firms. Even with the protection of patent laws, competitive firms cannot be sure of capturing the full monetary value of their inventions.

Such arguments cannot be definitively proved or disproved: economics, unlike the natural sciences, cannot conduct controlled experiments in which one alternative is compared with another in identical situations. The discussion in the following sections may however provide some relevant indications. Indeed, as will be seen, the agribusiness sector has been undergoing very rapid structural and technological change, which suggests that the dynamic effects are indeed important.

(b) The food chain

A graphical illustration of the food chain is given in Figure 3.2. This is a simplified representation: it is not possible to depict all possible channels, which vary from product to product (as will be seen below in discussing marketing). Also, it neglects imports and exports, which could occur at almost any stage.

The farm sector, though it may expand in absolute terms, tends in the process of economic growth to account for a declining share of national output and income: this topic will be analysed in Chapter 7. On the other hand, the "upstream" and "downstream" industries tend to expand in both absolute and relative terms in early stages of industrialisation, and subsequently at least to maintain their relative shares in national income.

Thus, in seven of the most advanced EC Member States (Belgium, Denmark, the Federal Republic of Germany, France, Italy, Netherlands and the UK), the "value added" in the manufacture of food, beverages and tobacco accounted in 1987 for about 4% of total value added in these countries, and this share had remained approximately stable for at least the previous decade. Value added in agricultural production (including forestry and fishing) was only about 3% of total value added, and this share had declined from about 4% some ten years earlier.

Employment in the food, drink and tobacco industry in the twelve EC Member States in 1989 accounted for 2.8% of total employment: the industry's contribution to gross domestic product was higher than this, at 3.2%, indicating relatively high labour productivity (in contrast to the farm sector, whose share in employment was 6.6% and contribution to GDP only 3.1%).

Figure 3.2—The food chain

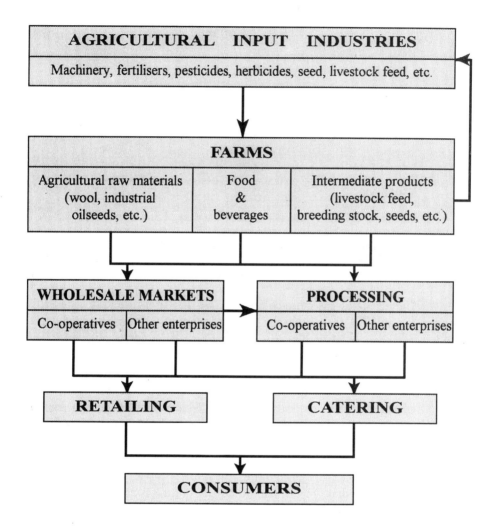

The margin between "farm gate" prices and consumer prices varies between products: naturally, it is greatest for products which undergo a substantial amount of transformation, so that the raw material accounts for a relatively small part of final value.

Table 3.1—US: Farmers' share of the consumer dollar, 1989

	Farm value	Consumer expenditure	Percentage share
	billion	*dollars*	*%*
Meat	35.1	130.0	27
Fruit & vegetables	15.8	108.5	15
Dairy products	19.6	64.2	31
Bakery products	3.5	48.1	7
Grain mill products	1.3	16.7	8
Poultry	10.5	31.2	34
Eggs	2.7	6.5	42
Other foods	12.7	56.6	22
All foods	101.2	461.8	22

Notes: "Fruit and vegetables" include soup, baby foods, etc. "Grain mill products" include flour, rice, pasta, etc. "Other foods" include fats and oils, sugar, nuts, etc.
Source: US Department of Agriculture, *Food Cost Review 1991*, Agricultural Economic Report No. 662 (Table 23).

The United States has more comprehensive data in this field than most EC countries. Table 3.1 shows that the farmers' share of the consumer's dollar in 1989 was only about 24%: this percentage has been declining steadily over time, as the importance and cost of the intermediate stages have increased. Figure 3.3a shows, for expenditure at food-stores, how the final cost is distributed between the various stages, processing and retailing being the biggest items: "farm value" is just under 30%. In the case of "eating away from home", which accounts for about 40% of total consumer expenditure on food in the US, "food service costs" are particularly important, and the "farm value" was only 26% in 1989. Figure 3.3b shows the various components of final cost: labour is particularly important.

In most Western European countries, the farmers' share of consumer expenditure is still somewhat greater than in the US, but the general tendency is for the share of marketing and processing to increase.

In all the market economies, the components of the food chain are, with few exceptions, in private hands. Agribusiness enterprises may be commercial or co-operative. Farmers' co-operatives mostly deal in the supply of inputs or in first-stage marketing and processing of farm produce: as will be seen below, their importance varies between countries and between types of activity. In both the "upstream" activities of supply of agricultural inputs and in the "downstream" activities of marketing and processing, commercial firms may be very large,

Figure 3.3—US: Components of consumer expenditure at foodstores, 1991

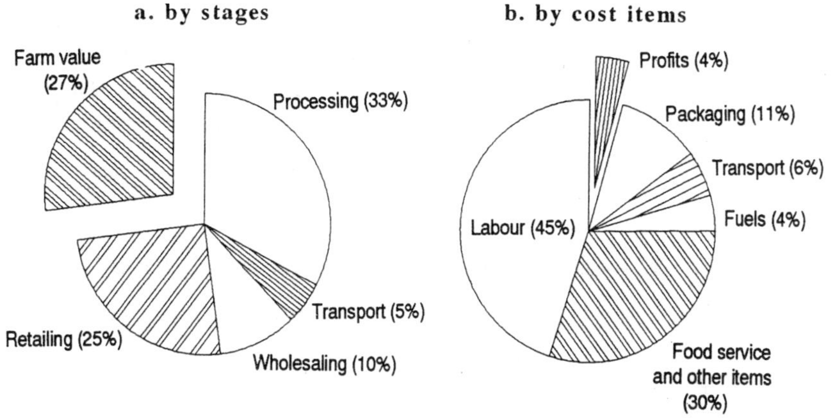

a. by stages   b. by cost items

Farm value (27%)
Processing (33%)
Retailing (25%)
Transport (5%)
Wholesaling (10%)

Profits (4%)
Packaging (11%)
Transport (6%)
Fuels (4%)
Labour (45%)
Food service and other items (30%)

Source: As Table 3.1 (Tables 24 and 25).

operating on a national or even international scale: the bigger firms are "joint stock" companies (i.e. owned by share-holders). In food distribution too, big retail chains, selling often through out-of-town supermarkets, account for a large share of the market.

Comprehensive data on the profits made by agribusiness firms are not easily available in Western Europe, though information on major companies which will be presented below (Table 3.5) shows profits for major food processors averaging around 6%.

Fuller information is available in the US: it appears from Figure 3.3b that "corporate profits before taxes" accounted for some 3.5% of the total marketing bill. Other data from the same source indicate "after-tax profits" of food manufacturers as 4.1% of sales in 1989, and the after-tax profits of retail food chains as 0.8% (some previous years showed slightly better results): data from thirteen selected supermarket food chains in 1989 show after-tax profits ranging as a percentage of sales from near zero to a little over 3%.

A more detailed discussion of the various stages of the food chain will be attempted below. It should be borne in mind that information in this field tends to be fragmentary and often not up-to-date (see Appendix, items 2 and 3, for main sources): some inaccuracies in the description are inevitable, especially as regards the activities of particular firms, in view of the rapid pace of take-overs and mergers.

(c) Agricultural input industries

In the European Community in 1990, the cost of purchased inputs amounted to about half the value of agricultural production; this share varied widely between the twelve Member States, being above-average in Belgium, Germany and the UK, and below-average in the southern countries. The biggest item was feed for livestock, followed by fertilisers, other agrochemicals, farm implements, fuel and seeds (see Table 3.2).

Table 3.2—Farm inputs (in 1991, percentage distribution)

	UK	DK	B	D	F	SP	GR
Animal feed	41	40	42	29	31	44	24
Farm implements, upkeep, repairs	19	18	9	17	10	16	15
Fertilizers and soil improvers	9	10	7	9	12	11	9
Energy and lubricants	7	8	8	16	8	8	24
Crop protection products	6	6	5	6	10	4	9
Seeds	4	3	6	6	12	4	6
Other inputs and services	14	15	23	17	17	13	13
All inputs	100	100	100	100	100	100	100
Share of inputs in production value	55	51	55	53	46	44	23

Source: Commission, *The Agricultural Situation in the Community—1992 Report* (preliminary data for Table 3.1.3). EC totals have been omitted as data for some countries are unreliable.

The agricultural supply industries have been going through a difficult time, as a result of the restrictions placed by policy measures on the growth of farm output (which will be discussed in Chapter 9); in the case of agrochemicals, environmental concerns have added to the pressures. Profits have been squeezed: some firms have gone out of business, some have enlarged their operations by acquiring other businesses. This process of restructuring is not yet complete.

Farmers' co-operatives sometimes play an important role as intermediaries, supplying inputs to their members. This is particularly the case in Germany (for feed and seed), in Italy (for machinery, agrochemicals and seed); in Denmark, the Netherlands, France, Ireland and the UK (for livestock feed). Sometimes—as in the case of feed—they are themselves producers.

In the following sections, the production of livestock feed, of fertilisers and other agrochemicals, of farm machinery and of seed will be discussed.

i) Livestock feed

Livestock consume various types of feed, some of which—the "roughages" such as hay, fodder beet, maize or grass silage— are mostly produced on the farms where they are used; or sugarbeet pulp, which is usually returned directly to the farmer from the sugar factory. Among "marketable" feeds, "energy-rich" and "protein-rich" items can be distinguished. The former include feed grains (mostly now produced within the European Community, apart from some maize), manioc (imported, mainly from Thailand and Indonesia), "corn gluten feed" (a by-product in the manufacture of "isoglucose" from maize, imported from the US), and citrus pulp (also mainly from the US). "Protein-rich" feeds include oilcakes, made from soya (mostly imported from the US and Brazil) and other oilseeds such as rape, sunflower or linseed (produced within Europe or imported), fishmeal (partly imported) and powdered milk.

Some livestock producers compound their own feed: possibly as much as 65 million tonnes may be produced in this way in the EC, of which 80% may be grain (data are uncertain). Farm-mixed feed has become a particular feature in Belgium, with the help of computerised programming.

The livestock feed industry produces mainly compound feed: production in the EC in 1990 was valued at about 28 billion ECU and amounted to about 100 million tonnes. Of this total, 35 million tonnes was for pigs, 32 million tonnes for cattle, 28 million tonnes for poultry.

The most appropriate ratios between the ingredients are precisely calculated according to price relationships and nutrient contents. In 1989, the raw materials used, amounting also to around 100 million tonnes, included:
* About 30 million tonnes of cereals (EC-produced and imported). The proportion of EC-grown cereals tends to be low in countries where imported energy-rich feed is easily obtainable: it is as low as 12% in the Netherlands, but as much as 63% in Spain.
* About 25 million tonnes of oilseed products (largely imported soya products).
* About 17 million tonnes of by-products from the food industry, including 6 million tonnes of imported "corn gluten feed" and 2 million tonnes of "citrus pellets".
* About 6 million tonnes of manioc (imported).

The biggest world producer is a branch of the oil company British Petroleum (BP Nutrition); other international producers include the Italian firm Ferruzi, the US-based trading companies Cargill and Bunge & Born, and the French firm Dreyfus. However, relatively small producers remain; co-operatives account for half or more of feed output in the Netherlands, Denmark, the UK and Ireland. In Germany, in the mid-1980s, about 40% of output came from 80–90 commercial producers, 30% from eleven large co-operatives within the "Raiffeisen" network, and the remaining 30% from small commercial and co-operative producers.

The sector employed 92,000 people in the EC in 1990: the number has fallen since 1984 as a result of mechanisation and automation; a large proportion of labour consists of highly-skilled technicians and engineers.

Since livestock feed is bulky in relation to its volume, transport is a relatively important cost item. As a result, the compound feed industry has developed in areas of dense livestock population, but also near ports where imported raw materials arrive. This in turn has promoted further development of livestock production in such areas—sometimes to the detriment of more traditional livestock producing areas.

Thus Brittany has become a major producer of compound feed (6.6 million tonnes in 1988), particularly for the intensive pig and poultry enterprises of the region. In Germany, the *Land* of Lower Saxony, with its North Sea ports, produces some 6.4 million tonnes.

The number of compound feed mills in the twelve EC Member States is falling steadily, as a result of abandonment and mergers, though some new mills have been built. In 1988 the total number of mills was 4,330. Although many small mills survive, especially in Italy, the tendency is towards increased concentration: 215 mills, 5% of the total, account for 52% of output.

Demand for feed is showing only limited growth, as a result of the general pressures on EC agriculture. One of the factors adversely affecting consumer demand for meat has been public concern with animal health, particularly following diseases in poultry and cows in the UK that have been attributed to the recycling of animal wastes in feedingstuffs. The production of cattle feed has fallen since 1983; there have been moderate increases in output of pig and poultry feed. Overall, profit margins are tight, and there is over-capacity in compound feed production to the extent of about 30%.

Mention may also be made here of the pet food industry, whose sales in the EC were valued in 1987 at 3.4 billion ECU but which, in contrast to the livestock feed sector, is expanding rapidly. This sector uses by-products, some of which would otherwise be waste, from meat production, from cereals and vegetables, and to a smaller extent from fish.

ii) Fertilisers

Fertilisers are produced as "single" fertilisers such as nitrogen (N) or phosphate (P), or as "compound" fertilisers including N, P and K (potassium). In the EC, the average consumption of N per hectare of agricultural land is around 80 kg., that of P somewhat below 38 kg., and that of K just over 40 kg.; but there are wide variations between EC countries, with much higher intensity of use in the north-western than in the southern regions.

Fertiliser use has been declining in countries where high levels of use had already been reached, as farmers try to adapt their applications more precisely to crop needs; also because of declining real product prices and supply controls. The cost of fertiliser has been partly responsible for this, but so has the growing concern over water pollution: manufacturers increasingly offer advice to farmers as the most appropriate quantities and periods of application (a "Code of Best Agricultural Practices" has been developed by the trade). Some countries, and now the EC, have introduced legislation aiming to control fertiliser use (see discussion of environmental issues in Chapter 10).

Prospects for fertiliser manufacturers within Western Europe have been further limited by the policy restrictions on the farm sector, already mentioned; the "set-aside" of arable land in particular is a negative factor for the fertiliser industry. There has also been growing competition from developing countries and from Eastern Europe: in 1990 about a quarter of EC fertiliser needs were met by imports, the value of which was three times as high as that of EC exports.

As a result, some firms have withdrawn from the market (the Germany company Hoechst) and others have reduced their involvement (particularly the British chemical giant ICI, which in 1990 sought to sell its fertiliser branch to the Finnish firm Kemira Oy, but this deal was blocked by the British Monopolies and Mergers Commission).

Economies of scale are important in fertiliser production, so the industry is characterised by a small number of large firms, co-existing with a larger number of small compounders operating locally. Kemira and the Norwegian-based firm Norsk Hydro are the two main European companies specialising in fertilisers, with branches in several European countries; other firms include BASF (Germany), Grande Paroisse (France), EniChem (Italy) and FESA (Spain).

The bulky nature of the product to some extent limits cross-border competition, and significant price differentials have been reported as between the EC Member States.

iii) Other agrochemicals

Agrochemicals other than fertilisers include herbicides, insecticides, fungicides, animal health products (antibacterials, antiparasitic drugs, vaccines, etc.), feed additives (vitamins, preservatives, growth promoters, etc.) and plant growth regulators. The market for these products is world-wide, and is dominated by a smallish number of very big multinational firms—mostly producing a variety of chemicals of which agrochemicals are usually not the most important. The thirteen leading world producers include three American firms (Monsanto, Dow and American Cyanamid); three Swiss firms (Ciba-Geigy, Schering and Sandoz); one British firm (ICI); three German firms (Bayer, BASF and Hoechst); two French firms (Rhône-Poulenc, which is state-owned, and Du Pont); and one Dutch-based (Royal Dutch-Shell).

For herbicides, Ciba-Geigy has an estimated world market share of 13%, followed by Monsanto with 9%, Bayer and BASF with 7% each. In the world insecticides market, Bayer holds 14% followed by Rhône-Poulenc with 10% and FMC and Hoechst with 5% each. In fungicides, the main companies are Bayer, with 18% of the world market, Ciba-Geigy with 14%, Rhône-Poulenc with 10%, Du Pont with 8%, BASF and Sandoz with 5% each. The EC is a net exporter, particularly of insecticides (ICI being largely responsible).

As with fertilisers, the agrochemicals industry has been put on the defensive by growing public concern over pollution and residues in food. It is responding partly by providing farmers with more precise advice, so as to reduce the environmental impact of the products while maintaining their effectiveness. It is also seeking to develop new, more "environment-friendly" products: this applies particularly to pesticides, with new methods of biological control being developed. In the case of animal health products and feed additives, the industry stresses the rigorous testing and registration process which, they claim, ensures the safety of the products.

Trade associations representing these industries at the EC level participate in—and seek to influence—the development of EC standards (cf. Chapter 11).

Research and development requirements are substantial, being estimated at 8–9% of sales. The heavy investments required to develop and register a new product reinforce the position of large companies, thereby promoting a continuing process of mergers and acquisitions. The range of products on offer to farmers remains wide, though each company tries to promote its own products by insisting on their specific characteristics. A sample of advertisements in one issue of the Belgian farming journal *Le Sillon Belge* (in April 1992—at other times of the year a different range would be on offer) gave the following results: seven fungicides for use on cereals, three anti-mildew preparations for potatoes, eight herbicides for cereals and four for sugarbeet. Almost all the major international companies mentioned above were represented, plus one smaller Belgian firm.

Although the production of agrochemicals takes place on an international scale, trade—even within the European Community—has remained subject to various "non-tariff barriers", while distribution to farmers has remained subject to varying national structures, with the result that prices to farmers can vary quite widely (twice as high in Germany as in the UK, for example). The removal of non-tariff barriers in the "Single Market" context (see Chapter 11) should help to reduce such disparities.

iv) Machinery

Farm machinery includes tractors (about half of the sector's turnover), other machinery and equipment for soil cultivation and crop harvesting, transport equipment, machinery and equipment for dairying and livestock raising.

For the big machines, economies of scale in production are substantial. Four huge American companies, which have reached their present size through past mergers, produce tractors and combine harvesters and sell them world-wide: Case-International Harvester, Ford-New Holland, Massey-Ferguson, John Deere. In European countries with a national producer, this producer tends to have the largest market share: Fiat and SAME in Italy, Deutz and Fendt in Germany, Renault in France. The American companies are present everywhere: Ford and Massey-Ferguson dominate in the UK.

A large number of small firms (three or four thousand in the EC) produce specialised equipment, such as for poultry or pig farming, wine production, storage, drying and so on.

The sector employs about 2.4 million people in the EC. Germany alone accounts for about 45% by value of total machinery production in the EC. The EC is a substantial net exporter.

On the whole, the market appears to remain competitive: a visit to any agricultural show suggests that a wide choice of machinery is available to farmers. However, the producing firms can try to restrict competition through agreements with their sales agents: John Deere was condemned and fined by the EC Commission for practices of this kind.

Since the early 1980s, as agricultural production growth has been constrained by policy measures, the European and North American markets for farm machinery have contracted; the decisions taken by the EC in 1992 (see Chapter 9), particularly as regards the "set-aside" of land, will further depress the market. The export trade is important for some European manufacturers: in particular, over 60% of UK production is exported outside the European Community. The prospects for the industry now depend largely on markets in developing countries and in Central and Eastern Europe.

v) Seed

Traditionally, farmers kept some of their harvest back as seed for the following year; commercial seed production tended to be localised and small-scale. But technical developments have changed this pattern. Most seed is now commercially produced on a large scale, under controlled conditions—often by farmers on contract to commercial firms. The seed may be treated against fungus, insects, parasites and bird attacks; it may be coated to give protection in storage and to incorporate substances that promote germination or regulate growth. In the case of hybrid varieties—hybrid maize being the main crop in question—a farmer has to purchase new seed each year, or there will be a loss of the hybrid vigour. Biotechnology will play an increasingly important role in developing plant varieties which are more resistant to diseases and fungus, thus reducing the need for chemical treatment.

These developments have shifted seed production increasingly towards the large multinational firms which can afford expensive research and development. "Plant Variety Protection" (PVP) legislation in most Western European countries and in North America provides some guarantee that firms can profit from the results of their research. Public research programmes also play a significant research role.

The expansion of hybrid maize in north-western Europe since the 1970s is a striking example of the impact which can be made by appropriate varieties. Original American varieties were unsuited to the relatively short growing season, but the development of new, early-maturing varieties made possible an expansion of cultivation into Northern France, the Benelux countries, Germany and even southern England (though in these regions most of the maize is cut when green and used for silage). In this case the basic research was initiated by the French official research institute, *Institut National de la Recherche Agronomique*: it was further developed by a co-operative seed firm, Limagrain, and then by others. This expansion, assisted by price support, caused maize imports from the US to be substantially reduced.

A few small co-operative seed producers remain, particularly in France, but most of these are localised and specialise in a single crop. Much the biggest international seed company is Pioneer (US); other firms specialising in seed production include KWS (Germany) and Limagrain (France), the latter—as has been seen above—being a co-operative. Seed production is also undertaken by companies for which this is not the main activity. This list includes oil firms such as Royal Dutch/Shell; chemical and agrochemical companies such as American Cyanamid, Bayer, Du Pont, ICI and Monsanto; pharmaceutical companies such as Upjohn, Ciba-Geigy, Dekalb-Pfizer and Sandoz; and some food traders and processors such as Cargill, Beatrice Foods and Campbell Soup.

This expansion of agrochemical firms into seeds may be a strategy linked to the problems of the agrochemical sector in an environment-conscious age, the development of plant varieties that are less dependent on chemical protection being seen as a growth area.

The seed industry seems to remain less concentrated than some other industries: in the mid-1980s, it was estimated that the top five firms had under 20% of the world market. But at national levels, and for particular crops, the degree of concentration is higher; and the process is continuing.

(d) Market structures

Market channels for farm produce are characterised by many suppliers (farms), who are in a weak position if confronted by a single buyer. This can indeed be a problem, particularly in backward regions where transport is difficult so that farmers cannot easily take their produce far afield, and particularly for produce that will perish if not sold quickly.

Returns to the farmer thus depend on an efficient market system; the consumer too has an interest in a system that will provide food that is fresh, of good quality and properly graded; growing health concerns make hygiene at all stages, and reliable labelling of "biological" or "organic" produce, increasingly significant; storage that can even out supply over the year is an important factor in ensuring variety.

Depending on the product and local circumstances, there are various ways in which the farmer may sell his produce.

Direct sales to the consumer. Farm shops may offer sales "at the farm gate" of dairy produce, eggs, fruit and vegetables; "pick-your-own" systems play some role for fruit and vegetables (particularly in the UK). Such developments depend on the proximity of a large urban, car-owning, population. They can provide valuable extra employment and income for members of the farm family, especially when some element of processing or packaging on the farm is involved. Overall, direct sales do not account for a large part of total farm sales.

Sales at product markets, usually by auction. Much livestock is sold in this way, likewise fruit and vegetables. Small markets in relatively remote rural areas are often unsatisfactory. The "Dutch auctions" or *veilingen* for fruit and vegetables have a particular reputation for efficiency, being equipped with push-button bidding systems. In contrast to the usual auction system, the dealer set in motion a hand on a dial starting *above* the price he expects. Each lot goes to the first prospective buyer to press his button when the hand reaches the highest price he is prepared to bid. The system is quick and transparent. Reliable grading is necessary for the system to work; streamlined transport and communications are also important. The system has been copied in other countries (see discussion of France below).

Sales to merchants or processors. Specialised merchants are often the main buyers of cereals and other crops, and some areas of cattle and other livestock. In the European Community, as will be seen in Part B, the cereals market is supported by "intervention agencies", which stand ready to buy the produce at the pre-determined intervention prices. In principle, farmers as well as merchants can sell into intervention, so the market price is unlikely to fall much below the intervention price. In these cases, storage is mainly undertaken by the intervention agencies.

In the case of sugarbeet, under the EC's Common Agricultural Policy, growers receive an annual quota, which they normally sell directly to the nearest sugar factory at a price mainly determined by the CAP support mechanisms.

Sales to co-operatives. "First-stage" co-operatives buy from the farmer and may carry out initial processing; "second-stage" co-operatives may co-ordinate marketing by a number of primary co-operatives and undertake further processing. As can be seen from Table 3.3, marketing co-operatives are particularly important in the following cases:
* Milk and pigmeat in Denmark. Here, co-operatives have traditionally played a vital role, purchasing milk from the farmers and, after separation, returning skim milk to them for feeding to pigs and calves. Many slaughter-houses are owned and operated by co-operatives.
* Milk in several other countries, particularly the Netherlands. A special situation has existed in the UK, where the Milk Marketing Boards have had a statutory right to buy all milk produced in the country, without having the legal form of a co-operative: it is however likely that they will be transformed into voluntary co-operatives.
* Fruit and vegetables in Denmark and the Netherlands.
* Cereals in France, Germany and Denmark.

Table 3.3—Agricultural products sold through co-operatives, 1989
(percentages of total sales from farms)

	UK	DK	NL	D	F	IT (1987)	SP (1985)
Pigmeat	17	98	23	..	78	15	2
Beef/veal	5	44	16	..	30	6	5
Poultry	0	0	23	..	40	–	4
Eggs	17	60	15	..	25	5	18
Milk	4	91	84	65	50	32	10
Sugarbeet	1	17	63	..	16	–	14
Cereals	19	47	65	52	75	35	10
Fruit	21	90	75	30–40	45	31	26
Vegetables	25	90	82	55–65	35	10	12

Source: Commission, *The Agricultural Situation in the Community 1991* (Table 3.5.6.1).

* Not shown on the table, but important in Southern European countries, are co-operatives for wine and olive oil.

The size and structure of co-operatives varies widely between countries. Italy has over 30,000 co-operatives (including co-operatives supplying farm inputs), with an average membership of only 50–60. At the other extreme, Ireland has only about 140 co-operatives, with an average membership over 1,000. In France, Germany, Denmark and the Netherlands, the average membership is in the range 500–900. (See sources in Appendix, item 5.)

Generally, the aim of marketing co-operatives is to promote members' interests through more efficient marketing and greater bargaining strength. Membership is voluntary; profits are re-invested or distributed among the members; by their voting rights, members can in principle control the management ("one member, one vote" is the basic principle). The need for efficient management, however, may conflict with this democratic principle, particularly in the larger and more complex co-operatives. In France, Germany, Denmark and the Netherlands, the co-operative movement is strongly organised on a three-tier system, with local, regional and national levels: this permits rationalisation (avoiding, for example, overlapping by primary-level co-operatives in geographical or product coverage), and makes possible a co-ordinated market strategy. On the other hand, it removes the decision-making still further from the individual members.

The degree of success of co-operatives depends not only on the quality of their management and the number of their members, but also on the market context in which they are operating. In recent years, with restricted opportunities for expansion in volume terms (particularly in the case of milk where output is regulated by quotas), many co-operatives in the EC have been trying to extend their processing activities "downstream", in order to increase their "added value". This however brings them increasingly into competition with the big commercial food processors.

Links with co-operative banks (particularly within the Raiffeisen movement—see Chapter 1) have facilitated access to funds from outside the farm sector, but finance for expansion and investment has always been a problem for co-operatives.

Sales on contract to processors. Under such contracts, the producer undertakes to supply specified quantities and, usually, to respect certain conditions as regards production methods; the processor undertakes to buy the produce at a specified price, and may provide credit and technical assistance. This form of "vertical integration" has become particularly important for fruit and vegetables for canning or freezing, especially in the UK (where practically all commercial production of peas is subject to contract) and in Italy (practically all production of tomatoes for canning). It also plays a role in several countries for poultry, eggs, and sometimes for calves and pigs (the processor may supply the young animals which the producer fattens before resale to the processor)

The advantages of such contracts to the farmer lie mainly in having an assured outlet and price, and often in obtaining credit and technical assistance. On the other hand, individual farmers have little influence over the price proposed, and such contracts have been criticised for causing the farmer to lose his independence. Advantages to the processor include security of supply and relatively homogeneous produce.

A further step in vertical integration occurs when the processing firm itself undertakes production: this has been the case especially for eggs and poultry (in the UK in particular).

Some features of the marketing system can be illustrated by reference to **France**, where a previously antiquated structure has been much improved in recent decades. Co-operatives, as has been seen above, play an important role in the storage and marketing of cereals, in the collection and processing of dairy produce, in the slaughtering and processing of meat, and for some other products. Their role tends to be particularly important in regions where farms are relatively small, including Brittany and Normandy, Languedoc, Pyrénées and Poitou-Charentes. *Groupements de producteurs* are a particular form of co-operative, officially recognised and granted certain powers to enforce discipline in marketing: they account for the greater part of sales of fruit and vegetables (where they are entitled, under EC regulations, to compensation for surplus produce that has to be withdrawn and destroyed) and of young cattle. They may be grouped in *Comités économiques agricoles*, which determine rules, particularly as regards minimum prices and the terms of compensation for withdrawn produce.

The "Dutch auction"—in French, *marché au cadran*—has been adopted by farmers' co-operatives in Brittany as the main channel for the sale of cauliflowers and artichokes, and plays an increasing role for other vegetables and for pigs, cattle and calves. The "descending" price system is used for fruit and vegetables, "ascending" for livestock. Apart from the technical features, important services offered include control of the quality of produce, checks on the reliability of sellers and buyers, clear information on prices and centralised arrangements for payments. Controls of this kind, together with precise product specifications and with the development of modern telecommunications, even make possible marketing at a distance: buyers and sellers can operate on more than one market at a time, and all produce does not necessarily have to be brought to the market (the first such "telematic" market, for livestock, was opened at Amiens in 1988).

Wholesale markets, where merchants sell to retailers, are a subsequent stage in the chain: these are located in or near the main French towns. Some are specialised in a particular product, others (such as the huge modern market at Rungis on the north-south motorway outside Paris) deal in all types of produce. Nineteen such wholesale markets are designated as *marchés d'intérêt national* and special efforts have been made to modernise them.

(e) Food processing

The food and drink industry is one of the biggest in the European Community, employing 2.4 million people in 1990. Production of food and drink in the EC has been rising steadily, and amounted to 419 billion ECU in 1991. The biggest items were meat and dairy produce, each accounting for around 18% of the total.

Tobacco production (sometimes but not always included in statistics on the sector) occupied 106,000 persons in the EC in 1988, and amounted to 37 billion ECU.

The industry is extremely diverse, ranging from many small firms to a few very large "multinationals". Data on small firms are unreliable, but it seems that in 1988 firms employing under 20 persons accounted for three-quarters or more of the total number of food firms in several EC countries. Their share in employment and output is much less. Small firms, often located in rural areas and many of them co- operatives, can make a valuable contribution to local employment and income, including opportunities for off-farm work by members of farm families. They contribute to regional diversity of food and sometimes innovate in this respect (for example, local cheeses, honey, speciality breads). They may be well placed to take advantage of the current consumer desire for "health foods", including "organically-grown" or "biological" produce. For such reasons, small- and medium-sized enterprises are the object of national and EC assistance, particularly in Southern European regions.

However, small food firms suffer from serious disadvantages: their equipment is often old and they lack finance to invest in new buildings and machinery; they are often one-product firms, subject to seasonal peaks in activity and with underemployment in the intervening periods; they may have little or no control over the quality of the produce they receive; and—perhaps the biggest limitation in present circumstances—they cannot easily undertake significant research and development.

Indeed, in the manufacture of some food products—though not all—there are important economies of scale: this applies, for example, to sugar, flour, animal and vegetable fats, processed fruit and vegetables. These economies may be technical, where mechanisation and automation of the production process bring cost reductions and permit uniform quality of produce. They also relate to product innovation, as regards both the research and development required to create new products and the marketing effort needed to promote and distribute them. Dynamic areas in the food market include "convenience foods": ready-made dishes, including frozen foods, suitable for re-heating in microwave ovens, or the recent development of "modified atmosphere packaging" whereby food is preserved in nitrogen or carbon-dioxide-sealed in plastic impermeable materials. The development of such technology requires expensive investment, and big production runs to recoup the costs.

So the greater part of food production comes from large firms, some of them very large indeed. World-wide, out of the thirty biggest producers of food, drink and tobacco, fifteen are American: most of these have subsidiaries in Europe too, particularly in the UK. The ten largest European companies include Nestlé (Switzerland), followed by Unilever (Netherlands and UK), five other British firms, two French and one Italian. (See Appendix, item 6, for a description of Nestlé.)

In relation to the food sector as a whole, no single firm approaches a monopolistic situation in any country. Table 3.4 indicates output shares in 1987 (the inclusion in Italy and Spain of very small firms affects in particular the number of firms shown, but has less influence on the shares of the largest firms).

In individual product categories, however, market shares may be much greater. Thus in the UK, the top three companies account for over 80% of sales of instant coffee, "savoury snacks" (mainly potato crisps), margarine, prepared soups and yoghurt.

In France, in 1986, one company (France Farine) had 84% of the flour market; two companies (Générale Sucrière and Beghin Say) had 75% of the sugar market; two companies (Lesieur and Astra) had 72% of the edible oils market; two companies (Kellogg and Quaker) had 73% of the breakfast cereals market.

In Germany (the pre-1990 Federal Republic), although the overall degree of concentration is less, there were quite high degrees of concentration for starch products (three firms accounting for 73% of the market in 1988), for margarine and related products (three firms with 77%) and for sugar (three firms with 55%). Even in the less-concentrated Italian market, the top three firms have over 80% of the market in frozen food, breakfast cereals, savoury snacks, baby food and prepared soups.

At the European level, cases where a single firm dominates are few but important, including breakfast cereals (Kellogg—up to 85% in Spain), instant coffee (Nestlé—up to 75% in Italy) and ice-cream (Unilever—up to 50% in Italy

Table 3.4—Food industry structure in 1987

| | Total output | Number of firms* | Percentage of output accounted for by: | |
			top 10 companies	top 50 companies
	$ bn.		%	%
UK	85.4	5,419	31	52
Germany	84.0	4,269	12	26
France	87.0	3,018	29	62
Italy	97.3	40,000	7	16
Spain	38.2	2,608	11	28

* Firms with twenty or more employees in the UK, ten or more in France and Germany, one or more in Italy and Spain.
Source: Confédération des Industries Agro-Alimentaires, reproduced by OC&C Strategy Consultants in *The Restructuring of the European Food Industry* (London), February 1990.

and Spain). Several companies dominate the European market for chocolate confectionery (Nestlé, Mars, Suchard, Cadbury, Ferrero, with cumulative shares up to 88% in the UK) and coffee (other than the "instant" variety—Jacobs Suchard, Douwe Egberts, General Foods, Nestlé, with cumulative share up to 65% in France). On the other hand, there is no dominant European company for bread, sugar confectionery, cheese and many other products.

Cases of *single-firm* domination are thus relatively few, and in at least two cases—breakfast cereals in Spain and instant coffee in Italy—seem to arise when the market is relatively small and underdeveloped: in the UK, where breakfast cereals have been a large market for many years, Kellogg remains the largest firm but has only some 43% of the market, and similar observations can be made about instant coffee. This might support the thesis that when profits can be made, competing firms enter the market.

On the other hand, there are several cases where the market is dominated by just a few very big firms. This raises the question whether competitive forces remain adequate, or whether some degree of collusion between these firms enables them to act against the consumer interest.

In Western Europe, data on profit margins are not often collected and published at national level. They are however available from individual company reports. The general impression is that margins are not high, especially after tax.

Table 3.5 gives information on the biggest European companies producing food and drink. Their average profit in 1988, after tax, works out at 5.9% of total turnover (including, in some cases, non-food activities). Since 1988, as a result of recession, many firms have declared reduced profits.

Table 3.5—Turnover and profits of major European food and drink firms, 1988

Company, with main food or drink activity	Turnover on food and drink	Total turnover	Net profits	Net profits as % of total turnover
	\$ million			%
Nestlé (CH) – coffee, confectionery	26600	27800	1390	5.0
Unilever (NL) – fats and oils	18835	31303	1526	4.9
Grand Metropolitan (UK) – beverages	9793	10726	733	6.8
Allied Lyons – brewing	8006	8006	558	7.0
Dalgety (UK)– various	7787	7969	529	6.6
Ferruzzi (IT) – sugar	6841	19079	425	2.2
BSN (F) – various	6383	7065	367	5.2
Sucres et Denrées (F) – sugar	4858	5495	12	0.2
Guinness (UK) – beer etc.	4700	4939	607	12.3
Hillsdown (UK) – poultry	4497	6320	368	5.8
Hanson (UK) – various	4448	13158	1994	15.2
Bass – beer etc.	4446	6644	574	8.6
Associated British Foods (UK) – bread, biscuits	4398	4398	346	7.9
Jacobs Suchard (CH) – coffee, chocolate	4354	4354	234	5.4
Cadbury Schweppes (UK) – confectionery, soft drinks	4241	4241	301	7.1
United Biscuits (UK) – bread, biscuits	4239	4239	291	6.9
Heineken (NL) – beer etc.	3683	3686	147	4.0
Tate & Lyle (UK) – sugar	3641	3715	125	3.4
Berisford (UK) – various	3558	4706	59	1.3
Whitbread (UK) – brewing, hotels	3280	3280	287	8.8
Unigate (UK) – dairy products	3113	4149	230	5.5
SME (IT) – various	3099	3099	68	2.2
Rank Hovis McDougall (UK) – cereals	2956	2969	186	6.3
Booker (UK) – various	2938	3275	131	4.0
Perrier (F) – mineral water	2443	2443	175	7.2
Pernod Ricard (F) – alcoholic drinks	2256	2256	130	5.8
Union International (UK) – meat	2196	2196	32	1.5
Koninklijke Wessanen (NL) – dairy products	1923	1923	47	2.4
Northern Foods (UK) – dairy products	1834	1834	91	5.0
Union Laitière Normande (F) – dairy products	1819	1819	14	0.8
MD Foods (DK) – dairy products	1686	1699	93	5.5
Sandoz (CH) – various	1648	6925	519	7.5
Besnier (F) – dairy products	1629	1629	63	3.9
LVMH (F) – wines and spirits	1484	2754	336	12.2
All above companies	169612	220093	12988	5.9

Source: Institut Agronomique Méditerranéen de Montpellier, *Agrodata: les 100 premiers groupes agro-alimentaires mondiaux*, 1990.

The United States has better information (cf. Appendix, item 2). The overall degree of concentration does not appear excessive: in 1987 the top 50 processing firms controlled 48% of the total food market. But as in Western Europe, concentration in some individual foodstuffs is high.

Several US studies suggest that undue market power is being exercised in those food industries with differentiated consumer goods and oligopolistic market structures, possibly causing consumers to pay 6–10% more than if the industries had been more competitively structured. Heavy advertising is undertaken to promote branded products. In 1989, according to the US Department of Agriculture, 12,000 new grocery products were introduced, resulting in 62,000 new products since 1983. Food-related advertising in 1989 probably reached $12 billion, and other promotion activities such as discounts to retailers, trade shows, etc. were probably twice that amount (total consumer food expenditure in 1988 was $506 billion). One American study (Connor *et al.*, p. 417—cf. Appendix, item 2) concluded :

...Market structure matters. Either high concentration or high product differentiation (and often times both) are positively associated with excess profits, elevated prices, technical inefficiency in the employment of labor, high and secularly rising wages, food price inflation, and excess consumption of foods. Moderately concentrated oligopolies may provide a congenial environment for inventive activity, but more important to technological progressiveness is keeping open the channels for the interindustry transfer of technologies from diverse sources.

Numerous mergers and acquisitions have taken place in the food and drink sector in recent years. In the USA, there were 351 acquisitions in the single year 1988. Table 3.6 shows the development in the European Community. Besides the "majority" acquisitions shown, there was a smaller number of acquisitions of minority holdings, and a number of "joint ventures".

Some American companies have been active investors in Western Europe, but overall, investment by Western European firms in the USA exceeds American investment in Europe. The firms concerned are mainly British (e.g. Brooke Bond, Allied Lyons, Rank Hovis McDougall, Cadbury), French (e.g. BSN, Lesieur, Pernod-Ricard, Perrier), Dutch (Unilever) and Swiss (Nestlé, Jacobs-Suchard).

Take-overs may be motivated partly by the economies of scale already referred to—although many of the companies responsible for take-overs probably reached an adequate size some time ago. Also important in current circumstances is the desire for increased market control. Particularly when profit margins are tight and there is little scope for overall expansion in the market, the acquisition of well-known brand names makes possible increased market share, and diminishes competition, without increasing total output in the sector.

A significant case of geographic integration was the announcement, in May 1992, that PepsiCo was to merge its production of salty and sweet snacks in

Table 3.6—Mergers and acquisitions of majority holdings in the EC food and drink industry

	National	Community	International	Total
1986/87	39	11	2	52
1987/88	25	18	8	51
1988/89	35	27	14	76
1989/90	41	44	17	102
1990/91	29	26	16	71

Source: EC Commission, *Report on Competition Policy*, Brussels (various annual issues).

Spain, Portugal and Greece, with similar production by General Mills in France, Belgium and the Netherlands: shared research and development, leading to "improved product innovation", was said to be a main motive.

Besides such "horizontal" integration, there is also some tendency towards "vertical" integration, both "upstream" to secure sources of supply, and "downstream" into the retail and, especially, the catering sectors, as will be seen in section (f) below.

There are suggestions that the scope for profitable acquisitions is diminishing, so that the pace of change may slow down during the 1990s. Possibly, by the late 1990s there may even be some "unbundling"—i.e. shedding of acquisitions that have proved unsuccessful.

(e) Food retailing

The number of food shops has been steadily falling, and their average size rising. In the UK, there were in 1976 1.9 food retail outlets per 1000 inhabitants: by 1985 the number had fallen by nearly half, to just 1.0 shops per 1000 inhabitants. In other countries of North-Western Europe, the fall has been only slightly less spectacular, and by 1985 there were, per 1000 inhabitants, 1.3 shops in Denmark, 0.7 in the Netherlands, 1.6 in Belgium, 1.3 in Germany, 1.4 in France. In Southern Europe, the trend has not gone so far: there were still 2.8 food shops per 1000 inhabitants in Italy, 3.0 in Spain, 4.4 in Portugal.

The main factor responsible has been the growth of self- service "supermarkets" (usually defined as having between 400 and 2499 m^2 of sales area) and "hypermarkets" (over 2500 m^2): for the latter, items other than food are relatively important. The share of these two categories together in total food sales was reckoned in 1987/88 to be around 80% in the UK, Belgium and France, 71% in the Netherlands, 56% in Germany, 46% in Denmark.

Some countries—including France, Belgium and Germany—have introduced legislation to curb the development of hypermarkets: this has been in response to pressures from small shopkeepers. However, large self-service stores, stocking a wide range of goods at competitive prices, with rapid turn-over, often located out-of-town with ample parking facilities, have responded to consumer preferences. Surveys in various countries find that consumers want low prices so far as is consistent with good quality, variety, freshness, clear labelling (including "sell-by" dates), easy access, quick and friendly service.

Consumer organisations in most countries regularly publish surveys of the prices of comparable items in different supermarkets, and generally help to maintain competitive pressures. Thus the Belgian consumer magazine *Test-Achats*, reporting in April 1992 on its latest findings, was able to list at least four competing supermarket chains even in quite small country towns and up to twenty in the bigger cities: a "basket" of 119 identical products cost about 20% less in the cheapest stores than in the dearest, but a basket of "distributor brands" (see below) could cost only half as much as similar branded goods in the most expensive stores.

There has been a considerable increase in the degree of concentration, as supermarkets and hypermarkets usually form part of large chains. In 1987, the largest five food chains were calculated to have around half the total food sales in the Netherlands, Belgium, Germany and the UK, and even more in Denmark. In some countries, the number of "decision points" has become even more concentrated, taking advantage of computerised information technology: in the UK, it has been reported that ten key decision points control the buying for over 3,000 food stores, accounting for 58% of grocery sales; in other countries, notably France, food chains maintain a policy of decentralised management. However, centralised purchasing and bulk distribution systems are essential features of the big food chains.

There has been some polarisation of store size: while small general food shops have been virtually eliminated in most countries of North-Western Europe, specialist shops can survive, and have even been able to develop where they meet a growing demand, such as for high-quality produce or "health foods".

In France, where the overall degree of concentration is somewhat lower than in neighbouring countries, small-scale specialised shops may have better chances of survival because of the preferences of French consumers. *Boulangeries-pâtisseries* still accounted in 1986 for about 7% of total food sales, butcher shops and *charcuteries* for 16%, other specialised shops for 11%. Nevertheless, the biggest food chain, Leclerc, possessing in 1986 103 hypermarkets and 344 supermarkets, was reckoned in 1985 to have 12% of the total food market, followed by six others totalling 32%. French hypermarkets had an average size of some $6,700 \text{ m}^2$, employed on average about 290 people each, had a total turnover of some 375 mn. frs. each, of which about half from food sales, made an average profit before tax of about 4% on groceries and drinks and 17% on fresh foodstuffs (there were somewhat higher rates of profit on clothing and other sales items). Supermarkets had an average size of just over 1000 m^2, employed 34 workers on average, had a turnover of around 35 mn. frs. of which about 90% came from food, and made pre-tax profits of 9.6% on groceries and drinks, 17% on fresh foods.

Since, in the countries of North-Western Europe, total food consumption in volume terms is rather static, as will be seen in the following chapter, expansion strategies by food distribution firms cannot simply aim at increased output.

One strategy, linked to the trends in the food processing industry already discussed, is *diversification*: new product lines, in areas where consumer demand is growing. Other means to attract customers include the improvement of services, such as simplified payment through credit cards and electronic "direct debit" of customers' bank accounts.

"Own brands", or "distributor brands"—i.e. goods bearing the label of the distributor and not of any processing firm, and sold below the price of processors' brands—are an important feature of some food chains. They were reckoned to account, in 1986, for 25% of food sales in the UK, 21% in the Netherlands, and somewhat lower percentages in other North-Western European countries. Sometimes the presentation of these products imitates well-known branded goods, and their quality is supposed to be equivalent. But advertising costs are negligible, since these items are sold on the basis of the general reputation of the food chain. In the case of the specific category of "generic" goods (sometimes called "white products"), which are usually basic foods such as sugar or flour, only the name of the product is indicated, and the price is kept particularly low. Since "own brands" are manufactured to the specifications of the distributor, and do not require individual promotion, they provide outlets for relatively small food processing firms, and may have caused some reduction in levels of concentration for specific foodstuffs.

Some chains have cut prices even further by "cash and carry" systems or other methods whereby distribution costs are minimised: shelf presentation is simplified, produce is sold in quite large quantities rather than in individual items, staff and labour costs are minimised. A more recent development offering significant cost reductions is computerised stock control (by "electronic point of sale" equipment, or EPOS), which enables stock-holding to be minimised.

There is also diversification into non-food activities; some "vertical integration" into food production; and some moves into the catering sector (discussed below). Co-operation with partner organisations may result in the formation of a new type of store, as in a number of agreements between French food retailers and oil companies to develop "convenience stores" on petrol station forecourts.

As with the food processing industry discussed in the previous section, numerous mergers and acquisitions have occurred in food distribution. The acquisition of existing companies is often a preferred means of expansion, as it avoids the potentially risky and costly business of funding internal expansion, and allows for rapid expansion over a short time period. Economies of scale are expected from operating a larger chain of stores. Targets for acquisition strategies include family-owned businesses which have lost their dynamism but also firms which are basically sound but have run into financial difficulties, or successful companies operating in regional markets which are complementary to those of the predator.

Another major structural trend has been increasing "internationalisation" of food retailing. The German firm Aldi, for example, has spread to several neighbouring countries. Some French firms, especially Carrefour, have set up numerous hypermarkets in Spain and Portugal. The Belgian firm GB-Inno-BM (already the result of successive mergers within the country) has interests in France and other Western European countries. Another Belgian firm, Delhaize Le Lion, controls a major American chain, Food Lion; it was for a while active in Portugal; in 1992 it acquired a majority share in a large Greek supermarket chain; it has an involvement in Prague which it is seeking to expand.

(g) Catering

The amount of food consumed outside the home, at work-place canteens, restaurants, "fast food" and "take-away" shops, continues to grow. Higher levels of income and new employment, occupational patterns involving higher female participation in the labour force, and social factors such as increased purchasing-power among young people, have been factors in this trend (see next chapter).

Up-to-date information is difficult to obtain, but it has been estimated that in the early 1980s, catering expenditure accounted for between 15% and 25% of total food expenditure in North-Western European countries. In the UK, in 1990, expenditure on "meals out" was thought to amount to about £20 billion, as compared with £42 billion for household food expenditure; total food consumption has been shifting steadily away from meals prepared and eaten in the home towards food purchased from the catering sector, and the upward trend is most pronounced for meals other than midday meals. In the US, in 1991, "meals and snacks" away from home accounted for about 43% of expenditure on food (excluding alcoholic drinks).

The structure of this sector is, on the whole, diverse and small-scale: most restaurants are in individual ownership and management. However, some large catering groups have emerged, sometimes to acquire leadership positions in specific sectors. New opportunities such as motorway and airport restaurants can only be grasped by large-scale companies. Both horizontal and vertical integration is occurring. Thus in the UK, Trusthouse Forte combines a restaurant and hotel chain with roadside and motorway catering, airport catering and in-flight services; the larger breweries—while obliged by recent legislation to divest themselves of their "public houses" or "pubs" (where food as well as beer is increasingly consumed)—are expanding into restaurant and fast food chains. In France, the Accor group is the leading catering company, controlling the foremost hotel-restaurant chain (Novotel) and numerous other outlets. In France too, as has been mentioned above, some major food retailers, having begun by installing cafeterias inside their stores, have expanded into restaurant and fast food chains.

Within the US, the hamburger chain McDonald's has the largest turnover, with sales over $11 billion in 1988, as compared with $4.9 bn. by the Burger King Corporation, owned by Grand Met, and $2.9 bn. by Kentucky Fried Chicken, $2.6 bn. by Pizza Hut and $1.6 bn. by Taco Bell—the last three being owned by PepsiCo.

With its various chains, PepsiCo claims to have over 3,000 fast-food restaurants outside the US, more than any other group. In some Western European countries, particularly the UK, Kentucky Fried Chicken and Pizza Hut outlets are widespread. Eastern European countries are PepsiCo's latest field of operation. In 1990 the first Pizza Hut was opened in Moscow, soon followed by a second; and in October 1992, PepsiCo announced a deal to expand its activities in the Ukraine, involving a joint venture to promote the sale and leasing of Ukrainian-built ships.

On the other hand, the British food manufacturer, United Biscuits, is competing in the UK with its subsidiaries Pizzaland and Wimpy (which, like McDonald's, sells hamburgers).

The French market has been comparatively resistant to American-style food, and has seen the emergence of locally-owned chains marketing French-style fast food: these include La Brioche Dorée, La Croissanterie and Franquette, which are having some success in penetrating markets outside France. The hamburger chain Quick is owned by a Franco-Belgian consortium consisting of Casino and GB-Inno-BM, and operates in both countries, in direct competition with McDonald's.

*   *   *

At the outset of this chapter the question was put whether the food industry as a whole remains sufficiently competitive. Though outright monopoly is not to be found, monopolistic practices do undoubtedly occur and excess profits are sometimes made. The greatest danger of restrictive practices arise in sectors where the market is relatively static, with weak demand growth, and where import penetration is below average, either because of the nature of the product (e.g. fresh milk) or because of barriers to trade, including non-tariff barriers.

Without public control, in individual countries and more recently in the European Community, restrictive practices would undoubtedly be more widespread and concentration would have gone further—the important issue of competition policy will be discussed in Chapter 11.

But on the whole, the answer must be positive, so far: the dynamism of the agri-food system, its ability to innovate, to develop and implement technological improvements of many kinds in the production, processing and distribution of food, have provided plenty of food, in great variety and at affordable prices. As will be seen in Chapters 4 and 11, average consumption more than meets nutritional needs in Western Europe and North America. The percentage of consumer expenditure on foodstuffs in the twelve EC Member States averaged 16.5% in 1989 (beverages were an additional 3.3% and tobacco 1.8%). The figure was lowest in the north-western countries (down to 11.6% in the United Kingdom, 12.3% in the Federal Republic of Germany). By international standards—including Central and Eastern European countries—these are low rates of expenditure, which leave a large share of consumer purchasing-power available for other purposes.

The power of the big food processors has so far been largely offset by that of the big distributors, and the result has been in the public interest. But any significant vertical integration between the processing and distribution sectors would need to be watched very carefully.

Perhaps the most effective guarantee of the consumer interest is provided by free trade: monopolistic power that might be attained at the national level is much more difficult in a competitive international context. Hence trade liberalisation, and in the EC the attempt to remove trade barriers in the 1992 "Single Market" context, are very significant. These issues will be considered in several chapters in Part B.

APPENDIX

1. Theory of imperfect competition. This field is not usually covered in agricultural economics textbooks, which concentrate on the farm sector. On the other hand, all economics textbooks set out the theory of imperfect competition, monopolistic competition, oligopoly, monopoly, etc.—see the references in the Appendix to the Introduction. It is better for the uninitiated to read these first, rather than the relatively complex works by the original authors such as Joan Robinson, Edward Chamberlin, etc.
The Schumpeterian view is set out *inter alia* in Chapter VIII of his *Capitalism, Socialism and Democracy* (Allen & Unwin, London: 4th edn., 1954).

2. Agribusiness: general sources. There is much less material available on the agribusiness sector than on the farm sector. General economics textbooks, such as those mentioned in the Appendix to the Introduction, deal at some length with the theory of monopoly and imperfect competition, but without relating it specifically to the food industry; while most textbooks on agricultural economics concentrate on the farm sector and have relatively little to say about either the theory or the practice of agribusiness.
Consequently, the descriptive and analytical material in this chapter has been based on a wide range of disparate sources, and it is not easy to obtain comprehensive and up-to-date information: some of the data quoted in this chapter are from specific surveys which have not been repeated. The most important general sources are mentioned below.
* Some basic data are produced annually, but with a time-lag of several years, by Eurostat in *Structure and Activity of Industry*. (Its *Statistical Yearbook on Industry* has not appeared since 1988.)
* The EC Commission publishes an annual report, *Panorama of EC industry*, which includes chapters on the food industry and several of the agricultural input sectors. (For 1992, only a statistical supplement to the previous report is available.)
* Under the Commission's FAST programme ("Forecasting and Assessment in Science and Technology"), a series of reports were produced on "The Future of the European Food System"; but as this series ended in 1988, its data are now somewhat old. The main papers, somewhat modified, were also published under the title *Prospects for the European Food System*, edited by Bruce Traill (Elsevier, London, 1989).

* A useful though specific Commission report is *Development Strategy for the Agro-Food Industries in the Mediterranean Regions of the European Community* (1985).
* Comprehensive information on the food markets in various countries, on product sectors and on major companies is regularly collected by the *Centre Français de Commerce Extérieur* in Paris. Its publications, unfortunately, are very expensive, being aimed primarily at the French business world.
* Certain consultancy agencies—such as OC&C Ltd. of London and Paris, and Nielsen of West Germany—specialise in the food industry sector, but most of their work is only available to their clients.
* The news agency Agra Europe (London) publishes a monthly report, *Eurofood*. Useful to those who have to keep regularly in touch: otherwise too expensive. It also publishes special reports, of varying quality, also very expensive.

Among academic institutions working more-or-less regularly on the food industry at the European scale, the following may be mentioned:

* The *Institut Agronomique Méditerranéen* in Montpellier (France) maintains a valuable "data-bank" on major food processing firms, which is published every third year under the title *Agrodata*.
* The *Institut für landwirtschaftliche Marktforschung der Bundesforschungsanstalt für Landwirtschaft*, Braunschweig-Völkenrode (FAL). See in particular *Wissenschaftliche Mitteilung* 1990:1, containing a series of useful articles.
* The Department of Agricultural Economics and Management, University of Reading. The following, though mostly concerned with the UK, include some European and international aspects:
    —A. Swinbank and J. Burns (eds.), *The EEC and the Food Industries*, Food Economics Study No. 1, 1984;
    —J. Burns and A. Swinbank (eds.), *Food Policy Issues and the Food Industries*, Food Economics Study No. 3, 1986;
    —J. Burns and A. Swinbank (eds.), *Competition Policy in the Food Industries*, Food Economics Study No. 4, 1988.

Other academic works used in preparing this chapter include:

* J. Pinard, *Les industries alimentaires dans le monde* (Masson, Paris: 1988)—a useful general introduction.
* G. Chalençon, *Le marché français des produits alimentaires* (Agra-Alimentation, Paris: 3e édn., 1987).
* E. Wöhlken, *Einführung in die landwirtschaftliche Marktlehre* (Ulmer, Stuttgart: 3. Auflage, 1990)—see chapter 4.
* S. Berndt, *Neue Entwicklungstendenzen in der Nahrungsmittelproduktion der Bundesrepublik Deutschland und ihre Auswirkungen auf Landwirtschaft und Konsumenten* (Herodot, Aachen: 1987).
* M. Breitenacher und U.C. Täger, *Ernährungsindustrie—Strukturwandlungen in Produktion und Absatz* (IFO-Institut, München: 1990)—contains a detailed description of the German food industry.
* J. Burns, J. McInerney and A. Swinbank, *The Food Industry: Economics and Policies* (Heinemann, London: 1983)—only on the UK, and now rather out-of-date.
* A. Swinbank, "The EEC's policies and its food", in *Food Policy*, February 1992.

The annual *Agrarbericht* by the German Ministry of Agriculture includes useful coverage of the "upstream" and "downstream" agricultural industries.

The United States is much better served by official reports. The US Department of Agriculture publishes annually an informative *Food Marketing Review* and a *Food Cost Review*. There are also numerous academic studies, among which the following is particularly useful: J.M. Connor *et al.*, *The Food Manufacturing Industries* (Lexington, Massachusetts: 1985).

3. Specific sectors.

Livestock feed. Useful feed balance sheets, but only up to 1987, appear in a special Eurostat report, *Animal Feed—Supply and Demand of Feedingstuffs in the European Community* (Luxembourg, 1990). The Agra Europe agency (London) has produced a series of reports on livestock feed, the latest being Special Report No. 49, *EC Animal Feed Industry 1989–95*.

For the present work, useful material has been obtained from FEFAC (*Fédération Européenne des Fabricants d'Aliments Composés*) in Brussels.

Fertilisers. The IFA (International Fertilizer Industry Association) in Paris has provided helpful information.

See also S. McCorriston, "Les déformations du marché européen des inputs agricoles en matière de concurrence", in *Economie Rurale* 196, mars–avril 1990 (this also deals with machinery).

Animal health products. Helpful information from FEDESA (or European Federation of Animal Health) in Brussels.

Feed additives. Helpful information from FEFANA (or European Federation of Animal Feed Additive Manufacturers), Brussels.

Seeds. See *inter alia* N. McMullen, *Seeds and World Agricultural Progress*, National Planning Association (Washington D.C.) 1987.

4. Marketing. For an excellent account of the French market system, see L. Lagrange, *La commercialisation des produits agricoles et alimentaires* (Lavoisier, Paris: 1989).

The Dutch *veiling* system was analysed in several articles in the French journal *Economie Rurale* in 1985: see in no. 165 articles by F. Lauret and J.F. Soufflet, by J. Vaudois, and by G. Opstelten; and in no. 170, an article by F. Naegelen.

5. Co-operation. The COGECA (*Comité Général de la Coopération Agricole de la C.E.E.*) in Brussels provides information on co-operatives in the various EC countries.

Background information can be found in "Agricultural Co-operation in the EEC", *Studies: Agricultural series no. 21* (EC Publishing Services, Brussels: 1967) (this covers the original six Member States in detail); and in M. Sargent, *Agricultural Co-operation* (Gower, Aldershot (UK): 1982). More up-to-date information is contained in Ministère de l'Agriculture (France), "La coopération agricole dans la CEE", *Bulletin technique d'information 6–7*, 1992.

There is a lack of critical analysis. See however G. Foxall, *Co-operative Marketing in European Agriculture* (Gower, Aldershot (UK): 1982).

6. The case of Nestlé. As the biggest European food company, this may be briefly examined (information from *Agrodata*, see above: data up to 1988).

About 96% of Nestlé's turnover comes from foodstuffs. The category "beverages", including soluble coffee ("Nescafé"), fruit juices and mineral water accounts for 28% of the total, dairy products (condensed and powdered milk, etc.) for 15%, chocolate confectionery for 12%, prepared foods ("Maggi" powdered soups, etc.) for 12%, deep-frozen foods and ice-cream for 10% ...

Although Nestlé is based in Switzerland, only 3% of its turnover takes place there: another 48% arises in other West European countries, 33% in North America and 16% in other continents. By the end of 1988 Nestlé had 178 subsidiaries, of which 94 in Western Europe, 22 in North America and 27 in Latin America.

The company has steadily expanded through a series of take-overs, which reflect a dual strategy:

* Reinforcement of its position within its sector of activity, for instance through the acquisition of the British chocolate firm Rowntree;
* Geographical reinforcement, especially within Europe, for instance in Italy (where Nestlé was previously not very prominent) through the acquisition of the Italian food and confectionery group Buitoni-Perugina, or—more recently—by the take-over of the French mineral water firm Perrier.

The group's total turnover in 1988 amounted to 28 billion US dollars; net after-tax profit was 5.0% (the average profit over the period 1977–1988 was 4.2%).

CHAPTER 4

FOOD CONSUMPTION AND DEMAND

This chapter will consider first the levels and trends of food consumption in the main market economies, then the factors which influence demand for foodstuffs. These two concepts should be distinguished. **"Consumption"** refers to physical quantities actually consumed (in the statistics, usually the amounts available or purchased, since we usually do not know just how much gets eaten). **"Demand"** refers to the underlying wishes of consumers as to how much to purchase.

(a) Consumption levels and trends

Table 4.1 shows data on *per capita* food consumption in a number of countries; figures for Central and Eastern European countries are included although some of these are now known to be unreliable.

In Western Europe and North America, the availability of calories appears adequate, indeed excessive in some cases from a nutritional point of view, with an increasingly sedentary population: in some high-income but health-conscious countries—most notably Sweden—calorie consumption is relatively low. It remains high in Southern Europe.

Consumption of animal protein reflects income levels, being on the whole higher in North-Western than in Southern Europe, though there are exceptions due to national eating habits. The intake of vegetable protein tends to be lowest where that of animal protein is highest.

North America has even higher consumption of animal protein. Overall, the contrast between the developed and the "developing" regions of the world is stark, with calorie intakes below recognised needs for much of the population in Africa and the Far East, and supplies of animal protein definitely inadequate by any nutritional standard.

Per capita consumption of individual products varies between Western European countries, and is evolving in different ways over time. Table 4.2 shows some major food groups in selected EC countries. (Note that these data include

Table 4.1—Availabilities of calories and proteins per person per day, 1987–89

	Calories	Protein from:	
		vegetable products	animal products
		grams	grams
Sweden	2945	28	65
UK	3181	36	54
Netherlands	3163	32	65
Germany (BRD)	3464	36	64
France	3449	34	62
Switzerland	3565	34	64
Italy	3508	49	57
Spain	3567	28	65
Greece	3793	55	57
Poland	3464	46	56
Czecho–Slovakia	3609	45	63
Hungary	3638	48	56
Romania	3252	56	43
Bulgaria	3683	58	52
USSR	3380	50	56
All Europe (excl. USSR)	3459	42	60
North America	3656	36	72
Latin America	2724	38	29
Africa	2218	43	11
Far East	2433	47	11

Source: FAO *Production Yearbook.*

processed products, expressed in terms of the quantities of the basic products used in their manufacture; also that the EC average data for the earlier period do not include Spain and Portugal, and are thus not strictly comparable.) Some significant points are as follows:

Cereals. Per capita consumption is generally between 60 and 80 kg. (this does not include grain fed to animals). Wheat bread, with some rye bread in the cases of Germany and Denmark, are the main items; but the high consumption in Italy is partly due to *pasta.*

Potatoes. Consumption is falling in some countries: the EC average is about 80 kg. In some countries, a large part of consumption is in the form of "chips" and "crisps": this probably accounts for consumption remaining relatively high in

Table 4.2—Consumption of major foodstuffs (kg. per head per day)

	Year	EC10 or EC12	of which:						
			UK	DK	NL	D	F	IT	SP
Cereals (flour equivalent, excl. rice)	>1973/74<	84	74	65	63	66	72	129	..
	1990/91	82	80	64	51	74	79	110	72
Potatoes	>1973/74<	82	100	69	83	93	94	38	..
	1989/90	78	98	65	89	71	71	38	85
Sugar (white sugar equivalent)	>1973/74<	37	46	49	44	36	38	30	..
	1990/91	36	41	40	40	35	33	29	27
Vegetables (incl. preserved)	>1973/74<	101	73	50	83	68	109	152	..
	1988/89	117	65	80	98	83	124	167	199
Fruit (incl. preserved)	>1973/74<	60	32	42	66	86	56	68	..
	1989/90	61	38	49	63	61	58	81	64
Milk (fresh products, excl. cream)	>1973<	99*	144	145	143	86	83	69	..
	1990	100*	129	145	135	93	101	75	92
Butter (fat content)	>1973<	5*	7	7	2	6	7	2	..
	1990	3	4	5	3	5	7	2	0
Eggs	>1973<	14	15	11	11	17	13	11	..
	1990	13	13	14	10	15	15	10	16
Total meat	>1973<	74	70	57	63	82	87	61	..
	1990	87	70	97	86	94	101	83	91
Beef and veal	>1973<	25	22	15	21	23	29	26	..
	1990	22	19	19	20	22	30	26	13
Pigmeat	>1973<	31	27	35	32	49	33	16	..
	1990	39	24	64	46	58	37	32	49
Poultrymeat	>1973<	12	12	6	7	9	14	15	..
	1990	19	20	12	19	12	22	19	23

* Author's estimate.   EC 10 for 1973/74 and 1973.
Source: Commission, *The Agricultural Situation in the Community* (various years—Table 3.7.2 in recent issues). Some recent data are provisional.

the UK, Belgium and the Netherlands. In Italy, low consumption of potatoes is the counterpart to high consumption of *pasta*.

Sugar. Another "energy" food, for which consumption is falling in almost all EC countries, especially as people become concerned about being overweight and about dental decay.

Vegetables. The variety of items and the importance of processed products make data on this group difficult to interpret. In Southern European countries, high consumption of tomatoes pushes up the total. On the whole, consumption is rising: probably a large part of the extra consumption is in processed form.

Fruit. Similar statistical problems arise as with vegetables (juices, for example, are an important outlet). Citrus fruit is not included: in this case, consumption is highest in the Southern European countries, as one would expect. Overall, in volume terms, consumption seems fairly stable, but there is probably considerable substitution of higher-quality and higher-price fruit, including exotic produce, for lower-quality grade and traditional items.

Milk and milk products. As regards fresh milk, there is quite a strong North-South differentiation, as British, Dutch and Danish consumers (as well as other Scandinavians) drink relatively large amounts. But there is some levelling tendency, as consumption falls in these countries and rises in the others.
Butter consumption reflects national characteristics even more strongly, but again, there is some levelling. Ireland (not in the table) had formerly the highest *per capita* consumption in the Community, but this has fallen substantially (from 11 kg. in 1973 to 6 kg. by 1989). There have been declines also in the UK and Denmark, formerly also high-consumption countries, but where health concerns over saturated fats have been prominent. Consumption in the Netherlands has risen slightly from a very low level, and continues to reflect high use of margarine: this may be related to the publicity of the main margarine producer, Unilever (a Dutch company) as well as to the health factor. In France, "taste" seems to remain much more important than the health factor, and consumption has risen to the highest EC level. In Mediterranean countries, both butter and margarine consumption remains low: neither is much used for spreading on bread, while olive oil is normally used in cooking.
Cheese consumption also reflects national attitudes. France, where many different types are available, has the highest consumption in the EC, together with Greece, where *feta* is widely used. Other major dairy producers, Ireland, Denmark and the Netherlands, also have relatively high consumption.

Eggs. There is no clear pattern, probably because eggs are used in different ways as between countries (manufacturing, cooking and fresh consumption). There is a slight declining tendency in some countries, possibly due to health concerns (cholesterol): this could accelerate.

Meat. Total meat consumption has risen in most countries, but the pattern varies widely between the different types, with much substitution occurring. This is partly due to changing price relationships, as the price of poultrymeat and to a lesser extent pigmeat has been reduced relatively to that of beef by intensive production techniques; while beef, in times of recession as in the latter half of the 1980s, is one of the first items on which consumers cut down, and the market may not subsequently be recovered. Changing consumer preferences are also a factor, as beef usually requires more preparation in the home than the other meats. Health considerations have also worked against beef consumption in some

countries (see section b iv below); but health concerns arise increasingly for the
other meats too.

Beef consumption has fallen particularly in the UK: after 1973 it rose somewhat
in most other countries, but the more recent trend is for stagnation or decline.
(Note that the averages for the EC of "Ten" in 1973 and "Twelve" in 1989 are
here somewhat misleading because of the non-inclusion of Spain and Portugal,
with their relatively low consumption, in the earlier period.

Pigmeat consumption, on the other hand, has risen sharply in Denmark, the
Netherlands and Germany—all countries where various types of *saucisson* as
well as fresh pork are traditionally much favoured by consumers. But it is also
rising from lower initial levels in France and in Southern European countries.

Poultrymeat consumption has risen sharply in all countries, though it remains
somewhat lower in the countries of high pigmeat consumption, demonstrating
the close link between the two "white meats".

(b) Determinants of demand

As has just been seen, several factors influence aggregate demand for a commodity. The factors which lend themselves most easily to economic analysis are
consumers' incomes and the prices of the product and of other products. A
simplified *per capita* demand function might thus be written:

$$Q_d = f(Y, P_p, P_1 \dots P_n)$$

where Y is average income per head, P_p is the price of the product and $P_1 \dots P_n$
are the prices of (n) other products.

However, changes in consumer *preferences* are becoming increasingly important as compared with the more easily quantifiable economic factors.

Per capita demand can in principle be multiplied by the size of the population
to obtain *aggregate* demand. However, the *distribution* of income within a
population should be taken into account. Changes in the age distribution can also
modify the pattern and volume of demand.

i) Incomes

Over time, rising *per capita* income gives rise to increased expenditure on
food, and to changes in the pattern of consumption.

Income growth in the developed market economies over the last two decades
has been moderate but on the whole positive, despite periods of recession. During
the 1970s in the EC (ten Member States), gross domestic product (GDP) per
inhabitant rose on average at 2.5% per annum (in constant prices, i.e. adjusted
for inflation). In the early 1980s, growth was slow or even negative, but over the
second half of the decade, the twelve EC Member States had an average growth
rate of 2.8% (strong growth in Spain and Portugal following their accession in
1986 helped to push up the average).

Food, however, differs from most other goods and services in that its physical
consumption cannot rise indefinitely. At some point, when people have more

than enough to eat, the overall *volume* of food consumed has to stop rising. *Expenditure* may continue to rise, with greater "added value" in processing and packaging: this, however, does not usually give extra returns to the farmer.

It has been statistically observed that increases in *per capita* income are associated with a less-than-proportionate increase in expenditure for food in general. This was first noted in the 19th century by the German statistician Ernst Engel and has become known as **"Engel's Law"**. It is valid over time; it can also be observed in international comparisons, and within a country between different income groups. Although *per capita* consumption is affected by factors other than income—i.e. prices and consumer preferences, which will be discussed below—the income-expenditure relationship is sufficiently precise to be represented statistically and for "income elasticities" to be derived.

Income elasticity of demand is defined as the proportionate change in expenditure on foodstuffs (or in the quantity demanded—see below) in response to a given proportionate change in consumer income, or:

$$E_{di} = \frac{\Delta X/X}{\Delta Y/Y}$$

The elasticity may vary at different levels of income, so the co-efficient E_{di} is usually related to a small—1%—change in income. Four different situations can be distinguished:

* Expenditure is rising more than in proportion to the change in income: the co-efficient is greater than unity, and demand is said to be *income-elastic*. This is unlikely in the case of food in general, but possible for individual high-quality (and expensive) foodstuffs.
* Expenditure and income rise in exactly the same proportion: *the co-efficient of income elasticity is equal to one*. This is possible for food in general at relatively low levels of consumption, and possible for individual foodstuffs.
* Expenditure is rising less fast than income: *the co-efficient is less than one, but still positive*. This is the typical situation for food in general and for most individual foodstuffs.
* Expenditure decreases as income rises: the co-efficient is *negative*. This is liable to arise for certain basic foodstuffs (such as bread or potatoes), often called "inferior goods".

The data necessary for calculating income elasticities can in principle be obtained either from "time series"—observations of the same or a similar population over a period of years— or from "household surveys", enabling comparisons of households in different income categories. Ideally, the effect of other factors— changes in prices and consumer preferences—should be eliminated, but this is not always possible.

In the United Kingdom, an extensive household survey (the "National Food Survey") is conducted annually. Income is not the only factor causing differences in consumption levels: the number of children per household is found to be a bigger influence. However, income elasticities of expenditure are calculated, and are shown in Table 4.3.

Table 4.3—UK: Income elasticities of expenditure

	Income elasticity	Standard error
All foods	−0.01	0.02
Bread	−0.25	0.03
Sugar and preserves	−0.54	0.08
Fresh potatoes	−0.48	0.07
Fresh green vegetables	0.13	0.06
Other fresh vegetables	0.35	0.04
Fresh fruit	0.48	0.05
Fruit juices	0.94	0.08
Milk	−0.40	0.05
Yoghurt	0.58	0.08
Cheese	0.22	0.06
Butter	−0.04	0.11
Margarine	−0.44	0.09
Carcase meat	−0.01	0.06
of which:		
Beef and veal	0.08	0.07
Mutton and lamb	−0.21	0.14
Pork	−0.05	0.11
Broiler chicken	−0.08	0.13
Eggs	−0.05	0.06

Source: Ministry of Agriculture, Fisheries and Food, *Household Food Consumption and Expenditure, 1989.*

The overall elasticity for all food consumed in the household (the National Food Survey does not cover meals taken outside the home) shows no significant relation to income. For most individual foods, elasticities are positive, but inelastic: fruit juices are the only commodity where the co-efficient approaches unity, and there are moderately high co-efficients for fresh fruit, vegetables and yoghurt. For several foodstuffs, elasticities are *negative*: this includes bread, potatoes and sugar, as might be expected for this group of high-energy foods, but also milk and probably (the margin of error is significant) mutton and lamb, possibly also eggs.

When income elasticities can be estimated with some confidence, they are an important element in *projecting* future demand trends. It is necessary to estimate the likely change in *per capita* incomes (most projection studies make two or three alternative assumptions). It is also desirable to take into account changes in income *distribution* within the population. Those who are made worse off by a redistribution of income (through taxation, for example) may reduce their purchases by a different amount from the increase in consumption by those who are made better off. On the whole, it is to be expected that a movement to greater equality of income will increase the demand for food, and *vice versa*, since an unequal distribution implies a concentration of income among people whose income elasticities of demand for food are relatively low.

It should however be remembered that changes at the level of the final consumer are only a partial guide to effects "at the farm gate". This is particularly the case as regards *expenditure* elasticities: extra consumer expenditure may be largely taken up by extra "added value" in processing, packaging and distribution. As the previous chapter has demonstrated, for most foodstuffs, only a small part of consumer expenditure reaches the farmer.

ii) Prices

The neo-classical analysis of demand was based on the concept of "diminishing marginal utility", and this will be first explained below. Subsequently, a less subjective approach has gained favour, which will also be discussed.

"Marginal utility" and "consumer surplus"

Starting from the concept of *utility* (or "satisfaction") derived from the consumption of goods or services, neo-classical economics developed the notion of *marginal utility*: i.e. the increase in total utility derived from the consumption of one additional unit of the product concerned. Marginal utility is held to *decline* as consumption rises: each additional unit gives less satisfaction than the one before, and eventually, marginal utility will become zero and even negative as the point of satiety is reached (more likely in the case of foodstuffs than for some consumer goods and services).

The analysis here in many ways parallels that already described in Chapter 2 in relation to supply. Table 4.4 shows a hypothetical demand schedule: the amounts a particular consumer (or household) would be willing to pay for each unit of a commodity diminish with increasing quantity. Smoothed out, this schedule produces a demand curve like that shown in Figure 4.1a.

Table 4.4—Demand schedule

Units of consumption	Amount consumer would pay	Consumer surplus at price 3 ECU
	ECU	ECU
1st	8	5
2nd	6	3
3rd	5	2
4th	4	1
5th	3	0
6th	2	–
7th	1.5	–
8th	1	–
9th	0.5	–
10th	0	–

Figure 4.1a—Demand curve and consumer surplus

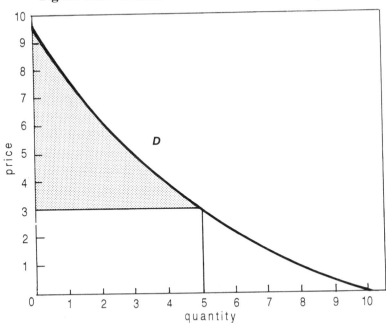

The consumer does not in fact have to pay a different price for each unit. If the prevailing market price in this case is 3 ECU, he can buy 5 units at that price. But for the first unit, he would have been willing to pay 8 ECU, for the second 6 ECU, and so on. Summing up the differences between what the consumer would have been willing to pay, and what he/she actually paid, we can obtain a total which we call "consumer surplus". The schedule indicates that this would total 11 ECU, and on the diagram this corresponds approximately to the shaded area below the demand curve and above the price 3 ECU.

If we are considering the aggregate demand of a number of consumers, among whom the "marginal utility" of the commodity differs, so that some consumers would have been willing to pay 8 ECU for one unit while others only begin to buy when the price falls below this level, the first group benefits from the lower market price.

Consumer surplus is thus the difference between the value consumers place on their total consumption of some commodity and the amount they must in fact pay for it. A utility-maximising household will consume any commodity up to the point where its consumer surplus on the last unit is zero.

The notion of consumer surplus is somewhat abstract, depending on a subjective assessment of "utility" which in practice could not easily be measured. However, it is used in comparing different situations from the point of view of consumer welfare: are consumers better-off with higher quantities and lower prices than with the reverse situation? It thus plays an important role in analysing

Figure 4.1b—Demand curve: price effects and shifts

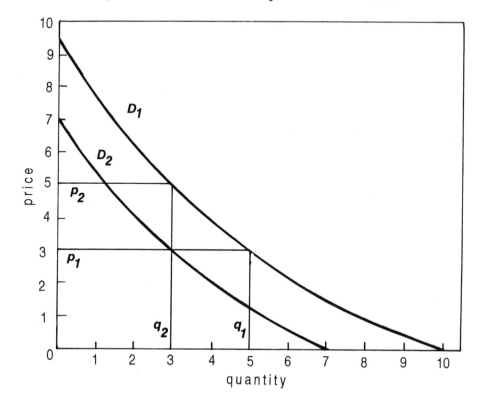

such matters as taxes and—as will be seen in Chapter 6—tariffs on trade. In such practical application, it is fortunately not necessary to know the shape of the whole supply curve and to estimate *total* consumer surplus at any particular price level: as the purpose is to evaluate the *change* in consumer surplus, it is sufficient to know (or estimate) the shape of the curve over the relevant range.

Effects of price changes

Figure 4.1b shows in the first instance the effect of a change in price. The initial price (p_1) is 3 ECU, at which point the quantity demanded (q_1) is 5 units. A rise in price to 5 ECU (p_2) causes a movement along the demand curve so that the quantity demanded falls to 5 units (q_2).

"Quantity demanded" and "demand" should be distinguished. With a change in price, the *quantity demanded* may alter as just shown, but the underlying demand schedule has *not* changed. The expression "a change in demand" should be reserved for a change in the schedule, or a *shift* in the demand curve—i.e. when the underlying conditions, such as income levels, have changed. (This parallels the distinction made, in the case of supply, between a movement *along* the supply curve, resulting from a change in price, and a *shift* in the curve, due to technological change.)

Figure 4.1b also shows a *shift* in the demand curve—in this case shown as a shift to the left, from D_1 to D_2. This could also cause a fall in quantity demanded (to 3 units at the price of 3 ECU, as the diagram has been drawn), but not for the same reason.

Price elasticity of demand is defined as the proportionate change in the quantity demanded in response to a given proportionate change in price, or:

$$E_{dp} = \frac{\Delta Q_d/Q_d}{\Delta P/P}$$

The co-efficient E_{dp} is usually related to a 1% change in price. Normally, price elasticity is *negative*. The following main cases can be distinguished:

* A change in price is associated with a *more than proportionate* change in quantity demanded: the coefficient has a negative value exceeding –1. Demand is said to be **"elastic"** in response to price.

* A given percentage change in price is associated with a *smaller* percentage change in quantity demanded: the coefficient is between 0 and –1. Demand is said to be **"inelastic"**. This is the case for many foodstuffs: it implies, for example, that when the market is oversupplied, a relatively large cut in price is necessary to induce a sufficiently large increase in quantity demanded.

There are three possible cases where the co-efficient of price elasticity is *positive*. The first of these introduces the notion that the effect of a price change on quantity demanded has two aspects: a **"substitution effect"**, in that a rise in price causes consumers to try to substitute other commodities for the one whose price has risen, and an **"income effect"**, in that the consumer's income is reduced (and *vice versa*). The latter effect will only be significant when expenditure on the product in question is a large part of total expenditure.

* In the case of a foodstuff which is regarded as an essential items of consumption, and which though cheap occupies a large part in expenditure, a rise in price, by curtailing income, may conceivably lead to reduced purchases of other, less essential items, and bigger purchases of the item in question. Such a situation was said to have been observed by the English economist Sir Robert Giffen in the 19th century in the case of bread among poorer working-class households (hence the term "Giffen good" to describe such items). It is an improbable outcome in high-income societies, though in the context of sudden and drastic price liberalisation in some of the former centrally-planned economies after 1990, such an effect for bread may have occurred.

* A rise in price might be taken by consumers as evidence that further price rises are likely to follow. This does not really contradict the basic theory, and such reactions are likely to be temporary.

* The price of the product is taken as an indicator of *quality*. This can occur for luxury goods (e.g. fashion clothes): it is probably a factor in the demand for wine and possibly other high-quality food and drink. It is also possible that below a certain price level, consumers buy less because they are doubtful about

the quality of a product: but the seller is likely then either to withdraw the product, or raise its price, or promote it more effectively.

On the whole, therefore, the occurrence of a positive correlation between price and quantity demanded (a "backward-sloping demand curve") is exceptional.

The responsiveness of the quantity demanded of one product to a change in the price of another product is known as **cross-price elasticity of demand**, and is defined as the proportionate change in quantity demanded of product A in response to a proportionate change in price of product B. Whether the quantity demanded of product A is increased or decreased by a change in the price of product B depends on whether the two products are *substitutes* or *complements* to each other.

Substitute (competing) products already mentioned are butter and margarine, or different types of meat: when the price of one rises, more of the other is likely to be demanded (the co-efficient of cross-price elasticity is *positive*.

Complements are, in theory, goods which are normally consumed together: British and American textbooks—referring to eating habits in their respective countries—give examples such as bread and jam, bacon and eggs, milk and breakfast cereals or even gin and tonic. This is not very convincing: much depends on national consumption patterns, and even in the cases mentioned it is doubtful whether the complementarity effect is very strong. Sugar, for example, is complementary to breakfast cereals, tea, coffee and various other items: but each of these uses accounts for quite a small part of total sugar consumption.

Most foodstuffs are, in fact, substitutes for each other in the housewife's shopping basket, so that cross-price elasticities are usually *positive*: a rise in price of product B causes an increase in the quantity demanded of product A. This is an important consideration in attempting to predict the effect of price changes. However, income effects can also be important if expenditure on the products concerned is substantial. This may be one reason why attempts to derive cross-price elasticities from empirical data often give unexpected and conflicting results (even the British National Food Survey, which as observed earlier has excellent data, is having difficulties in deriving price and especially cross- price elasticities—cf. Appendix, item 2).

An alternative approach: "indifference curves"

Many economists have felt unhappy with the subjective nature of the assumption of "diminishing marginal utility": how can the satisfaction derived from consumption of a product be measured? There is an extensive literature on this point, which need not be fully discussed here.

An alternative approach is based on the distinction between "cardinal" and "ordinal" utility. The former supposes that consumers can place a value on each item of their consumption, in the manner described above. The latter supposes only that consumers can *rank* alternative bundles of goods according to the utility they provide. It does not require that they should *quantify* this utility, for example by deciding that one bundle yields twice as much utility as another: only that they can decide that one bundle is better than, or worse than, or exactly as good as another.

On this basis, **"indifference curves"** can be constructed. These take into account different amounts of two commodities between which the consumer can choose, and seeks to represent alternative *combinations* which offer the same satisfaction, or between which the consumer is "indifferent".

Figure 4.2 illustrates this, supposing that the choice lies between beef and poultrymeat. Any point on an indifference curve represents a combination of the two products that is preferred to all combinations *below* that curve, but the consumer is held to be "indifferent" as between different points on the curve. Thus, with the curve IC_1, one combination could be 6 kg. of beef and 1 kg. poultrymeat, another could be 14 kg. of poultrymeat and 0.5 kg. of beef. Combinations *above* this curve would be even better (in principle, there can be an infinite number of indifference curves).

The curves are *convex to the origin*: this implies that if the quantity of one product is reduced in a series of equal amounts, increased amounts of the other product are required to leave the consumer indifferent to the change.

The consumer's actual choice will depend on the prices of the two commodities. If for example the price of beef is 10 ECU per kg. and that of poultrymeat is 5 ECU, with 50 ECU the consumer could purchase *either* 5 kg.

Figure 4.2—Demand indifference curves

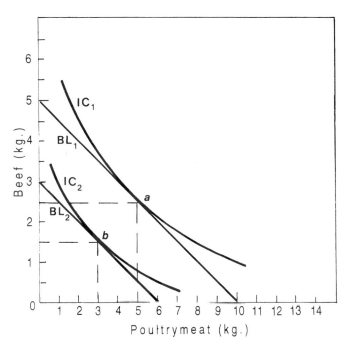

of beef *or* 10 kg. of poultrymeat, and various combinations between these extremes are possible: this is shown by the **"budget line"** BL_1. Reference to the indifference curve shows that the combination which would give greatest satisfaction is 2.5 kg. of beef and 5 kg. of poultrymeat (point *a*).

If the sum available is less, say 30 ECU, the consumer would have to be content with smaller quantities: the lower indifference curve IC_2 indicates that the most satisfactory combination would then be 1.5 kg. of beef and 3 kg. of poultrymeat (point *b*). At this point, the consumer maximises his "utility" or satisfaction, and can be said to be **"in equilibrium"**.

At points *a* or *b*, the relevant indifference curve and budget line have the same slope. The slope at any point on the indifference curve shows the rate at which one product can be substituted for the other at that point: in other words, the *marginal rate of substitution*. The slope of the budget line is determined by the *price relationship* between the two products.

Extension of this reasoning to consumer choice as between all the goods and services on offer leads to the formal statement that *the consumer is in equilibrium when his marginal rate of substitution is equal to the inverse ratio of the prices of any pair of products.*

iii) Demographic and social factors

In Western Europe, population growth is slowing down. Declining fertility rates are to some extent offset by increased life expectancy, but the average annual rate of natural increase in the twelve EC countries, which was around 0.8% in the 1960s, has fallen to below 0.2%. Up to 1987, net immigration—especially of workers from North Africa, Turkey, Yugoslavia—added slightly to population growth: with the influx from Eastern Europe, this has been a more important factor since 1988, particularly in Western Germany (but since many of these immigrants were refugees from Eastern Germany, recalculation on the basis of the unified territory will show a smaller net increase).

Figure 4.3 shows population trends for the five biggest EC countries, including projections till the year 2020. Marked falls are expected in Germany (but this is the pre–1990 territory), in Italy and in Spain; in other countries, modest growth is projected.

There are other demographic and social factors which can have important effects on demand for food, though these effects are not so easily measurable.

One such factor is *an increasingly old population.* This is the result of declining birth-rates with increasing life expectancy. For the EC as a whole, the share of people aged 60 or over is expected to rise from 20% of the total population in 1990 to 22% by 2000 and to 27% by 2020, with a rising proportion of women among the aged. Older people, on the whole, eat less—in particular, less of the expensive items and those requiring preparation in the home, including meat, fish, eggs and vegetables: so the likely effect is to reduce consumption of food in general and these items in particular.

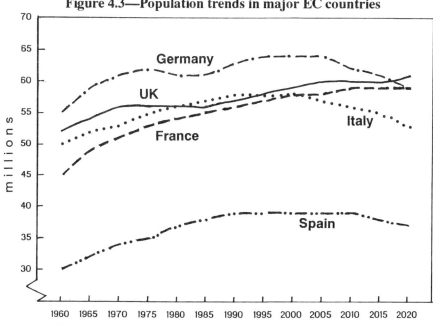

Figure 4.3—Population trends in major EC countries

Source: Eurostat, *Demographic Statistics 1991*

Different influences, however, may arise from the following two factors:
* **A decline in family size.** This arises from later marriages, from couples postponing the arrival of their first child, from family planning practices which reduce the average number of children per family (the latter trend being particularly marked in most Western European countries). There is also an increase in the number of households, in particular single-person households, partly due to higher divorce rates.
* **Increased participation of women in the work-force.** This also shifts demand towards "convenience foods": ready-prepared items, deep-frozen and "microwaveable" foods. Following the entry of the refrigerator into most households, the spread of deep-freezers and of micro-wave ovens is having a significant effect on eating patterns.

These changes seem unlikely to increase the total demand for food in volume terms, but they certainly change the *pattern* of food consumption, with for example increased demand for "convenience foods" with a higher value-added through processing and packaging: farmers may not benefit, but there are growth prospects for processors and distributors.

There are also important implications for the *marketing strategy* of food distributors in particular. The trends just mentioned, together with other factors such as increased car ownership, have implications for the *type and location* of food stores, reinforcing the move to out-of-town supermarkets with ample parking facilities; social changes also intensify demands for food shops to open longer hours.

It also likely that these developments, together with rising per capita incomes, will continue to promote increased eating-out (cf. Chapter 3), in terms of midday meals at or near the work-place as well as evening meals.

Increased leisure time is another social factor, though its effects on food demand seem less clear.

v) Health and nutrition

Changes in food consumption in recent years also arise from health concerns. Policies on nutrition will be discussed in Chapter 11. Official guidelines have played a role in influencing consumer choice, though sometimes "fads" whose scientific basis is doubtful have had bigger effects. One result has been the move away from animal fats, particularly in dairy products. Food processors, Unilever in particular, have developed brands of margarine which both respond to the health concern through being made from polyunsaturated vegetable oils and are more attractive, indeed often almost indistinguishable from butter, with the advantage of being easier to spread. Many consumers are also shifting away from full-cream milk, yoghurt and cheese to skimmed or semi-skimmed products.

The decline in the direct consumption of sugar (increased quantities are liable to be consumed in processed food and drink) is another case in point. Here the link is with obesity, sugar being the most concentrated source of calories, and with dental decay.

On the other hand, there is increasing interest in so-called "health foods", in particular food produced without the use of agro-chemicals ("organic" or "biological" produce). Such items are no longer confined to specialist shops, but are finding a place—often a special area—in supermarkets. They usually command a considerable price premium.

Meat consumption has been influenced by concerns over the use of growth-promoting hormones in rearing meat animals, a practice which is now banned in the EC. Health considerations are reinforced by growing concern over animal welfare issues; some consumers turn to vegetarianism as a result.

Some dramatic demand changes have occurred in recent years as a result of major health scares. In the UK, in 1989, egg consumption fell sharply following an ill-advised statement by the current Minister of Health to the effect that "most" eggs were infected by salmonella: the resulting egg surplus necessitated a cutback of the egg-laying flock. Poultrymeat consumption was even more affected by listeria and salmonella scares. Media attention in 1990 to "mad cow disease", or "bovine spongiform encephalopathy" (BSE), found among cattle in the UK, caused demand for beef to fall off sharply, not only in the UK but in France and other countries, and contributed to a collapse in beef prices. Coming on top of the hormone scares, this created considerable consumer resistance to beef, though consumption in the UK recovered somewhat in 1991 and 1992.

APPENDIX

1. Sources. The theory of demand is set out in all economics textbooks, though not always very fully in agricultural economics textbooks (see Appendix to Introduction). However, Ritson gives a very full development of the "indifference curve" approach.

Statistical sources have been indicated in the notes accompanying tables and diagrams.

See also articles in *The Food Consumer*, eds. C. Ritson and J. McKenzie (Wiley, London: 1986).

2. Demand elasticities. While the principles upon which income and price elasticities can be derived are clear, empirical evidence is often hard to interpret. Even the British "National Food Survey", to which reference has been made in the text and which provides very comprehensive data over a long period of time, gives some surprising results for price elasticities, with big variations from one year to another and large "standard errors" especially in the calculation of cross-price elasticities.

Unpublished calculations on the basis of 1980–89 NFS data, communicated to the author, indicate a number of foodstuffs for which demand appears to be relatively price-elastic (negative co-efficients exceeding –1). These include wholemeal bread and brown bread, cheese, most kinds of meat, fresh fish and oranges: these could be regarded to some extent as "luxury" items. On the other hand, price elasticities appear low for white bread, sugar, potatoes, milk, broiler chicken (a relatively cheap type of meat), frozen fish, eggs, apples and tea. Most of the cross-price elasticities from the same source are less statistically significant: there appear to be some positive cross-price elasticities as between some types of meat, but no significant cross-price elasticities as between different fruits. It is not even evident from the data that price is significant in the choice between butter and margarine: probably dietary considerations are more important.

The *European Review of Agricultural Economics*, no.19 of 1992, contains two methodological papers that are relevant in this context: J. Michalek and M.A. Keyzer, "Estimation of a two-stage LES–AIDS consumer demand system for eight EC countries" (pp.137–163); and M. Burton and T. Young, "The structure of changing tastes for meat and fish in Great Britain" (pp. 165–180).

In applying demand elasticities, calculated at the consumer level, to the analysis of changes in the farm sector, further difficulties arise in view of the large share of value-added in processing and distribution, as for example in the food chain from wheat to bread, from milk to dairy products or from carcass meat to prepared and packaged cuts of meat.

Despite such methodological difficulties, price elasticities of demand are included in econometric models of the kind already referred to in item 3 of the Appendix to Chapter 2 (where supply elasticities are discussed). Thus the USDA "SWOPSIM" model gives complete sets of price and cross-price demand elasticities for all major commodities. As with the supply elasticities, virtually the same co-efficients appear for each individual EC Member State as for the EC total, which seems inherently improbable. Another set of co-efficients, significantly different for some commodities, is given by Tyers and Anderson.

CHAPTER 5

PRICE DETERMINATION

The previous chapters have explained the fundamental factors determining supply and demand in a market economy: this chapter will discuss their interaction, and the resulting formation of prices on the market. Many of the essential concepts, including the "price elasticity" of supply and demand, have already been covered.

The "market" is to be understood in a very general sense, as any place or arrangement whereby sellers and buyers transact business. It may be a small street market, or a wholesale market dealing in produce from a wide geographic region; it may even consist of a network of contacts such as those which are made increasingly possible by modern telecommunications.

The concept of "market equilibrium" has practical value in helping to understand and to predict market behaviour. It also help to define a theoretical optimum under which all markets in an economy are in balance, with productive resources being allocated according to the criteria of economic efficiency described in Chapter 2, and consumer preferences being accurately expressed as described in Chapter 4. Although such an optimum is unlikely ever to be fully realised even in a static situation, and although it must change over time, requiring constant adjustments in the allocation of resources, this is a useful paradigm against which the reality can be compared.

(a) Market equilibrium

In the normal situation, a rise in price causes the quantity supplied to increase and the quantity demanded to decrease, and *vice versa*: then a balance between the two is possible (though not certain, if for example even the lowest price at which any quantity will be supplied exceeds the highest price at which there is any demand).

The theory is is most easily illustrated by diagrams. Figure 5.1a illustrates a normal short-run situation with a rising supply curve and falling demand curves. In the first instance, with demand curve D, a balance can be found at the price level p where the quantity exchanged is q. At any price above this level, suppliers

Figure 5.1—Supply and demand

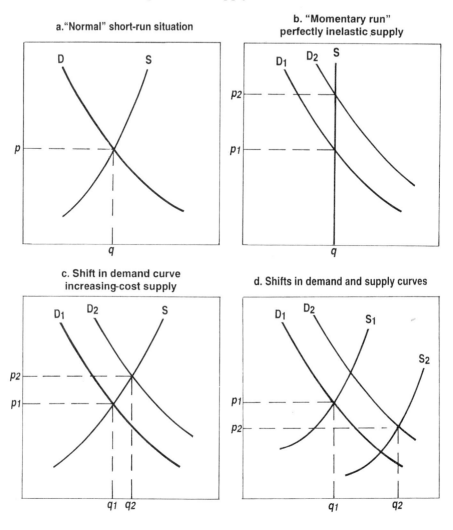

a."Normal" short-run situation

b. "Momentary run" perfectly inelastic supply

c. Shift in demand curve increasing-cost supply

d. Shifts in demand and supply curves

will offer more than consumers want to buy; at any lower price, consumers want to buy more than suppliers are willing to sell.

This point of balance may not be immediately found, and indeed may never be found at all (a particular case of such continuing disequilibrium is discussed below). Whether balance is established, and how quickly, depends on the efficiency of the market in question: on its "transparency"—how well information circulates among buyers and sellers—and on how well they can act on such information. (In respect of food markets, the Dutch *veiling* system, described in Chapter 3, is particularly efficient; financial markets dealing in currency exchange, or stock exchanges, are still more efficient, nowadays on a world-wide scale.)

In practice, markets are hardly every static, so it is important to consider how they may react to *shifts* in demand or supply.

Figure 5.1b shows a situation corresponding to the "very short run" as defined in Chapter 2, during which supply is fixed or "perfectly inelastic": i.e. a vertical straight line, indicating that whatever the price, the same quantity must be sold. This could be the case for a perishable product brought to market to be sold on a particular day. Price is then determined by demand: a shift in the demand curve to the right, for example (which might arise from the arrival of more buyers) would raise the price from p_1 to p_2.

Figure 5.1c demonstrates a short-run situation during which supply can adapt to some extent, but there are rising marginal costs due to the fixity of some of the factors of production. The quantity supplied can now rise in response to a shift in the demand curve to the right: a larger amount is exchanged, and the new price p_2, though higher than in the initial situation, is less than in the case of perfectly inelastic supply.

Figure 5.1d relates to a long-run situation in which the supply curve has also shifted (as a result of increased factor use with economies of scale and/or improved technology). Even though the demand curve has shifted as in the previous examples, a higher quantity can be supplied at a *lower* price than before.

The *direction* of change can thus be explained quite simply. The *magnitude* of change depends on the slope and position of the supply and demand curves—in other words on their respective "functions". If it were possible to derive empirically functions covering the whole relevant range of supply and demand, price levels and changes could be accurately predicted. In practice, this is hardly possible, but the basic principles can be described. Figure 5.2 illustrates the effects arising from different demand curves with the same rightwards shift in the supply curve, the demand curve in Figure 5.2b being steeper than that in Figure 5.2a—i.e. less "elastic", although it should be recalled that elasticity depends on the position as well as on the slope of the curves. The increase in supply causes a larger fall in price in the second case than in the first.

Figure 5.2—Shifts in supply curve

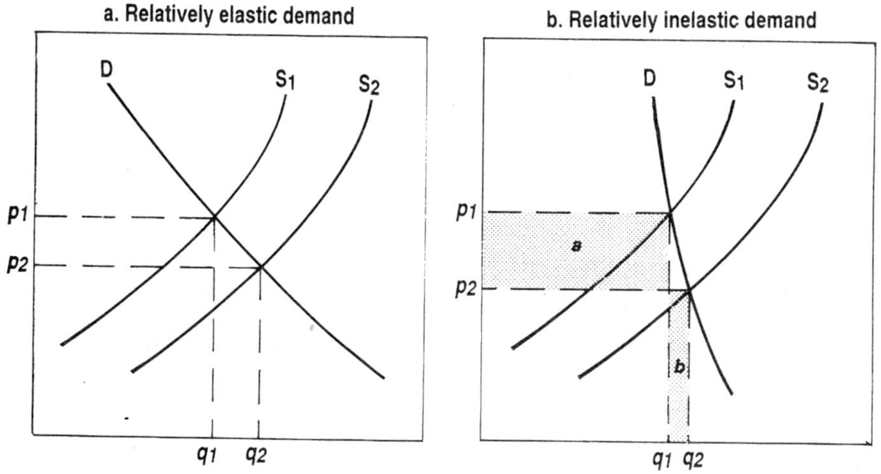

a. Relatively elastic demand

b. Relatively inelastic demand

In fact, as has been seen in Chapter 4, demand for foodstuffs is usually price-inelastic: the implication is therefore that changes in supply tend to be associated with relatively large changes in price. As agricultural supply is subject to unplanned variations, due to weather and other causes, this demand inelasticity explains why prices for agricultural products tend to fluctuate widely, and is often used as a justification for some form of intervention to stabilise the market.

It can also mean that if producers can combine to restrict supplies, they may get a higher total receipt from sales. Thus in Figure 5.2b, with relatively inelastic demand, the revenue from sales (price times quantity) is greater with the smaller supply, S_1, than with the larger one, S_2: the rectangle a is greater than the rectangle b. (See also Appendix, item 1, on "King's Law".)

Given the large number of agricultural producers, it is difficult for them to combine to restrict production, unless public legislation gives a producers' organisation the authority to do so. A major example is provided by the Milk

Figure 5.3—The "cobweb" theorem

a. Consecutive time periods

b. Repetitive cycle

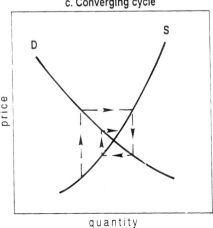

c. Converging cycle

d. "Exploding cycle

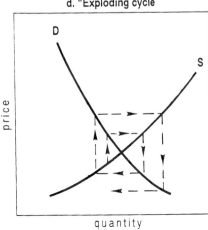

Marketing Board for England and Wales (there are similar Boards for Scotland and Northern Ireland). The MMB has had the exclusive right to buy milk from farms. It has then imposed a high price for its sales of liquid milk, for which demand is particularly price-inelastic, and where in the past, before the advent of "long-life" (ultra-high temperature) milk, natural protection against imports was provided by the need for freshness; other dairy products, for which demand is comparatively elastic, were priced more competitively. These practices, however, have come under attack, and it is now likely that the MMB will be transformed into a voluntary producers' co-operative.

(b) Market instability

As was pointed out above, the market may never find the point of equilibrium. A particular case—to which some agricultural products are subject—is that of *cyclical* fluctuations around the equilibrium point.

Such a pattern may arise in the following circumstances:

* Producers are numerous, so that an individual producer has insignificant influence on total output.
* There is a specific *time-lag*, more or less the same for all producers, between production decisions and actual output. For arable crops, this time-lag is one year; for tree crops considerably longer; for pigs, less than a year; for beef cattle, at least eighteen months; and so on.
* Production decisions, however, are largely influenced by *current* prices. Each producer decides without taking into account what other producers may be planning to do. In other words, expectations as to future prices are "naïve": most producers do not learn from their mistakes. (If most producers acted rationally, the cycle would not be perpetuated).
* Once produced, the commodity has to be sold: fluctuations in output cannot easily be absorbed by storage. Perishable products in particular fall into this category.

Such conditions may apply to fruit and vegetables and to certain livestock products, in particular pigs, poultry, eggs, and sometimes beef cattle: the classic textbook examples usually refer to one or other of these commodities. The conditions do *not* usually apply to grain or other crops which can be stored at fairly low cost; nor to milk, which is a continuing production process.

The characteristic cycle is one where, initially, high prices stimulate optimistic production decisions by most producers: their combined increased output comes on the market at about the same time, depressing prices; most producers then decide to cut back production; reduced quantities then cause higher prices; and so on.

A graphical illustration is given in Figure 5.3: this, because of its appearance, is called the **"cobweb theorem"**. Over time (Figure 5.3a), prices and quantities are shown as fluctuating in opposite directions. The length of the cycle, from peak to peak, will be double the production period (e.g. two years for arable crops).

On the traditional prices-quantity diagram (Figure 5.2b), a rise in price initially causes the quantity supplied to rise; but this quantity is excessive in relation to demand, so price falls back; production is then reduced, and the cycle begins again.

Depending on the relative slopes of the supply and demand curves, the cycle may *converge* (Figure 5.2c) or *diverge* (Figure 5.2d). These patterns reflect the fact that the more inelastic is demand in relation to supply, the greater the likelihood of a divergent pattern.

The cycle can be broken in various ways. Better market information helps: rational producers can then more easily anticipate the cycle and act accordingly. Storage may become economic, even for perishable produce, if the market price is very low. The underlying supply or demand curves may shift, so that over time the cyclical pattern is overshadowed, especially for products with a long production cycle.

Moreover, producers may combine to even out their supplies, or to withdraw produce from the market in times of oversupply; or governments may introduce stabilisation schemes ("buffer stocks"). In fact, such measures have been widely practised in most Western countries since the 1930s, and more recently under the EC's Common Agricultural Policy: relevant policies will be discussed in Part B. As a result, there are not many clear examples of cyclical behaviour in recent experience: the textbook cases usually refer to earlier developments so far as Western Europe is concerned. In the US and Canada, on the other hand, there is recent evidence of cyclical behaviour, particularly for products such as pigs and lamb with a short production cycle.

The tendency of some agricultural markets to behave in a cyclical pattern may provide justification for stabilisation measures. It is however very difficult, in practice, to know where the equilibrium point lies: supply and demand curves cannot be drawn in real life with any accuracy. The tendency, given the inevitable political pressures, is almost always to set prices too high—particularly if the underlying trends call for a long-run decline in the relative price of the product concerned. So stabilisation measures all too easily become support measures, and lead to overproduction.

(c) Price and "value"

The foregoing analysis has explained price formation exclusively in terms of the interaction of supply and demand. Is there any sense in which a commodity has a *value* that is independent of the price established by these market forces?

Reference has already been made in the Introduction to the Marxist "labour theory of value", which implied that such a value existed as the consequence of the effort used up in producing the commodity. Marx did recognise that if there was no *use* for a product, it would have no value (see Appendix, item 2); and subsequent interpretations stressed the notion of "socially useful" production, which implied some reference to demand.

The idea that some such independent value exists is not confined to Marxists. In discussion of agricultural policy issues in the West, farmers' representatives constantly claim a "fair return" for their work or—more specifically—a price to cover their costs of production. A particular claim has been for "differential pricing", to give a relatively high price for small producers: such demands have frequently been put forward by small farmers associations and their supporters, including some economists (usually French—see Appendix, item 3). Such arguments, though frequently confused, reflect a widespread feeling that the act of production in itself confers some kind of value on the goods produced, and often a genuine concern with the underprivileged sectors of the farm population.

It is therefore important to be clear as to the function of price. The vast majority of Western economists would insist that this function is to provide correct market signals, and to allocate productive resources throughout the economy in accordance with consumer preferences; and that any attempt to use prices for other purposes, in particular for providing a particular income level to producers or for covering their costs, will lead to inefficiencies and distortions.

This point is not only crucial in relation to pricing policy in the former centrally-planned economies (see Appendix, item 2): it is also the main objection raised by economists to the high rates of price support for agricultural products provided in most of the developed market economies, including the EC's Common Agricultural Policy.

However, it is important now to consider how far market forces can be left to determine prices and allocate resources, and how far the goal of economic efficiency may need to be tempered by other considerations, in particular that of *equity*.

(d) "The invisible hand"?

Adam Smith said that every individual, in pursuing his own advantage, was "led by an invisible hand to promote an end which was no part of his intention", namely to "render the annual revenue of the society as great as he can".

This implies that competition leads to economic efficiency. More recent analysis is based on the work by the Italian economist Vilfredo Pareto (1848–1923). The economic literature on the subject is vast, and well beyond the scope of the present work. However, some essential features should be briefly explained.

An economy can be said to have attained a **"Pareto optimum"** if there is *no possibility for making any individual better off without making some other individual worse off*. Competitive equilibrium is theoretically Pareto-efficient, subject to certain important restrictions, because the independent actions of producers setting marginal cost equal to price, and of consumers setting marginal benefits equal to price, ensure that the marginal cost of producing goods and services just equals their marginal benefits to consumers.

More precisely, the conditions for the Pareto optimum may be stated as follows:

* **Production equilibrium.** Each firm allocates its factors of production efficiently between the output of different commodities, along the lines discussed in Chapter 2: i.e. the marginal rate of transformation between any two inputs must be the same in the production of any two products. Each firm also adjusts its output of different commodities so as to equate, in each case, marginal cost and price. These conditions should be attained under perfect competition by producers seeking least-cost (or profit-maximising) solutions.

* **Consumers' equilibrium.** Each consumer chooses between available goods and services so as to maximise his satisfaction or "utility", along the lines discussed in Chapter 4: i.e. each consumer substitutes one product for another until his marginal rate of substitution for any pair of products equals the inverse ratios of their prices. This condition too should be attained in perfect competition when consumers are free to choose the combinations they prefer.

* **General equilibrium.** As a result of all the individual decisions by producers and consumers, relative prices and relative amounts of goods and services adjust so that no other combination could increase the satisfaction of one individual without decreasing the satisfaction of another. It can be shown that this condition will also apply if all firms are operating under perfect competition, all consumers are also price-takers, and all prices are free to adjust.

These are abstract concepts, which in practice are immeasurable. It is unlikely that they would ever be fully achieved in a market economy, since fully perfect competition does not exist. However, it is much more likely that the Pareto optimum will be realised under even an imperfect market economy than in a planned economy. In the latter case, the government would need vast amounts of information, and would have to be able to make a multitude of computations and to put them precisely into effect: conditions which, even assuming an entirely benevolent and uncorrupt authority, are quite unrealistic in a complex modern economy. To that extent, Adam Smith's concept of the "invisible hand" remains valid.

Indeed, the Pareto theory could mean that governments should not interfere at all in the market process. There are however important restrictions to the Pareto optimum concept.

One such restriction relates to **market failure**, or deviations from the model of perfect competition. As was seen in Chapter 3, a firm operating in imperfect competition can exploit the falling demand curve for its products by producing less and at a higher price than a firm in perfect competition. So there may be a case for government intervention to limit the market power of such firms.

Another concerns **"externalities"**, a point that has already been raised on several occasions in this book. "Social costs" (or benefits) may diverge from the direct "private costs" of a productive process—e.g. through pollution, or on the contrary through some environmental improvement from which many people benefit. This provides theoretical justification for government action, in the form of taxes or subsidies, to bring private and social costs into line. Some applications of this principle to agriculture will be discussed in the context of environmental measures in Chapter 10.

(d) Inequity and compensation

The concept of the economic optimum must also be qualified by reference to *equity* considerations: a matter of particular significance for agricultural policy.

All Western governments intervene to correct inequalities, though to varying extents. Through welfare programmes for groups such as the old, the poor and the unemployed, governments seek to modify the distribution of income that would result from a totally-free market economy. But most policy measures aiming to make one group of people better-off—e.g. farmers—tend to make other groups worse off—e.g. taxpayers and consumers. Distributional issues cannot be ignored in policy-making, but are usually very controversial. Is there any objective way in which costs and benefits can be weighed against each other?

The **"compensation principle"** developed under welfare economics (see Appendix, item 4) holds that if the gainers can compensate the losers and still be better-off themselves, then there is an objective justification for a policy measure. This has potential application in relation to action to reduce farm product prices, through policy reform and/or trade liberalisation: the price cut may be justified if the benefit to consumers and taxpayers is sufficient to compensate farmers, through some form of direct payment. (Some recent developments under the CAP, involving compensation for price cuts, can be seen in this light.)

Still, this principle is open to criticism. One limitation is that any measure of redistribution itself involves costs, in raising and distributing the necessary money; and because the information available to the authorities is never complete, and administration is never perfect, errors in implementation will be made. Although direct payments seem generally superior to price support in terms of allocative efficiency, we are here dealing with "second-best" solutions, a complex field of welfare economics where policy recommendations cannot be clear-cut.

Further, the compensation principle assumes that the welfare losses and gains of different individuals, or groups of individuals, can be *compared*. To assume that a given sum of money means the same to different people is to ignore the likelihood that subjective valuations are different (in technical language, the marginal utility of income is not the same for all gainers and losers). This may be partly because a given sum seems more important to someone with a low income than to someone with a high income. It is also arguable that what matters is what a person *notices*: price cuts for agricultural products are certainly noticed by farmers, since they affect their main activity, but may be hardly noticed by consumers because they are not always fully passed down the distribution chain, because their effect may be gradual over time, and because food is only part—for most people, quite a small part—of total expenditure.

Because of such difficulties, some writers on welfare economics have said that the community as a whole can only be regarded as being better off following a particular measure if *no* individual is made worse off by it: a condition which if strictly observed would preclude almost any government action. A more realistic position is to the effect that it is not sufficient to affirm that losers *could* be compensated by gainers: the compensation *must actually take place*. This seems also to imply that the recipients of compensation should be *satisfied* with the compensation.

Farmers, however, dislike the whole idea of receiving direct payments, which they see as a welfare programme, in compensation for price cuts: they regard product prices as their "income" and treat any drastic cut in these prices as an affront to their dignity. Such attitudes may be irrational, but in politics they cannot be ignored.

The compensation principle in welfare economics remains a useful starting-point for dealing with farm policy issues, but it does not provide simple answers. The issue will be further discussed at the end of the Chapter 7, and will recur in later chapters too. But it is questionable whether any compensation system that is acceptable to the rest of the population will make price cuts acceptable to farmers: if governments want to reduce prices they must expect such action to be unpopular.

APPENDIX

1. "King's Law". This is often mentioned in French economic literature—cf. for example J.-M. Boussard, *Economie de l'Agriculture*, Economica (Paris) 1987 (p.131).
The reference is to the English statistician Gregory King (1648–1712), who observed from study of the London grain market that the total revenue to sellers increased when the supply diminished: a consequence of what we now term "inelastic demand".
Alfred Marshall, in his *Principles of Economics*, makes a footnote reference to Gregory King (p.88 in the 8th edition), but "King's Law" is not usually referred to as such in English-language textbooks, though the phenomenon is well known. It is, in any case, erroneous to refer to it as a "Law", as it only holds good under certain conditions.

2. "Value" and price. Marx's theory of value has been much criticised in the West—see for example Joseph Schumpeter's *Capitalism, Socialism and Democracy* (pp.23 sq. in fourth edition). Two concepts appear in the first chapter of *Das Kapital*:

> *Ein Gebrauchswert oder Gut hat also nur einen Wert, weil abstrakt menschliche Arbeit in ihm vergegenständlicht oder materialisiert ist... Endlich kann kein Ding Wert sein, ohne Gebrauchsgegenstand zu sein. Ist es nutzlos, so ist auch die in ihm enthaltene Arbeit nutzlos, zählt nicht as Arbeit und bildet daher keinen Wert.*

> [So an object of use or a commodity only has value because abstract human labour has taken shape or been materialised in it... In the end, no item can have value if it is not an object of use. If it is useless, then the labour contained in it is also useless, cannot be counted as labour and therefore constitutes no value.]

Marx's approach, however, could not adequately solve the inherent contradiction between these two statements; and in practice, the "labour theory" has dominated.
Mikhail Gorbachev, in his book *Perestroika* (Collins, London 1987) showed awareness of the problems arising from application of the labour theory of value when he wrote (p.19):

> *The worker or the enterprise that had expended the greatest amount of labor, material and money was considered the best... The consumer found himself totally at the mercy*

of the producer and had to make do with what the latter chose to give him... It became typical of many of our national executives to think not of how to build up the national asset, but of how to put more material, labor and working time into an item to sell it at a higher price.

Unfortunately, Gorbachev—like many brought up in the Marxist context—showed limited understanding of the economic remedies: one finds in his book only vague references to "full cost accounting", undefined. Indeed, it could be said that his inability to grasp the essential elements of market economics, by causing him to hesitate over the adoption of a systematic reform plan, was largely responsible for his downfall in 1991.

3. Differential pricing. In France, before the Common Agricultural Policy, a "quantum" system was applied for cereals, under which the relatively high guaranteed price was paid only for a certain amount of sales per producer, thus giving an advantage to smaller producers. French small-farmer movements, and left-wing groups supporting them, have regularly demanded the restoration and generalisation of such a system: currently, this is requested by the *Confédération Paysanne* which in 1987 regrouped several previous left-wing farm organisations.

The former Agriculture Minister Edgar Pisani has been a frequent advocate of differential pricing in the European Parliament; in a full-page article in *Le Monde* of 27th May 1992 he repeated this claim, stressing in particular the "social role" of price support—which he does not define. The case for this demand (in the form of a *quantum financier*) was also presented in *Agriculture: changer de politique* by Jean-Christophe Kroll (Alternatives Economiques, Paris 1990).

The arguments used are generally characterised by a rejection of "neo-classical" economics, regarded as a product of "Anglo-Saxon liberalism" (usually misunderstood) and by anti-Americanism (Britain being regarded as an American "Trojan Horse" in the EC). The specific interest of small farmers is emphasised and the general interest disregarded; "productivism" is opposed; the approach to foreign trade is neo-mercantilist ("imports are bad, exports are good"); and long-term implications for the allocation of resources are ignored.

Though such views are not often directly challenged, they are probably no longer widely held. The French (Socialist) government did *not* follow this approach in the negotiations on the "MacSharry Plan" in 1991–92 (see Chapter 9): on the contrary, it opposed the proposal for differentiating compensatory payments in favour of small producers. Apparently the government opted for the "productivist" line, favouring the more competitive large producers. But it then had to affront demonstrations by outraged small farmers (cf. Chapter 14).

4. Welfare economics. This branch of economics was initiated in the 1920s by the Cambridge economist Arthur Pigou. It has developed a vast and complex literature, associated with the names of Maurice Dobb, J.R. Hicks, N. Kaldor, I.M.D. Little, E.J. Mishan, Tibor Scitowski and others. The subject is however better approached through one or other of the general economics textbooks previously cited.

The specific issue of the "Pareto optimum" is well discussed in Ritson's textbook on agricultural economics (cf. Appendix to Introduction). The demonstration of general equilibrium requires rather more elaborate use of diagrams combining production possibility curves and indifferences curves, and/or use of algebra, than has been attempted here. See, for example, Chapter 19 in the textbook by Begg *et al.*

On the application of the compensation principle to agriculture, and particularly on the relevance of the theory of the "second-best", see K.J. Munk, "Price support to EC agricultural sector: an optimal policy?" in *Oxford Review of Economic Policy*, 5:2, 1989 (pp. 76–89); and "The rationale for the Common Agricultural Policy and other EC sectoral policies" in *European Economy* (special issue on "The Economies of Community Finance", forthcoming 1992 or 1993).

CHAPTER 6
INTERNATIONAL TRADE THEORY

In international trade, theory and practice come sharply into conflict. As will be seen below, economic theory demonstrates how the general principle of specialisation, if permitted to operate internationally through reasonably free trade, can lead to significant benefits. But international trade in general, and agricultural trade in particular, has been and remains subject to numerous and sometimes severe barriers, taking a variety of forms.

(a) Comparative advantage and gains from trade

The benefits of specialisation, which Adam Smith (1723–1790) demonstrated as regards the division of labour between different tasks, apply also as between regions within a country, or as between countries and continents. The broader the geographical range, the wider the opportunities for mutually advantageous trade arising from differences in natural conditions, population densities, human skills and economic structures.

However, in the international context, there are specific constraints. National frontiers obstruct the movement of labour, maybe also of capital, and land is by nature fixed: the costs of the factors of production may thus vary widely between countries. In the absence of a common currency (such as was once provided by the widely-accepted "Gold Standard"), exchange rates complicate the picture.

The general principle is that, if the greatest possible advantages of foreign trade are to be secured, each nation should devote itself to what it can do "most cheaply". But this expression should be carefully defined. The **theory of comparative advantage** (or "comparative costs"), due originally to David Ricardo (1772–1823) and often called a "law", can be restated along the following lines (see also Appendix, item 1).

The simplified case. The following table considers two commodities—grain and timber—and two countries, which we shall call Ruritania and Sylvestria. The main difference between these hypothetical countries is that Sylvestria has a colder and wetter climate, a shorter growing season, and poorer-quality land.

	Cost of production in Ruritania	Cost of production in Sylvestria
Unit of grain	x	$2y$
Unit of timber	x	y

A unit of grain and a unit of timber are defined as *those amounts of each which in Ruritania have the same production costs (x)*. In Sylvestria, the cost relationship is different: a unit of grain costs twice as much to produce as a unit of timber—$2y$ as against y. The *units* are the same in both regions, but no assumption is made as to whether the cost x is greater or less than y.

It follows that if Ruritania shifts productive resources from timber to grain and exports grain to Sylvestria, while Sylvestria shifts from grain to timber and exports timber to Ruritania, the same amounts of both commodities can be produced in the two regions combined at less cost—or more can be produced at the same cost. This assumes that there are no restrictions on trade, and that transport and other marketing costs are not so great as to wipe out the benefit.

Nothing has been assumed as regards the relation between the cost x in Ruritania and the cost y in Sylvestria. Ruritania might have an *absolute* advantage over Sylvestria in the production of both grain and timber (i.e. lower costs at the prevailing rate of exchange). Potential benefit is dependent on different *comparative* costs, not *absolute* differences between the two regions.

Gains from trade. The greater the initial differences in the cost ratios as between the two regions, the greater the potential gain from trade.

As resources shift in each region, the cost relationships will change. Probably the cost of producing a unit of grain will rise in Ruritania, as less suitable land is brought under cultivation, or more fertiliser is applied, and so on; in Sylvestria, the cost of producing a unit of timber will rise for similar reasons.

The cost ratios will therefore move more closely together: once they are the same (or before this point, if transport costs etc. are taken into account), further trade will cease to be beneficial.

The less cost ratios change—i.e. the smaller the slope of the "cost gradients"—the greater the potential benefit from trade.

If Sylvestria is a small producer of grain and timber and Ruritania is a large one, the impact of trade will be proportionately less in Ruritania, where in consequence cost ratios are likely to shift relatively little: Sylvestria can gain greater benefit from trade.

If on the opening of trade, extra output enters a range of *decreasing* costs (possible with economies of scale in manufacturing—cf. Chapter 3), production will expand until increasing costs are encountered (or complete specialisation occurs). The benefit from trade is correspondingly great.

Several countries and commodities. When several commodities are taken into account, they can be arranged in order in each country according to their comparative cost. The most advantageous situation and the optimal trading pattern depends on *all* the cost ratios and cost gradients in the country concerned, and in its trading partners. It may be then that Ruritania should not export grain but some other item, perhaps manufactured goods. Maximum advantage will be obtained once all the ratios have been approximately equalised as between the trading partners.

For one country, the rest of the world can be regarded as a single region: it has an interest in trading and adjusting its own pattern of production until its cost ratios correspond to those existing as between the most efficient foreign suppliers of each commodity. Multilateral trade offers more scope for benefit than bilateral trade.

Factor endowment. In the first example given above, the differences in cost relationships were attributed primarily to varying physical conditions as between the two countries. More generally, such differences may arise in that production factors are *needed* in different proportions as between products, while they are *available* in different proportions as between countries (the "factor endowment" varies). To take examples within the agricultural sector: cereals or other arable crops need a high proportion of land, while milk production by traditional methods is labour-intensive. Thus a country or region such as North America, where land is abundant and relatively cheap, is likely to have a comparative advantage in the production of cereals; Western European countries, where land is relatively expensive in relation to labour, may have a comparative advantage in producing milk.

It is however immediately apparent that cost ratios are not eternally fixed: to some extent, one factor can be substituted for another. Milk production can be mechanised—i.e. capital is substituted for labour. Factors can also move from one line of production to another: e.g. farm labour can be moved from cereal to milk production.

Returns to factors of production. The opening-up of trade, as compared with a no-trade situation, tends to raise the price of goods that can be exported (for which demand is increased) and lower the price of goods subject to competition from imports: it will thus tend also to raise the returns to those factors of production upon which the exportable goods particularly depend, and *vice-versa*.

Thus free trade in cereals and milk products between North America and Western Europe will tend to raise returns to land but lower returns to labour in North America, with the opposite effects in Western Europe. In theory, this process might continue until the cost proportions are equal.

In the case of a country or region which has a comparative disadvantage in most branches of agriculture as compared with other sectors—which may be the case for Western Europe in relation to the rest of the world—the consequence of free trade may be to lower returns to *all* the factors of production used in agriculture. This result can be offset only in so far as the factors can move to other employment—but, as has been seen, farm labour is not very mobile.

The above reasoning as regards the international context complements the concept of optimal allocation in the national context, which has been discussed in previous chapters (cf. especially Chapter 5, section (d)). Within a country, "perfect competition" should lead to an optimal position in which, *inter alia*, output of different items is at levels where marginal cost equals price for each item: if the free trade condition is also realised, the same condition should apply in the world generally.

Full economic optimality in the world context would require that factors of production should be free to move across frontiers in response to different rates of remuneration, until these rates are equalised. Trade would still be profitable in view of differing natural conditions, or different consumer preferences, but not because—for example—labour costs in one region were significantly below those in another. This, of course, is an economic Utopia: such economic migration does occur—as with the *Gastarbeiter* in Germany or other immigrant worker groups in Western Europe and North America—but since one result of such movement is to reduce wage levels (or increase unemployment) in the host country, the movement of labour across frontiers remains limited, and differences in wage levels persists.

As with other aspects of economics, the theory of comparative advantage should not be taken as a description of how trade *is* or *should be* conducted: it only explains why, in certain circumstances, trade is beneficial. Although it is theoretically possible for countries with planned economies to work out their comparative costs and advantages and to determine their trade on that basis, in practice the amount of empirical data that would be required and the task of computation would be enormous. But when, in a free market with realistic exchange rates, traders export what is cheaper at home than abroad and import what is more expensive, they are in fact implementing the principle of comparative advantage.

(b) Exchange rates

It is implicit in the above arguments that exchange rates should be realistic. (The Gold Standard enabled the "classical" economists to bypass this issue.) Exchange rate theory is complex and often controversial, but its practical implications can be very significant for the agri-food system. Recent issues concerning the role of exchange rate policy in general macro-economic management will be touched upon in the next chapter.

In its simplest expression, the exchange rate between two national currencies is the equilibrium price at which they are traded in the foreign exchange market. When, say, German goods are exported, a *demand* for D-marks arises because exporters want to convert the foreign currency they have earned into D-marks; there is also a demand for D-marks on the part of holders of foreign currencies who want to buy German assets (or simply to hold bank accounts in D-marks). The *supply* of D-marks arises from the reverse processes.

In other words, the exchange rate is influenced by the various components of the **balance of payments**: the "current account", including both "visible" trade in goods and "invisible" trade in services such as banking, tourism or shipping; and the "capital account", i.e. financial transactions.

An overvalued exchange rate would make a country's exports too expensive and its imports too cheap, and *vice versa*: adjustments should then occur until an equilibrium is reached. In the extreme case where one country initially had higher costs at the ruling exchange rate for *every* item, it might begin by importing on a wide scale: but since it could not export, the demand of its citizens for foreign currency to pay for imports would soon outrun the amount of foreign currency it could earn. The rise in the price of foreign currency relative to its national currency (i.e. "depreciation" of its own currency) would eventually lower the price of its produce until some exports became competitive and a balance was reached.

One hypothesis as to the exchange rate which would result, in the absence of official intervention (a "free float"), is the **purchasing power parity** (PPP) theory. This holds that the exchange rate, at least in the long run, will reflect the relative prices of goods and services as between the countries concerned. Efforts are made by international bodies such as the OECD to measure PPPs on the basis of a "basket" of similar goods and services in different countries, to serve at least as a bench-mark against which actual exchange rates can be compared. (See Appendix, item 2, on the "Big Mac" illustration.)

Figure 6.1—Economic cost of a tariff

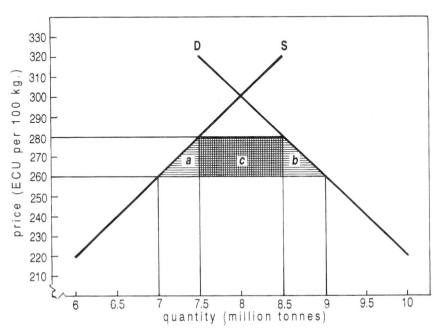

But in fact, exchange rates, if free to float, often do diverge from PPPs, causing "appreciation" or "depreciation" of the currency concerned. There is much argument among economists as to whether such deviations are likely to be only temporary, in which case intervention is probably undesirable, or whether they may set the currency in question—and hence the economy of that country—on a different path, in which case action may be needed.

The main cause of deviations is to be found in financial transactions, which are influenced not just by the underlying competitiveness or otherwise of the countries concerned but also by relative interest rates: *expectations* as regards possible changes in the interest rate and as regards the exchange rate itself play a major role. As there are nowadays very large funds which can move around the world, the resulting swings can be very big. This is often described as "speculation" and "hot money", and it is indeed partly due to financial operators aiming to make a quick profit by anticipating an exchange rate movement: but it is also due to the managers of pension funds, investment trusts and so on who have a duty to their clients to protect their assets, a task which may involve shifting the money into a safer currency.

Since 1971 (when the attempt to maintain an international "dollar standard" was abandoned), three of the major world currencies—the US dollar, the Japanese yen and the British pound—have "floated", but subject from time to time to central bank intervention, buying or selling the currency to stabilise the exchange rate: a process described as a "managed float".

Such action can quickly become a trial of strength between the financial operators and the central banks. If the latter co-operate and pool their resources, they have a better chance. A key feature of the European Monetary System (EMS), set up in 1979 by the Member States of the EC, was the creation of a fund for concerted short-term intervention. Further, the countries participating in the Exchange Rate Mechanism (ERM) undertake to keep their exchange rates within a narrow band, i.e. a maximum spread at any given time of 2.25%, or 6% for a few countries. Although it is hoped that the support arrangements will reduce the need for "revaluations" or "devaluations", the ERM rules do not preclude them. Experience with the EMS, and some implications for the agri-food system, will be discussed in the next chapter. It should already be stressed here that exchange rate issues are inseparable from interest rate policy and from other aspects of macro-economic policy.

(c) The effect of a tariff

Supply/demand analysis can illustrate how prices and quantities are determined in international trade, and help to analyse the impact of tariffs.

To come closer to reality, we shall consider a case where the world price is undoubtedly lower than the domestic price: that of beef in the European Community. Figure 6.1 shows hypothetical supply and demand curves. In a no-trade situation, market equilibrium might be found at a price of around 300 ECU/100 kg., with production around 8 million tonnes. Suppose that the EC could import

2 million tonnes at a price of 260 ECU/100 kg. (allowing for the rise in the world price that would result from large EC purchases). At that price, the total quantity demanded in the EC would be 9 million tonnes, the amount supplied from within the Community falling to 7 million tonnes. "Consumer surplus" (cf. Chapter 4) is increased as consumers can now obtain greater quantities at a lower price.

The imposition of a tariff (or levy) of 20 ECU per tonne raises the domestic price to 280 ECU (on the assumption that the import price remains unchanged). Domestic production expands from 7 to 7.5 million tonnes; consumers buy 8.5 instead of 9 million tonnes; imports fall from 2 to 1 million tonnes. (These figures are used just for illustrative purposes: in fact the EC has imposed much larger levies on beef imports and has moved into a net *export* position.)

The diagram makes it possible, on certain assumptions, to estimate the gains and losses:

* **Consumers** lose (their welfare as measured by consumer surplus is reduced) to the extent that the price is higher and the quantity purchased lower: this loss corresponds to the whole area $a + b + c + d$ (it can easily be worked out that this amounts to 175 million ECU in this illustration).
* **Producers** obtain an extra *gross* revenue corresponding to the rise in price multiplied by the rise in quantity sold. But they also incur additional production costs. As the supply curve represents the aggregate marginal cost of all producers (cf. Chapter 2), the area below this curve (cost times quantity) represents the total cost of production for any point on the curve: the *additional* cost therefore corresponds to the triangle b. The *net* producer gain is the area a (145 million ECU in the illustration).
* **The government** (or in this example, the EC budget) gains revenue from the tariff, consisting of the unit rate of the tariff multiplied by the amount of imports following imposition of the tariff: i.e. the area c (here, 20 million ECU).

Since consumer loss is represented by $a + b + c + d$, while producer gain is only a and "government's" gain only c, it follows that there is a *net national loss* corresponding to the triangles b plus d (8 + 5 million ECU) (on the very optimistic assumption that the extra government revenue is spent only for socially-useful purposes). Of these:

* The triangle b represents a loss due to a part of supply being obtained at a relatively high cost from domestic production when it could have been obtained more cheaply abroad—often called the "production effect".
* The triangle d represents that part of the loss to consumers that is not offset by gain to either producers or to the "government"—often called the "consumption effect".

While in all cases there is a net economic loss, the size of this loss depends entirely on the position and slope of the supply and demand curves, i.e. on their *elasticities* over the relevant range. This approach is the basis for much econometric analysis aiming to assess the effects of alternative trade policies (cf. Appendix, item 3).

In analysing trade *liberalisation*, the issue arises in reverse: what happens if an existing tariff (or levy) is *removed*? Would the gain to consumers exceed the loss to producers? In the above example, abolition of the tariff would enable consumers to regain 175 million ECU as against a loss to producers of 145 million ECU and a loss of "government" revenue of 20 million ECU. In principle, there is a net national gain, and if 165 million ECU were transferred from consumers to producers and "government" (e.g. via taxation), consumers would still be better off to the extent of 10 million ECU.

However, the welfare issues already touched upon in Chapter 5 are highly relevant here. Can equal weight be attached to the gains and losses of different groups of people?—in other words, can valid "interpersonal welfare comparisons" be made? Hence, is one entitled to recommend a measure whereby one group of people gain and others lose, even if the gain exceeds the loss in monetary terms? Can some compensation system adequately resolve the dilemma? In the context of agricultural trade, these are real issues.

Finally, some important qualifications to the foregoing arguments should be noted. In illustrating the effects of a tariff, the diagram represents only a *partial equilibrium* situation: it neglects other changes which might occur, especially if the tariff is large. In particular:

* **"Factor costs"**—the price of inputs used in domestic production—could change (causing a *shift* in the supply curve and not just a movement along it). Thus, workers could be encouraged by the higher price level to demand higher wages.
* **The "terms of trade"** might change: with reduced import demand, the import price could fall. The likelihood of this depends on the size of the tariff and on the significance of the importing country in relation to total trade in the commodity concerned. While a low tariff imposed by a minor importer may cause little or no change in the world price (the "small country effect"), a high tariff imposed by a big importer is likely to drive down the world price, shifting some of the domestic losses to exporters. This argument plays an important role in trade theory, suggesting that for a large country there may be an "optimal tariff level" at which the terms of trade effect offsets the loss due to misallocation of resources: the point is further discussed in section (e) below.

Such an effect is indeed highly likely in the example of beef imports by the EC, potentially a very large importer. The above example deliberately supposed a rather small tariff, so that effects on the import price could be ignored. In reality, the combined protective effect of a 20% tariff plus a much higher import levy keeps the world price much lower than it would otherwise be. It follows that abolition, or substantial reduction, of EC protection for beef, or other commodities of which the EC is or could be a major importer, is likely to lead to an *increase* in world prices.

(d) Customs unions

Customs unions which create free trade among their members while imposing common tariffs against non-member countries do not fully exploit comparative advantage, but they can bring about a more efficient use of resources. The removal of barriers to their internal trade will lead to a *creation* of trade among them. There will on the other hand be a *diversion* of trade away from more efficient external suppliers in the case of any member country which previously had tariffs lower than the new common tariffs. Whether or not trade creation outweighs trade diversion will depend on whether the new external tariffs are less than the average of the previous individual tariffs. A number of other conditions influence the extent of trade creation or diversion (see Appendix, item 4).

The General Agreement on Tariffs and Trade (GATT) has given effect to this argument by stating, in its Article XXIV.5:

> *The provisions of this Agreement shall not prevent... the formation of a customs union... provided that the duties and other regulations of commerce imposed at the institution of any such union... in respect of trade with contracting parties not subject to such union... shall not on the whole be higher or more restrictive than the general incidence of the duties and regulations of commerce applicable in the constituent territories prior to the formation of such union.*

The "common market" formed by the European Economic Community is the most significant case of a customs union to date. The Treaty of Rome declared (Article 110) that "by establishing a customs union between themselves, Member States aim to contribute in the common interest to the harmonious development of world trade, the progressive abolition of restrictions on international trade and the lowering of customs barriers". Following negotiations in the early 1960s on the basis of Article XXIV of GATT, the Community was held to be generally in compliance with GATT rules.

In the case of agriculture, however, the maintenance of high internal prices and high rates of protection in the EC has caused considerable *diversion* of trade away from third countries, leading to a number of trade conflicts. These matters will be more fully discussed in Chapter 13. Broadly, it can be said that agricultural trade within the EC has expanded, particularly during the 1970s among the original six members; but the extent of trade creation and specialisation has not been as great as might have been hoped, largely because high prices and other features of the CAP have enabled high-cost production to persist, partly also because obstacles to trade have remained in the form of "monetary compensatory amounts" and "non-tariff barriers".

(e) The case for protection

The "law of comparative advantage" has been described as "elegant" and "beautiful" (Samuelson), even as "conceptually impeccable" (Harrod). Yet it has had remarkably little impact on policy.

Some of the arguments by which the free-trade case is presented are too complex, and the diagrams too abstract, to impress non-specialists. References to "consumer surplus" and to "areas below the demand curve" are not likely to convince the uninitiated.

Arguments for protection, on the other hand, often have direct and immediate appeal. Of these arguments, some are bad economics, some have a valid basis in economics, others have nothing to do with economics and cannot be assessed by economic analysis.

The category of "bad economics" includes the following:

* **Mercantilism and neo-mercantilism.** The "mercantilist" writers of the 17th and 18th centuries considered a country fortunate if it sold more goods than it bought, because this meant that gold would flow into the country to pay for its export surplus. This confuses the means and ends of economic activity. To go on indefinitely accumulating gold—or, in the modern context, "hard currency"—beyond the needs of a reasonable reserve will not in itself improve a country's living standard: on the contrary, this will drive up prices, making the country less competitive. Money is worthwhile not for its own sake, but for what it will buy from other countries.

In the present-day context, the same sort of argument frequently arises in the context of agricultural trade, and may be described as "neo-mercantilism". This is particularly prevalent in France, where the concept of *"vocation agricole"* is treated as virtually a dogma and rarely subjected to any kind of analysis: imports of food and feed are regarded as undesirable, exports as desirable.

* **The balance of payments.** This is closely related to the previous argument: it is held that an importing country that can achieve greater self-sufficiency in foodstuffs (or can even move to a net export position) improves its balance of payments with the rest of the world. In the United Kingdom in the 1950s and 1960s, there was much discussion of this issue, involving some eminent economists. The case turned on whether labour and other factors of production were better employed producing food and thus saving imports, or in other sectors of the economy where their productivity might be higher and where they might contribute to exports. The balance of expert opinion favoured the latter course, but the farming lobby was able to use this argument to secure continued government support.

* **Retaliation.** It is argued that if other countries impose protection, one's own country should do the same in self-defence. This does not in fact improve one's own economic welfare, on the contrary. It is true that a *threat* of retaliation may deter another country from raising tariffs, or cause it to remove them: the US threat, announced in November 1992, of prohibitive tariffs against certain goods from the EC, aimed at forcing the EC to reduce its subsidies on oilseeds, falls in this category.

Arguments that may have economic validity in certain circumstances include the following:

* **The "infant industry" argument.** This has a long and respectable history: in the 19th century it was associated in particular with the German economist Friedrich List and his school of nationalist economics. It points out that protection may enable industries to develop which after a period of time may become internationally competitive—particularly if they can exploit economies of

scale. This argument draws attention to the weakest point in the "comparative advantage" theory: that it is essentially *static*.

Some contemporary economists apply the argument to developing countries as a whole: this discussion goes beyond the scope of this book.

The counter-argument is that once an industry (or economic sector) enjoys protection, it will prove very difficult to remove that protection. That has certainly been the case for agriculture, as the present author has sought to show in another work (see Appendix, item 5).

* **The anti-dumping case.** If a foreign country can be shown to be practising "dumping"—i.e. selling below costs to eliminate competition—there may be a case for temporary protection. In this form, the argument is not very relevant for agriculture; but a similar point is frequently made with regard to export subsidies, American export subsidies in particular being held to justify EC protection. It is of course preferable that such conflicts be dealt with by bilateral negotiation or through GATT.

* **The terms of trade argument.** This has already been touched upon above. It is a rather complex argument, to the effect that a country which imposes a tariff may gain by pushing down the price of its imports relatively to its exports. It may be valid for a country that accounts for a large part of world imports of the commodity or commodities concerned; even then, it neglects the likelihood that other countries will retaliate, causing a decline in *every* country's economic welfare. This is, in fact, a "beggar-my-neighbour" policy.

There is no doubt that agricultural import restrictions by the EC have contributed to pushing down the world prices of major agricultural commodities. That has not actually benefited EC consumers, since EC import levies are then raised still further (see Chapter 9). On the other hand, the result has been to aggravate tensions in trade policy.

* **The unemployment issue.** This has been the most widespread and effective argument for protection, particularly in recent times. Protection against Asian textiles or Japanese cars and video recorders for example, aims to maintain employment in the corresponding industries in the West. The economic counter-argument is that this means propping up uncompetitive industries, a loss in economic efficiency and even, in the long-term, less employment overall. It is also a "beggar-my-neighbour" policy, since it acts against the export countries concerned, and ultimately reduces their import capacity.

The same argument forms the main justification for agricultural protection: to maintain jobs in farming which would be lost if agriculture were exposed to the full force of competition. Economic analysis can demonstrate the costs arising from protection, in terms of higher prices to consumers, adverse effects on world trade, and so on. It can also demonstrate that a move to free trade would give overall gains exceeding the losses to farmers: numerous econometric studies take this line (see Appendix, item 3). But these arguments make little impact on policy since they do not sufficiently answer the threat to farming jobs and incomes, and since, as has already been observed several times, it is difficult to devise satisfactory compensation schemes.

* **Balanced protection.** In the real world, the ideal situation does not exist: the assumptions of perfect competition are only partly fulfilled, and the starting-point in trade matters is not free trade but some degree of protection. The theory of the "second-best" under welfare economics holds that if distortion cannot be removed from one market, it is better to spread inevitable distortions thinly over many markets than to concentrate their effects in a few markets. On this basis, it can be argued that as complete free trade is unattainable, it is better to have a *balanced* degree of protection as between sectors and commodities than for some to be highly-protected and others with little or no protection.

This argument has been relevant to the EC's demand in the Uruguay Round context (cf. Chapter 13) for a "rebalancing" of protection: i.e. the imposition of some degree of protection on imported feed (especially oilseed products), currently imported levy-free, in return for reduced support and protection on cereals and other products. (See Appendix, item 6).

Among the *non-economic* arguments for protection, the following are significant.

* **Food security.** Particularly in the past, this has been an important argument for protection to raise domestic production of food. It is no longer so significant with the development of surpluses, although some countries—Japan and Switzerland, for example—still attach importance to their food security.

The EC, while more than self-sufficient in most agricultural products, is in fact highly dependent on imports of livestock feed: but the case against this (the "rebalancing" controversy—see Chapter 13)—rests mainly on economic grounds.

* **The "way of life" argument.** This is particularly relevant to agricultural protectionism. There are many references, in discussions of agricultural policy, to the importance of the traditional values which the farming community, more than any other, is seen as preserving. Coming from politicians, this can be demagogic—an easy way to gain farm votes. Still, it is often a sincerely-held belief, deserving of respect.

APPENDIX

1. General sources. All economics textbooks and most textbooks on agricultural economics include a discussion of international trade theory. There are also numerous more specialised works. R.F. Harrod's *International Economics* (4th edition, Cambridge University Handbooks, 1957) gave clear and simple explanations. More recent works have introduced greater sophistication though not always greater clarity (e.g. the later Cambridge Economic Handbook, by A. Dixit and V. Norman, *Theory of International Trade*, 1980). However, *International Economics*, by C.P. Kindleberger and P.H. Lindert (6th edition, Irwin, Illinois, 1978) is comprehensive and readable; useful points are also made in *International Trade and Agriculture: Theory and Policy*, edited by J.S. Hillman and A. Schmitz (Westview Press, Boulder, 1979). Other specialised works should only be tackled by advanced students: these include W.J. Ethier, *Modern International Economics* (Norton, New York: 1988); or R. Pomfret, *International Trade* (Blackwell, Cambridge (US) etc.: 1991).

The theory of "factor endowment" is frequently described as the "Heckscher-Ohlin" theorem; the demonstration that trade tends to raise returns to the factor used intensively in the production of exportable, rising-price goods, and *vice versa*, is referred to as the "Stolper-Samuelson" theorem. Fuller explanations will be found in the works referred to above. In view of problems in the definition of "costs", when the cost relationships of the various production factors differ as between the trading partners, recent works prefer to use the "opportunity cost" concept, whereby the cost of one item is expressed in terms of the quantity of the other item that *could* be produced instead. The "indifference curve" method— in this case using "production possibility" and "community indifference" curves—is suited to this approach, and can be used to demonstrate the welfare gains from trade.

2. Purchasing power parity and the "Big Mac". As mentioned in the text, sophisticated official calculations are made by bodies such as the OECD. The weekly *Economist* has used a simpler approach, based on the price in different cities around the world of a McDonald's hamburger, on the grounds that this is virtually identical wherever it is produced, and incorporates a wide range of inputs. In the absence of more serious information, this may serve as a rough guide. In April 1992, for example, this calculation suggested that the rouble (on the basis of the price in McDonald's Moscow restaurant) was then *over*valued by 273% (but subsequently the rouble continued its fall against the dollar and other currencies).

3. Costs of protection and benefits from free trade. The type of analysis briefly outlined in this chapter forms the basis of much econometric work, which has become increasingly sophisticated as the development of computer power has enabled complex and comprehensive "models" to be built. The costs of agricultural protection, under the EC's Common Agricultural Policy and in other countries, and the benefits that could be gained from agricultural trade liberalisation, have been a particular object of study: the OECD, the Australian Bureau of Agricultural and Resource Economics (ABARE), and the US Department of Agriculture, have been particularly active in this field. For a review of the main models, see D. Blandford, "The costs of agricultural protection", in *Agricultural Protectionism in the Industrialized World*, edited by F.H. Sanderson (Resources for the Future, Washington D.C., 1990).
It is however questionable whether knowledge of all the necessary parameters has advanced to the same extent as skill in model-building. The costs and benefits of price changes resulting from trade policies are crucially dependent—as can be seen from Figure 6.1—on the position and slope of the supply and demand curves, i.e. on the price elasticities. Previous chapters have indicated the difficulty in obtaining accurate elasticities (see in particular the Appendices to Chapter 2 (item 3) and to Chapter 4 (item 2). Studies in this field often fill in gaps in information by making alternative assumptions. As is indicated in Annex IV of the OECD report *National Policies and Agricultural Trade* (Paris, 1987), such alternatives can cause substantial differences in the outcome as regards the distribution of gains and losses between producers and consumers.

4. The customs union issue. The theoretical issues were extensively discussed in the 1950s, particularly in writings by J. Viner and J.E. Meade. The latter's *Theory of Customs Unions* (North-Holland Publishing Company, Amsterdam, 1955) gave a clear statement of the criteria (additional to those mentioned in the text above) for judging whether a customs union is likely to have as its net effect the creation or diversion of trade. Later writings—discussed in the specialised sources mentioned in item 1 above—have extended this "partial equilibrium" analysis to incorporate dynamic and "general equilibrium" effects. Note that customs unions do not achieve the theoretical "Pareto optimum" even for their members, because of the existence of tariffs, but they may represent an attainable "second best".

5. Agricultural protectionism. The author's work *Government and Agriculture in Western Europe 1880–1988* (Harvester–Wheatsheaf, London etc.: 3rd edn., 1989) describes the evolution of agricultural policies starting from the protection granted in the late 19th century by France, Germany and other continental European countries against North American grain. With qualifications, the general thesis is that this protectionism was an improvised response to an immediate crisis, but that once installed it proved difficult to remove; and that its long-term effects have been harmful, not only to consumers and the economy in general, but also to the farming community by delaying structural adjustment.

Some authors take a different view. In particular, Paul Bairoch, in *Commerce extérieur et développement économique de l'Europe au XIXe siècle* (Mouton, Paris, 1976) contested the advantages of free trade, on the basis of a statistical analysis indicating that phases of rapid economic growth in the latter part of the 19th century did not correspond to periods of free trade. This interpretation has in turn been criticised by others, and the present author, following debate with Bairoch (cf. *Economie Rurale* 184–186, mars–août 1988, "Un siècle d'histoire agricole française"), maintains his opinion.

6. **Balanced protection.** The argument in relation to the EC was first advanced by L. Mahé in "A lower but more balanced protection for European agriculture", in *European Review of Agricultural Economics*, 1984:11 (pp.217–234). His reasoning, though not necessarily his specific calculations, remains valid. A major study sponsored by the Commission, *Disharmonies in EC and US agricultural policy measures* (1988), was carried out by a team of experts (including Mahé): it explored the effects of price cuts under various options, involving for the EC a 20% cut in prices for cereals and related products and a 10% tariff on imports of animal feed and oil. It concluded that reducing disharmonies in one sector would lead to smaller overall gains than reducing them across a wide range of commodities.

CHAPTER 7

AGRICULTURE IN A CHANGING ECONOMY

In countries at an early stage of economic development, most of the population live and work in the rural sector; agriculture contributes a large share of national income, maybe the largest; but productivity of labour in agriculture remains low. The process of economic growth involves a movement of labour into other occupations, permitting increased productivity by the remaining farm labour force, and the growth of non-farm sectors, with a smaller part of a larger national income coming from agriculture. In later stages of growth, the service sector overtakes industry as the major employer.

Many developing countries, however, and some centrally-planned countries, have found to their cost that to *neglect* agriculture, in particular by keeping down the prices of farm produce relative to non-farm items, endangers the whole process. Agriculture contributes to development not just by releasing labour: rapid growth of agricultural productivity enables extra food supplies to be made available to the growing urban population at lower prices. This is all the more necessary when *per capita* food supplies are initially low and population is growing fast, as is the case in most developing countries. The growth of farm incomes made possible by higher productivity creates a larger market for agricultural inputs and consumer goods from the industrial sector. Agricultural exports earn foreign exchange which can be used to buy capital goods needed for industrial development.

The role of agriculture in the developed market economies is different. An efficient food system continues to make its contribution to the economy as a whole. But agriculture is already a relatively small sector of the economy. Its productivity is high and the food needs of the non-farm population can be easily satisfied, even though the farm work-force is relatively small. Although labour continues to move from agriculture into other occupations, this no longer contributes much to economic growth. Domestic and international markets for agricultural produce tend to be oversupplied, and extra output can often be sold only at falling prices. The agricultural sector has to undergo a difficult adjustment—made all the more difficult in recent times by problems in the general economy.

(a) General economic trends and policies

Until about 1973, it was possible to discuss agricultural problems in terms of adjustment to economic growth: how could farm incomes keep pace with the rise in living standards in the urban economy? (See references in Appendix, item 1). The economic climate after 1973 was a very different one. A major shock to Western economies was caused by the first oil crisis, provoked by the Arab–Israeli war: the price of oil rose from under $2 per barrel before the crisis to about $11 in 1974. Inflation in Western Europe accelerated into double figures, while the growth of national income slackened and became negative in 1975: the phenomenon of "stagflation" (stagnation plus inflation) was born. Unemployment rose sharply. Monetary instability was aggravated: Germany, with a relatively low inflation rate, maintained a strong currency, but most other EC currencies depreciated against the Deutschemark.

A second oil crisis in 1979–80, provoked this time by revolution in Iran, raised the world oil price to over $30 per barrel, causing renewed inflation and world-wide economic recession. These problems persisted despite a sharp fall in the oil price in 1986: subsequently, it oscillated between $15 and $20 in most years, with a temporary sharp increase in 1991 during the Gulf War.

In the 1980s, most Western governments gave less priority to combating unemployment than to reducing inflation, through restrictive monetary policy (high interest rates in particular). Especially in the US under the Republican administrations of Ronald Reagan and George Bush, and in the UK under the Conservative government of Margaret Thatcher, "supply-side" measures—tax cuts, deregulation and privatisation of previously-regulated sectors—were pursued in efforts to relaunch growth by encouraging private enterprise in a more competitive environment, while attempts were made to reduce budget deficits by cutting public expenditure. The advice of the "monetarist" school of economists, led by Milton Friedman in Chicago and by several British economists, was currently in the ascendancy over the neo-Keynesians, and played a role in this process.

In Western Europe, the German economy provided a model of relative stability and progress: economic growth continued while inflation was kept low, partly because wage demands by workers remained moderate, and partly through firm monetary policy in which the *Bundesbank*, independent of political control, played a major part. The strength of the D-mark made it a pole of attraction.

In France, even the Socialist government elected in 1981, after some initial populist measures which caused renewed inflation and precipitated further devaluations of the franc, found it necessary to adopt restrictive policies: gradually inflation was brought under control: after 1987, the franc held its parity with the D-mark.

Meanwhile, world monetary instability was aggravated by continuing US budgetary and trade deficits, as a result of which the dollar fell steadily against the ECU from a peak in 1985, with only a short recovery in 1989.

In the EC, the European Monetary System (EMS) was introduced in 1979, incorporating the Exchange Rate Mechanism (ERM) which provides for mutual currency support. This kept short-term fluctuations within a narrow band—normally a maximum spread at any given time of 2.25%, though Italy was initially allowed a range of 6%. Still, within the system, the D-mark was periodically revalued against most of the other currencies: between 1979 and 1987, there were seven re-alignments, in each of which the D-mark was revalued by amounts varying between 2% and 5.5% (in terms of its "central rate" against the ECU). The Dutch guilder was also revalued, by the same amounts except on one occasion. The Belgian and French francs, initially weak, gradually gained strength. The British pound, which had remained outside the ERM and steadily lost value against the D-mark, was finally—in 1990—brought into the ERM, with the wider 6% band, which was applied to the Spanish peseta when it entered the ERM in 1989 and to the Portuguese escudo in April 1992. By then, among EC currencies, only the Greek drachma remained outside the ERM; Sweden and Finland too had pegged their currencies to the ECU.

Growing confidence in the system was a key factor leading to the signature, in December 1991 in Maastricht, of the Treaty on European Union, in which a key element was a three-stage programme to bring about economic and monetary union, at the latest by 1999. It was recognised that this target was dependent on achieving "a high degree of sustainable convergence", defined by reference to price stability (i.e. inflation rates), the absence of "excessive" budget deficits,

Table 7.1—EC 12: Major economic indicators

	GDP (volume)	Prices	Unemployment rate	Interest rate	$/ECU rate
	average %	annual change	%	%	$1 = .. ECU
1970–72	+4.9	+ 6.8	2.2	8.4	0.94
1973	+6.2	+ 9.0	2.5	9.1	0.81
1974–75	+0.5	+14.0	3.6	11.2	0.83
1976–79	+3.6	+11.5	5.3	10.9	0.82
1980–83	+0.9	+10.7	8.4	13.8	0.94
1984	+2.3	+ 6.8	11.7	11.8	1.27
1985	+2.4	+ 6.0	10.7	10.9	1.31
1986	+2.8	+ 5.6	10.3	9.2	1.02
1987	+2.9	+ 4.1	9.7	9.4	0.86
1988	+4.0	+ 4.5	8.9	9.4	0.85
1989	+3.3	+ 5.0	8.3	9.9	0.94
1990	+2.8	+ 5.3	10.8	11.1	0.79
1991				10.4	0.81

Notes and sources: see Appendix, item 6.

observance of the "normal" fluctuations margins under the ERM, without devaluations against other Member States; and the durability of convergence, as reflected in long-term interest rate levels.

Unfortunately, monetary stability within the EMS was sharply interrupted in September 1992, partly as a result of political uncertainties related to French ratification of the Maastricht Treaty, partly because the British pound and the Italian lira were being held within their ERM limits by high interest rates, and the markets clearly considered them to be overvalued. Unprecedentedly large international movements of funds by private operators overwhelmed the attempts of the central banks to support these currencies, which within a few days were forced out of the ERM and fell sharply in value; the peseta stayed within the system but had to be devalued. In November 1992, more turbulence caused a further devaluation of the peseta, along with the escudo, and other currencies came under pressure. By the end of 1992, the path towards monetary union looked much less smooth than it had seemed a year earlier.

Economic growth rates had improved during the 1980s, but as a result of restrictive monetary policy, they remained far below pre-1973 performances. The years 1991 and 1992 saw renewed recession in several countries, with major firms reporting losses or reduced profits, some being taken over by other companies, and many smaller firms going out of business. Workers were laid off, and unemployment, which had been somewhat reduced, was on the rise again, remaining a major problem in most countries.

Indeed, the central and largely unsolved issue of "macro-economic" policy was still how to achieve stable growth while maintaining reasonably full employment yet without inflationary overheating. Given the political aim of cutting taxes yet reducing budgetary deficits, Keynesian-type remedies—government expenditure to stimulate economic recovery—were officially out-of-fashion and were criticised by "monetarist" economists. The prevailing view was that inflation must be brought under control before measures to promote growth could be risked. In particular, the tight monetary policy of the *Bundesbank*, coupled with the determination of governments in other countries to tie their currencies as closely as possible to the D-mark, left little leeway for bringing down interest rates in other countries.

After the monetary crisis which began in September 1992, a re-assessment of macro-economic policy became inevitable. In Britain, with the pound floating once again, the case for maintaining a high interest rate was weakened: in November, the British government announced measures to stimulate economic growth, and cut interest rates in stages by several points. In other countries too, interest rates were being edged down. In Germany, however, the need for public borrowing to finance restructuring in the new Länder in the East kept interest rates high, and with continuing fear of inflation the *Bundesbank* remained reluctant to make more than token interest rate cuts.

Nevertheless, the European Council session in Edinburgh in December 1992 approved the outlines of a "growth initiative": a new European Investment Fund would guarantee loans to small and medium-sized companies, as well as infra-structural projects, while the existing European Investment Bank would raise new funds especially for cross-border transport links, including projects in central and eastern Europe.

This turbulence of late 1992 was a reminder of the complexity and vul-nerability of macro-economic policy, and of the links between the main economic components—growth, inflation, unemployment, trade—and of the policy instruments available to guide the economy—interest rates, taxation and the exchange rate in particular.

These events were also a reminder that, even within the EC and despite the "Maastricht" undertaking to move towards monetary union, exchange rate stability could not be taken for granted.

*   *   *

These various economic developments have significant consequences for the agricultural sector. In the following sections, there will be reference to the increased difficulty, arising from widespread unemployment in the non-farm sectors, for people leaving farms to find other jobs. High interest rates have created problems for farmers with big debts. Costs of agricultural production were raised in periods of high energy costs.

Currency changes within the European Community, particularly the ascen-sion of the D-mark and the devaluations of several other currencies, caused major difficulties for the Common Agricultural Policy, necessitating complex "agrimonetary" arrangements, which will be discussed in Chapter 9. The evolu-tion of the dollar also created severe problems, particularly because world prices of major agricultural commodities are expressed in dollars. The rise in the dollar in the late 1970s and early 1980s concealed for a time the extent of the growing supply-demand imbalance within the Community, as the cost of subsidising exports to the world market was kept down. The subsequent collapse of the dollar reversed this situation, provoking a sharp rise in the costs of support under the CAP.

(b) The agricultural adjustment problem

Though economic growth is not what it was, it has been historically significant and continues to have important consequences for the farm sector. Chapter 4 has underlined the significance of "Engel's Law": the tendency, as incomes rise, for consumer expenditure on food to decline as a *proportion* of total consumer expenditure. It has been seen that income elasticities in the high-income market economies are less than unity for most foodstuffs, and are even negative for certain "inferior" goods. Put differently, rising incomes mean that demand for non-farm products will tend to increase more rapidly than demand for farm products.

The implication is that the agricultural sector may expand in absolute terms, but it will be a progressively smaller part of the economy. Increased exports and/or decreased imports of agricultural produce may offset this tendency: indeed, agricultural policies in most developed market economies have had this effect, as will be seen later. But clearly, what one country's agriculture may gain in this respect can only be what agriculture in some other country loses. (In fact, traditional exporters of temperate-zone foodstuffs have had to look increasingly to new markets, including the Middle East and Japan.)

The role of prices must also be taken into account, since the farm sector's share in national income is a matter of value as well as volume. But farm product prices have tended to *fall* relatively to prices in general. Historical series of world market prices since the 19th century are not entirely convincing, partly due to abnormal influences, the two World Wars in particular. More recently, prices have been prevented from falling as much as they would otherwise have done, under the pressure of increased supplies, by various support measures. Even so, in the EC, the overall index of producer prices for agricultural products, "deflated" by the consumer price index, fell by 23% between 1980 and 1991. ("Nominal" prices continued to rise, though less than inflation.)

In terms of the analysis made in Chapter 2, the continuing growth in farming productivity is constantly shifting the supply curve to the right. The growth in output, however, encounters demand which is price-inelastic as well as income-inelastic: a fall in relative prices of agricultural produce becomes inevitable.

This argument is valid for the developed market economies, where—as has been seen in Chapter 4—growth in population and in *per capita* demand is limited: it may not apply in many developing countries where population is rising fast and per capita consumption is still at low levels. Food deficits in these countries could lead to increases in world market prices for major foodstuffs, with major implications for the developed countries too: but such an outcome is largely dependent on growth in purchasing-power in the poorer countries.

Figure 7.1 illustrates the crucial relationships for a number of developed market economies (for notes and sources, see Appendix, items 7 and 8). The horizontal axis shows average income per head, expressed in "purchasing power parity" for better comparability. The upper set of seven arrows relates to the share of total consumer expenditure spent on food: this declines over time in each country and is significantly lower in the higher-income countries. There are some differences due to national attitudes: British consumers, for example, spend less of their incomes on food than French consumers. (Note that these data relate only to food: the inclusion of beer, wine and other beverages would alter the pattern to some extent.)

The lower set of arrows relates to the share of agriculture in national income, or gross domestic product (GDP). Here too the inverse relationship with income is evident, and again, the various countries follow a similar path. Variations can arise because of different degrees of self-sufficiency in foodstuffs: the UK, which imports a substantial part of its food supply, has a lower share of agriculture in

GDP than France, which has a similar income level but is a net exporter. In the case of Portugal, there has been a fall in self-sufficiency in food combined with slow growth in agricultural productivity.

It is noticeable that the distance between the two sets of points does not diminish significantly with rising income: this implies that the processing and distribution elements remain important.

If agriculture's contribution to GDP is a declining share of the total, it follows that the average product per person employed must also decline in relation to the national average, unless there is a proportionate fall in the agricultural work force. Changes in product per head can be considered as roughly equivalent to changes in income per head (i.e., income arising from work within the sector). *Absolute* product per head can of course continue to rise: people dependent on agriculture can continue to become "better-off". But if they find their living-standards falling behind those of people in other occupations, they are likely to be dissatisfied.

Agriculture is not alone in such a situation: adjustments are continually taking place in the economy, as people move from lower-paid to higher-paid jobs. The problem for agriculture arises from the relative *immobility* of the farm work-force.

For most farm families, the farm is a home as well as a place of work. A decision to give up farming usually means moving to another area, possibly distant. The family may be able to continue living on the farm, while one or more members of the family travel to other jobs, provided alternative employment is available locally: but this is not the case in all regions. In fact, off-farm earnings have become increasingly important, and this point will be further discussed below: but it cannot solve all the problems.

In some rural areas, moreover, the type and level of education does not prepare people well for urban employment; nor does practical experience on the farm. Beyond a certain age, it is more difficult to learn new skills. These factors can limit the opportunities for farm employees, who otherwise might be more mobile than farmers and their families.

So the tendency is for the adjustment of the farm labour force to lag behind the rate that would be required to keep average earnings in agriculture in line with the national average. High rates of unemployment in the non-farm sectors are a further obstacle.

Figure 7.2 shows developments in some key indicators for EC agriculture between 1980 and 1991 (see Appendix, item 7, for notes and sources). Production rose by 13.5% in volume and by 74% in "nominal" value: in "real" terms (adjusted for inflation), it *fell* by 13%. Value-added by agriculture (deducting the cost of purchased inputs) fell by 18% in real terms. The farm labour force—expressed as "annual work units", thus allowing for part-time work—diminished by 30%, enabling the average value-added per work unit to rise by 18%. Annual fluctuations were considerable.

Figure 7.1—Food expenditure and agriculture in economic growth

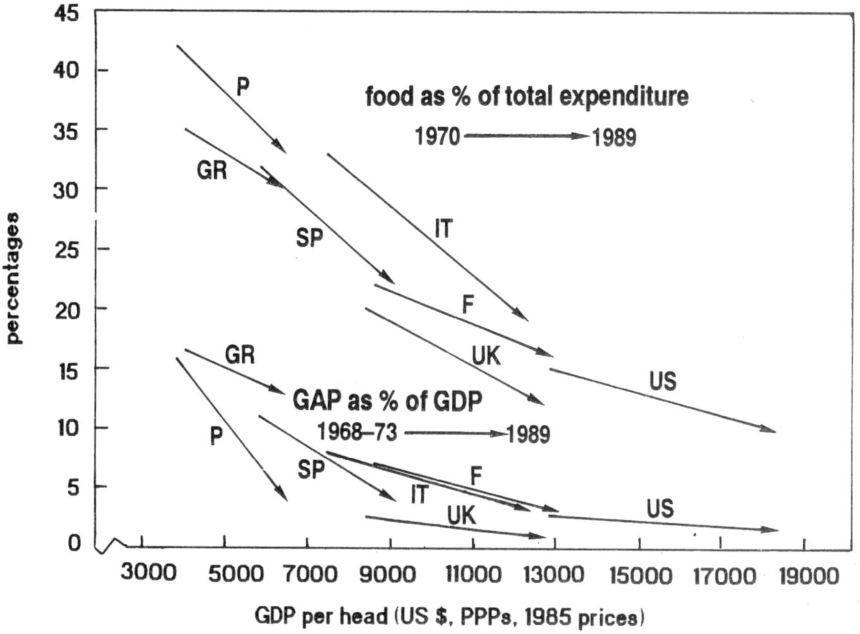

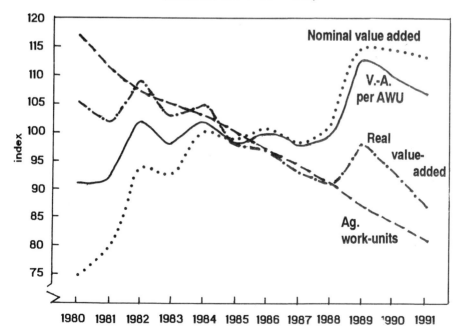

Figure 7.2—EC: Agricultural value-added and employment (indices, 1984–86 = 100)

Without the continued fall in the farm labour force, earnings per head could not have increased. Table 7.2 shows data covering all persons working on farms, *including those working part-time*. This substantially affects the results, particularly in Italy, where the apparent *increase* in the number of farmers is entirely due to an increase in the number working less than half-time on their holdings. Elsewhere, the number of farmers has fallen. The data on family members and on hired workers should be treated with caution, because of problems of classification (the series for France are particularly doubtful). Still, a fall in the number of family members has occurred in most countries, presumably reflecting mainly the increased tendency for sons and daughters to seek work elsewhere. The number of hired workers also seems to have fallen in the EC as a whole, but in most countries their absolute numbers is much less significant. It is noticeable that in the Netherlands the number of hired workers appears to have risen, and in the UK to have remained stable: the explanation is probably that in these countries, adjustments had already taken place at an earlier period, and the remaining workers are mostly skilled workers whose numbers cannot easily be further reduced.

The outcome of these various trends can be seen from Figure 7.3, which compares, for a number of countries, the share of agriculture in GDP with the

Table 7.2—The farm labour force (thousands)

	EC9	of which:				
		UK	NL	D	F	IT
Farmers						
- 1975	5783	267	161	904	1303	2646
- 1987	5157	232	129	702	923	2772
- index	89	87	80	78	71	105
Family members						
- 1975	5951	258	138	1221	(1473)	2479
- 1987	4512	258	116	835	(772)	2287
- index	76	100	84	68	(52)	92
Hired workers						
- 1975	974	223	33	90	(293)	264
- 1987	861	235	48	87	(339)	94
- index	88	101	145	97	(116)	36
Total						
- 1975	12708	758	332	2215	3069	5390
- 1987	10529	724	293	1624	2034	5153
- index	83	96	88	73	66	96

Source: Eurostat, direct communication. NB that the published data in *Farm Structure Survey 1987* (pp. 338 sq) contain numerous errors for 1987. The classification as between family labour and hired labour is doubtful, and in the case of France probably inconsistent as between the years.

share of the agricultural work-force in total employment. Approximate "parity" of product per head (which is *not* necessarily income per head, as will be seen below) is attained only in the Netherlands, though the situation appears reasonably satisfactory also in Belgium, Luxembourg, Denmark and the UK. On the other hand, the gap is wide in Germany, France and Ireland, and wider still in the Southern European countries, where a relatively high proportion of the work-force remains in agriculture but is unproductively employed. Indeed, a considerable degree of "hidden unemployment" lies behind these figures.

The data on agriculture's share in GDP (relating to "net value added at factor cost") include subsidies and the implicit "transfer payments" from the rest of the economy made through the price support system, without which the situation would appear still less favourable.

Such comparisons between agriculture and other sectors do not tell the whole story. "Product per head", derived from national accounts and manpower statistics (see Appendix, items 2 and 3) is only an approximation to farm income, and takes no account of revenue by farm families from off-farm sources. These are significant, as will be seen below.

Moreover, average results conceal the wide range of farm incomes. There are in fact different types of "farm income problem". One is related to the size of farm: despite substantial structural change, there are still many farms that are too small (in terms of area and capitalisation) to give a family an income comparable with other occupations (cf. Chapter 1 and in particular Table 1.1). The other problem is not necessarily dependent on farm size, but rather on the economic

Figure 7.3—Share of agriculture in GDP and in total employment, 1989

Source: Eurostat, *Agricultural Income 1991* (Series 5D), Luxembourg 1992 (Tables 1 and 2).

results, in particular on the level of debt: as has also been pointed out in Chapter 1, farmers who have invested heavily at a time of low interest rates can find themselves in difficulties if interest rates rise and farm profits are squeezed.

Information on income from farming in EC countries is gathered annually under the "Farm Accountancy Data Network" (FADN— commonly known as RICA after its French initials), though there is considerable delay in publication (see Appendix, item 4). The sample data are "grossed up" to represent all commercial farms. Table 7.3 is based on the latest data available at the time of writing. For reasons of space, it is not possible to include more than a small part of the information. This table however takes four countries, ranging from the Netherlands, which has the highest incomes from farming, down to Spain, and shows in each country both average data and figures for the smallest and largest size groups (omitting however groups which are numerically insignificant). This illustrates the wide range both between countries and within each of them, especially in respect of size of business (ESU) and farm net value-added (FNVA). In the case of Denmark, the smallest group has *negative* FNVA, largely due to a heavy burden of interest charges. FNVA per agricultural work unit (AWU) is a reasonably good indicator of earnings from farming.

An analysis of the FADN data over the period 1983/84 through 1988/89 (see Appendix, item 9) showed, in all EC countries except Belgium and the Nether-

Table 7.3—Characteristics of farms by ESU classes, 1988/89

	ESU category	% of all farms	ESU	AWU	UAA	FNVA	FNVA /AWU
					ha.	*ECU*	*ECU*
Netherlands	All farms	100	75	2.0	22	69362	34211
	Medium–high	38	35	1.4	13	31364	22094
	Very large	11	200	4.8	34	182865	37800
Denmark	All farms	100	46	1.1	34	33849	31417
	Small	15	7	0.3	9	– 902	–3261
	Very large	6	196	3.5	114	173764	49327
France	All farms	100	41	1.6	44	28486	17376
	Medium–low	24	15	1.4	24	10279	7583
	Large	22	71	2.0	67	48511	24821
Spain	All farms	100	10	1.4	20	9547	6849
	Very small	40	3	1.1	8	4364	4364
	Medium–high	10	28	2.0	56	10477	10477

Notes: ESU are "European Size Units"; AWU are "Agricultural Work Units"; UAA is "Utilised Agricultural Area"; FNVA is "Farm net value-added". See Appendix, item 4, for fuller explanations.
Source: Commission, "Farm Incomes Report 1988/89" (preliminary version).

lands, very low percentages of "commercial" farms earning sufficient profit to give the family an income comparable to other occupations and a return on capital comparable to the national interest rate (Table 7.4). Note that the "comparable income" criterion used was much lower in Southern European countries than in North-Western Europe, so farms in Southern Europe which showed a "profit" only did so at relatively low levels: with rising income expectations, this situation could change.

Much higher proportions of farms in all countries showed some increase in "own capital": this may be because they have other sources of income (see next section), or because the family has given priority to investment over current consumption. The study in question considered that such farms could be regarded as "viable" even if their current income appeared inadequate. The situation varies considerably between countries and between regions within countries. However, farms in less-favoured regions (including mountain areas), though they have low profit rates, do not show significantly worse results in terms of increase in "own capital", no doubt for the reasons just given.

(c) Off-farm sources of income

Faced with the difficulties of adjustment described above, many farm families have resorted increasingly to off-farm work to complement their incomes. "Multiple job-holding" or "pluri-activity" are better terms to describe the variety of solutions than the more usual expression "part-time farming".

Table 7.4—"Profitable" and "viable" farms, 1983/84–1988/89

	Average profit per farm	Farms making a profit	Farms increasing "own capital"
	ECU	%	%
Ireland	9526	5	62
UK	18342	19	59
Denmark	6679	14	59
Netherlands	29657	30	53
Belgium	27144	35	58
Luxembourg	20719	19	59
Germany	11810	8	29
France	13564	14	61
Italy	10663	8	16
Spain	6417	16	70
Portugal	3957	17	49
Greece	7109	11	46

Note: The two categories of farm are not mutually exclusive.
Source: Commission, *Viability of Farms*, 1991 (see Appendix, item 9).

The 1987 EC survey of farm structures indicated that 70% of "farm heads" had no other gainful employment (though many of these were not fully employed on their farms): 23% had other *main* gainful employment and 7% had other *secondary* gainful employment. In Germany, 38% of farmers had their main employment off the farm, reflecting both the small-farm structure in the southern *Länder* and the dispersion of industrial and service activity in the rural areas concerned. In Southern European regions, in view of the extent of under-employment on farms, off-farm activity rates would certainly be higher if the opportunities were greater.

It is more difficult to obtain reliable information on the incomes obtained from off-farm sources: farm families are generally reluctant to reveal all the sources and amounts of their income. However, official statistics in some countries do try to include such information, and a Eurostat project (see Appendix, item 2) is seeking to fill this gap at the EC level. Though differences in methodology and in the availability of data prevent firm conclusions, the first results indicate that "agricultural households"—i.e. those where farming is the main income source of the head of household—receive substantial amounts of income from outside agriculture, though with wide differences between Member States. In some countries, when these additional sources are taken into account, agricultural households seem to have average disposable incomes (i.e. after tax) *above* the average for all households. This is partly due to the larger average size of agricultural households, and incomes *per head* are less favourable. Their non-agricultural income is typically less variable from year to year than income from farming.

There is relatively full information on the situation in Germany. There, since 1980, agricultural households have received less income from farming than from other sources; and income from farming has grown less rapidly.

(d) Some policy implications

The analysis of price formation in the previous chapter, underlining the characteristic instability of agricultural prices, suggested that an economic case can be made for intervention to stabilise the markets, although it also stressed the risk of setting prices too high.

The case for *income* support is, from an analytical point of view, different. It is based on the tendency, described in this chapter, for earnings in agriculture to lag behind those in other occupations, due to the relative fall in agriculture's share in national income combined with the limited mobility of farm labour. This tendency is ineluctable, and can be avoided by individual countries only by increasing their degree of self-sufficiency in agricultural products. In *equity* terms, this can be a justification for some form of support, provided such support can be given in ways that do not aggravate or perpetuate the problem.

In practice, the two aims—stabilisation and support—have been mixed up in agricultural policy: most countries have used price support to fulfil both purposes. (In Chapter 12, it will be pointed out that Canada, which has stressed the stabilisation goal more than most other countries, has been increasingly drawn into support measures). In many cases, prices have been supported well above the levels at which national (and international) markets would be balanced. This has not only provoked excess supply, putting further pressure on market prices and raising the costs of support: it has also worked against the necessary long-term adjustment, by reducing the pressure on farm people to seek other occupations.

For many years, numerous economic studies have stressed these points, including a series of reports by the Paris-based Organisation for Economic Co-operation and Development. Already in 1964, a major OECD study on *Low Incomes in Agriculture* had concluded (p.10):

The main factor directly responsible for the low-income farm problem is the existence of excess manpower in the agricultural sector and its under-employment... In the long-run, the solution can only lie in reducing the number of farms and the number of persons working on farms, thus raising the average size of farm business.

A communiqué issued by the OECD Ministers of Agriculture in February 1964 on the basis of this report declared:

Price supports have a useful role in ensuring price stability and may have some value in alleviating farm incomes in the short-run; however, they are of less benefit to low-income farmers than to other farm groups and should not be allowed to impede long-term structural adaptations.

Such reasoning lay behind the development of structural policy, most notably the "Mansholt Plan" of 1968—this will be discussed in Chapter 10. As will be seen, however, the resources devoted to structural measures have been small by comparison with expenditure on price support, and the results have been limited.

Since the mid-1970s, the case for promoting the movement of farm labour to other jobs has been weakened by high unemployment in the general economy. In such circumstances, the "opportunity cost" of farm labour is reduced. It can also be argued that unemployment benefits under social security schemes would cost more than subsidies to maintain underemployed people in farming. Attitudes have also changed with growing realisation of the high social and economic cost of urban congestion, and with greater awareness of certain advantages of rural living.

So policies to deal with the farm problem have become more complex and sophisticated. They will inevitably continue to include an element of price support: but most economists would argue that this should be limited to the stabilisation function, that even in this context great prudence is needed in setting prices, and that farm income problems should be dealt with through other means.

Many economists have therefore advocated direct income aids, related to the *person* rather than to the product, to avoid giving a stimulus to overproduction. The conclusion to the previous chapter, however, has pointed out the theoretical as well as the practical difficulties: compensatory payments that are fully "decoupled" from production and linked to income needs are unpopular with farmers, and are difficult to devise and implement. Chapter 9 will discuss the compensatory payments introduced by the EC.

More constructively, there is growing support for payments for "services" which are increasingly demanded by society as regards maintenance and improvement of the rural environment; and perhaps most important, policies are being developed to promote economic growth and employment in rural areas, thus providing farm households with nearby job alternatives. These developments will be described in Chapter 10.

Finally, and returning to the issues discussed in the first section of this chapter, it should be stressed that the fortunes of the agri-food sector are inseparable from those of the economy as a whole. Recession, unemployment, high interest rates, and exchange rate instability seriously impede the process of agricultural adjustment, which on the contrary would become very much easier in a context of renewed growth and stability.

APPENDIX

1. Agriculture and economic growth. There is a vast economic literature on this subject, most of it related to developing countries and outside the scope of the present work. A pioneering study was Colin Clark's *Conditions of Economic Progress*, first published in 1940. Another important early contribution was by J.R. Bellerby, *Agriculture and Industry: Relative Income* (first published 1956).

In 1965, a panel of distinguished experts produced a report entitled *Agriculture and Economic Growth*, published by OECD (Paris): its conclusions, however, reflect the optimism of the period as regards economic growth, and need to be qualified in the light of subsequent developments.

For recent developments, the annual Commission reports on *The Situation of Agriculture in the Community* are a valuable source, though without deep analysis. Eurostat's *Agricultural Income 1991* (Series 5D, Luxembourg 1992) includes a useful retrospective covering the period 1980–1991.

Other major sources are mentioned below, or in the text. Much of this chapter, however, is based on the author's own work and experience in international organisations, and on studies too numerous to cite individually.

2. National income concepts. Since this chapter makes extensive use of statistics from national accounts, some explanations are desirable.

The most commonly-used measure is "gross domestic product" or GDP, often loosely described as "national income". This can be derived by adding up all incomes in the economy, or all expenditures, or the output ("value-added") by each economic branch. In principle, the same total should be arrived at in each case. In considering agriculture's relation to the economy, it is the "value-added" approach which is relevant. Value-added for each "firm" (or farm, in this case) is the value of its output *minus* the value of the inputs that it purchases from other firms.

GDP can be measured at "market prices" or at "factor cost": the latter *includes* subsidies and *excludes* indirect taxes, in particular value-added tax (VAT), which is the main indirect tax in the EC.

(Gross *national* product differs from GDP by including net earnings from abroad. *Net* national product (NNP) differs from GDP by deducting an amount needed to replace capital—i.e. depreciation. These two concepts are not used here.)

GDP can be expressed in *current* or in *constant* prices. In the latter case, an adjustment is made for changes in prices. This is the "implicit price deflator" of GDP, sometimes used to adjust other price series too. The "consumer price index" is similar but not identical. Series of data are described as "nominal" or "real" depending on whether or not they have been adjusted for price changes.

The Eurostat series on *Agricultural Income* (see below), is based on national accounts data. On income by farm households from non-farming sources, see the report prepared for Eurostat by Berkeley Hill of Wye College on *Total Income of Agricultural Households: 1992 report.*

The system of national accounts used by the former CMEA countries ("material product balances") did not include some items (particularly services) that are covered in the Western system, and generally gave lower figures for the agricultural sector than would have been obtained under the Western system.

National accounts are an indispensable means of *measuring* various economic magnitudes. They should not be treated as necessarily indicating *welfare.* In particular, they make no distinction between "private" and "social" costs, so that— for example—increased pollution associated with increased industrial activity is not deducted (on the contrary, pollution control measures are counted as additional "value-added"!). Nor do they allow for the depletion of non-renewable resources.

3. Employment statistics. In national statistics, people are normally classified according to their main occupation. Thus people who declare their main occupation to be farming will be included in agricultural employment, although they may have a second job; on the other hand, people whose main job is *not* in agriculture but who work part-time on a farm are *not* included. These statistics, however, have to be used for comparing agriculture with other sectors.

The periodic EC surveys of the structure of agricultural holdings (see below) cover all persons employed on farms, whether farming is their main activity or not; they also record working hours. On this basis, by conversion into full- time equivalents, the farm work-force can be expressed as "annual work units" (AWU).

In former CMEA countries, "agricultural employment" included various agriculture-related activities which in the West would be counted under "services" or "industry".

4. Farm income statistics. While national income and employment data can provide a rough comparison of incomes as between agriculture and other sectors, more precise information is given by the EC "Farm Accountancy Data Network" (FADN). A sample survey is conducted annually, covering about 57,000 "commercial" farms in the twelve Member States: the results are "grossed up" to represent all commercial farms, largely by reference to the periodic Eurostat surveys of farm structures (see below). "Farm net value added" (FNVA) is obtained from the value of total production, less purchased current inputs and depreciation of buildings, machinery, etc.: it thus represents the remuneration of family and hired labour, own and borrowed capital, and management. It can be expressed per AWU (see previous note).

If wages, interest charges, rents and social security charges are deducted from FNVA, gives "family farm income" is obtained. Expressed per unit of "unpaid labour", this represents the return to the labour of the farmer and his family and to their own capital. There are however difficulties in obtaining reliable information on family labour input.

FADN results are unfortunately published only with considerable delay (an advance copy of the main results for 1989/90 was made available by Commission staff for the present work). The system has also been criticised, particularly for the omission of off-farm incomes: cf. analysis by Berkeley Hill in the Commission's *Green Europe* series, no. 3/91: "Measuring farmers' incomes and business performance". As with the Eurostat approach mentioned above, attempts are being made to extend the FADN coverage to fill this gap.

5. Farm structure surveys. Eurostat conducts periodic surveys of farms throughout the Community: at the time of writing, the last for which results are available refers to 1987. These surveys provide detailed information on the number and size of farms, on farm employment, etc. (Note however that tables on the farm labour force in the 1987 report contain major errors.)

In this and in the FADN, farms are classified according to the European Size Unit (ESU) as well as by area. The ESU is a measure of economic size. A farm has an economic size of 1 ESU if its total "standard gross margin" (production minus certain variable costs) has a certain value in ECU: this amount is periodically adjusted, but was 1,100 ECU for the 1987 survey. Gross margins are not actually measured for every farm, but are calculated from the average for each type of farming in the region over a three-year period: the results can then be applied to individual farms on the basis of physical data as to their crop area, livestock numbers, etc.

The main results of both the FADN and the farm structure surveys are contained in the Commission's annual report on *The Agricultural Situation in the Community*.

6. Table 7.1. GDP volume changes are derived from the index, at market prices, in Eurostat *National Accounts 1970–1990*. Price changes refer to the "implicit GDP deflator", from the same source. The unemployment rate is from Eurostat *Basic Statistics*; before 1983, it refers to EC 9. Interest rates are long-term rates, from *European Economy* no. 50, December 1991 (Table 48). The dollar–ECU rate is from Eurostat *National Accounts* 1970–1990 and from Table 1.0.2 in the Commission annual *Agricultural Situation* report.

7. Figure 7.1 The data cover all twelve Member States. Value-padded is net value-added at factor cost. Nominal value added is adjusted by the "implicit GDP deflator" to obtain real value-added. Employment is expressed in annual work-units (AWU). The trend in real value-added per AWU can be considered as an approximation to the trend in average earnings from farm work. Source: Eurostat, *Agricultural Income 1991*.

8. Figure 7.2. OECD *National Accounts: Vol. I—Main Aggregates, 1960–1989* gives GDP per head, converted into US dollars for each country and in each year using "purchasing power parities" (PPPs), on the basis of an internationally-agreed "basket" of goods and services). For this diagram, the results for 1970 and for 1989 have been expressed in "1985 prices" by reference to the implicit price deflator of GDP for the US.

Expenditure on food and total consumer expenditure are taken from OECD *National Accounts: Vol. II—Detailed Tables*. Only *food* has been included, not beverages or tobacco. For Germany, separate data on food are not available, so Germany is not included in this diagram.

Value added in agriculture as a percentage of GDP is taken from OECD *Historical Statistics 1960–1989*. This source gives an average of the five years 1968–73, which has been used rather than the single year 1970.

It is not possible to match perfectly the two series. Expenditure on "food" includes imported produce. It does *not* cover some agricultural products, such as wine (which is important in Southern European countries), but to include all "beverages" would bring in items whose agricultural content is very limited. Agricultural production includes some non-food items, such as industrial oilseeds and cotton.

The diagram has been restricted to seven countries, at different stages of economic growth: other countries would fit within the same general trends.

9. Viability of farms. Table 7.4 is based on a study with this title—unfortunately using rather old FADN data—carried out by J. Zeddies of the University of Hohenheim and published by the Commission in 1991. The definition of a "profitable" farm is entirely dependent on the comparison with earnings on labour and capital in other sectors. The "comparable incomes" used (with reference to 1988/89) varied from over 20,000 ECU per head in Germany, Denmark and the three Benelux countries down to 5,000 ECU in Portugal: the author used only 80% of these figures in his calculations, on the grounds that the "comparable incomes" include the remuneration of highly-skilled employees, also because some farming capital (especially land) gives security and can appreciate in value. "Real" interest rates (i.e. allowing for inflation) varied from 7.2% in Ireland to 3.9% in Portugal.

PART B

PUBLIC POLICY

CHAPTER 8

THE EVOLUTION OF AGRICULTURAL POLICIES

This chapter will describe briefly how agricultural policies in various countries of Western Europe and North America have evolved. Protectionism in the late 19th century when Europe was faced with increased competition in foodstuffs from overseas, market intervention during the economic crisis of the 1930s, and income guarantees after the Second World War, form the background to the Common Agricultural Policy of the European Community.

(a) The late 19th century: the first wave of protectionism

i) The challenge of overseas competition

In the mid-19th century, trade between European countries was nearly free from tariffs and other restrictions. Britain had been the first to abolish duties, not only on grain but on almost all other agricultural imports. France practically removed agricultural protection in a treaty of commerce with Britain in 1860. Farmers in Germany were still interested mainly in exporting grain and therefore wanted free trade: the Zollverein's duties on grain had been abolished in 1853. In Italy, after treaties with France and other countries, agriculture was protected only by low duties on grains. Belgium in 1871 decreed free entry for the main foodstuffs. The Netherlands dropped its grain duties in 1862. In most other countries agricultural trade was free or nearly so.

Trade in agricultural products was not yet very significant. But from the 1870s onwards, exports of grain from the United States rose sharply. Russia too increased its exports, Canada began to make an impact on the world market, and the Suez Canal facilitated trade from India and Australia. Grain prices reached their lowest point in 1895: the world price of wheat was then little more than half the previous level.

In its early stages, the crisis affected mainly the grain market. Later on, techniques of refrigeration began to be applied on a commercial scale: the United States started to ship frozen meat in 1875, Australia in 1877, and shipments grew enormously from then on. However, production of livestock products was rising much less rapidly than that of grains, and with the gradual improvement in the standard of living the demand for livestock products was increasing comparatively fast. So prices of meat and other livestock products never fell as much as grain prices.

The effects of falling prices were thus felt mainly by arable farmers in Europe. Livestock producers also suffered a fall in value, but it came later and was not so serious; moreover, they *benefited* from the much greater fall in the price of feed grains.

ii) The protectionist revival

In **France**, a reversal of policy was marked by the tariff of 1881, which introduced moderate protection for industry and made large increases in the duties on livestock and livestock products. In 1885 and 1887, the duties on all major agricultural products were very substantially raised. The "Méline Tariff" of 1892 (named after the current Minister of Agriculture) gave increased protection to both industry and agriculture.

Germany's reconversion to protection began with the tariff of 1879, which restored duties on various manufactures and also imposed moderate duties on agricultural products. In 1885 and 1887 there were further and substantial increases in the grain duties. This protectionist policy was the work of Bismarck: after his dismissal in 1890, Germany for a while followed the opposite course. Germany by then needed outlets for its industrial exports, and in a series of commercial treaties Bismarck's successors made limited reductions in the agricultural duties in return for advantages for German exports. But this led to violent opposition from the farming sector and in particular from the powerful Prussian landowners. It also gave rise to controversy as to the desirability of Germany becoming an increasingly industrial nation. Satisfaction was finally given to the agricultural interests with the tariff of 1902.

Italy re-established protection in 1878, mainly with the object of protecting her infant industries, but the duties were initially moderate because of the desire not to provoke retaliation against Italy's agricultural exports. In 1887, however, duties on both industrial and agricultural products were raised substantially.

In **Belgium** too, the agricultural crisis caused a revival of protectionist agitation and led in 1887 to the imposition of tariffs on livestock and meat. The protection remained moderate. In 1895 the duties on a number of agricultural products were raised, but grains (other than oats) remained free.

In **Switzerland**, protection for agriculture was first introduced with the tariff of 1891. Like the Belgian tariff, this left grains largely unprotected, but concentrated protection on beef cattle and meat.

From the late 1870s onwards, measures of protection for both agriculture and industry were adopted also by **Austria-Hungary**, **Sweden**, **Spain** and **Portugal**, while **Russia** and the **United States** sheltered their growing industries behind prohibitive tariff walls; in the United States the McKinley Tariff of 1890 extended protection to agriculture, with increased duties on grains and new duties on some other products.

A few European countries were left holding to Free Trade principles, the most important of these being **Britain**. Agriculture in Britain was no less subject to overseas competition than that of other European countries. In fact a large sector of British agriculture was ruined in the course of the depression; many agricultural workers moved to the towns, much arable land was turned over to grass, and the previous "high farming" standards went into decline. Yet the British government refused the slightest degree of protection. Moreover, there was no effective move for protection among the farmers themselves. It was only after the end of the agricultural depression, from about 1903 to 1905, that a campaign for "Tariff Reform" was started, but this was based on the desire to secure preferences for Empire trade rather than on the wish to protect British agriculture.

Denmark too held firmly to Free Trade, but while in Britain the policy was one of pure laissez-faire, Denmark's reaction to overseas competition was to carry out a fundamental transformation of its agriculture. There was a large shift from crops to livestock production, with the co-operative movement playing a very important role in the development of dairying and pig-farming. Danish exports of livestock products became established on the British and German markets.

Developments in the **Netherlands** were similar to those in Denmark. The importance of foreign trade to the economy had led to a long-standing attachment to Free Trade principles, and the government resisted demands for protection. The farmers thereupon accepted the Free Trade policy, set up associations to improve the processing of their products and made use of the training institutes set up by the government. A justification for this policy could be found in the subsequent increase in exports of livestock products, fruit and vegetables.

iii) Some consequences

Where protection was adopted, it succeeded in restraining the fall in prices, though not in stopping it. Figure 8.1 shows the trend of wheat prices in the United States, England, France and Germany, using a five-year moving average to eliminate annual fluctuations. It also indicates the rate of duty on wheat in France and Germany. This shows clearly that till the mid-1880s wheat prices in all four countries followed a similar downward course. Then, as greatly increased tariffs were imposed in France and Germany, prices in these two countries parted company from the "world" price: the French and German prices in fact remained

Figure 8.1—Wheat prices and tariff rates

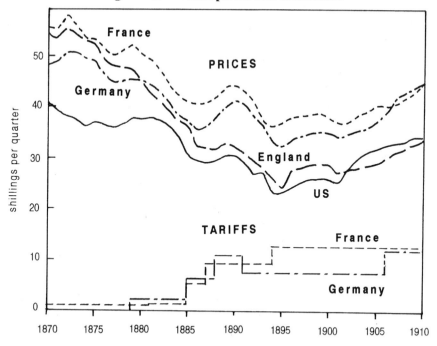

Source: Board of Trade (UK), *British and Foreign Trade and Industry* (1909); data for later years compiled from national sources. A "quarter" was a measure of capacity, equal to about 2.9 hectolitres.

above the US and English prices by roughly the amount of the tariffs, or by nearly a third.

Shielded from the worst of the depression, farmers in countries where protection was adopted probably suffered a smaller loss of income than those in Britain. The benefit of protection went mainly to the large grain growers, and gave much less benefit to the livestock-producing peasantry—perhaps it even harmed them by keeping up the price of bread and the cost of purchased feedingstuffs, as well as by maintaining land values.

Denmark and the Netherlands showed the possibility of meeting the crisis by adapting the pattern of agricultural production to the new situation, and thereby laid the basis for a prosperous agriculture making an important contribution to export earnings and to general economic progress. In France and Germany, though the livestock sector did expand, no such adaptation took place: the area under wheat actually expanded during the period, and in Germany the cultivation of rye, under the influence of various protective measures, rose quite out of line with trends in demand at home and abroad.

The preoccupation with tariff policy diverted attention from more constructive measures. In Germany, the co-operative movement did make some progress,

particularly the *Raiffeisen* credit co-operatives, and there was substantial technical progress. The need to consolidate fragmented holdings was realised and
several of the German states passed legislation to this effect, without achieving
very much. In France *syndicats* and *mutuelles* were promoted by rival political
groups with little initiative being shown by the peasants themselves; there was
no attempt at farm consolidation. In general, farmers in France and Germany
came to rely increasingly on tariff protection, and their governments did little to
encourage them to improve their position through higher productivity, better
marketing and so forth. The habits of mind thus created proved difficult to shake
off.

The movement of manpower off the land seems to have been comparatively
slow in France and Germany. In Britain the population occupied in agriculture,
even though it was already relatively small by the 1880s, fell substantially between 1881 and 1901—this at a time when total population was rising fast. In
France, according to the available data (not very reliable), the population occupied in agriculture appears to have fallen to some extent during the crisis and
then to have recovered. In Germany there was a reduction in agricultural employment, involving in particular emigration from the rural areas of the east to the
areas of industrial growth. This movement mainly concerned farm workers,
domestic servants and members of farm families: the number of farmers
remained approximately unchanged or even increased. These differences between Britain, France and Germany probably reflect, above all, differences in
the rate of industrialisation. Nevertheless, it seems likely that if France and Germany had not adopted agricultural protection, or if Britain had, the results in
terms of labour movement would have been different.

The effects of protection on consumers were probably not obvious to those
concerned, partly because of differences between countries in consumption patterns and also because the general price trend at the end of the 19th century was
downwards, so that the effect of protection was to restrain the fall rather than to
cause an increase in food prices. Protection thus did not give rise to an obvious
burden: but consumers in countries such as France and Germany were largely
deprived of the benefits that could have come from cheap imported food, and
changes in consumption patterns which might have taken place were impeded.

(b) The 1930s: the second wave of protectionism

During the First World War, farmers in both European and overseas countries
benefited from high prices, which persisted for a few years after the war owing
to the shortage of food supplies. But agricultural production gradually recovered,
while overseas production, which had expanded greatly during the war, continued to rise. The increase in food supplies, combined with the effects of general
economic depression, caused prices to fall. By the middle of 1929, world stocks
of wheat stood at 28 million tonnes, the equivalent of more than a year's exports
by all exporting countries.

After the New York stock market collapsed in October 1929, the industrial slump in the United States was rapidly communicated to other countries: prices fell, industrial output was drastically cut, unemployment rose.

The fall in the prices of grains was sharply accentuated by the general economic depression: by 1931 the wheat price was barely half the pre-crisis level. The prices of livestock products at first held up better, but by 1931 they too were drawn into the depression through the reduction in consumer purchasing power. Importing countries reacted to the fall in prices by raising their tariff barriers and by a series of other measures through which their markets became more and more insulated, while exporting countries were in many cases forced to get rid of surplus stocks at almost any cost, and dumped their produce abroad with the help of export subsidies.

i) The first line of defence—tariff protection

During the First World War and the immediate post-war period of food shortages, agricultural tariffs had been generally suspended. In subsequent years they were gradually re-introduced, at levels generally not exceeding those of the pre-war period.

When the crisis broke over European agriculture, agricultural tariffs were raised as a first line of defence in both France and Germany. They reached levels which in normal times would have been prohibitive: with the fall in world prices, they came by 1931 to represent twice or even three times the world market price for some products, in particular grains and sugar. Several other countries raised their duties on agricultural products.

The most spectacular development in the tariff field was Britain's conversion to protectionism in the autumn of 1931. The measures taken did not at first give any great benefit to British agriculture. Fruit, vegetables, wheat and some other agricultural products were made subject to duty. But since Empire produce continued to enter free of duty, tariff protection remained of limited importance to British agriculture.

ii) The second line of defence—non-tariff measures

At a time when exporters were prepared to sell at almost any price, tariffs, however high, were an ineffective means of protection. It became necessary to control imports more precisely and directly, and for this purpose a variety of new measures made their appearance.

The first of these, and one of the most effective, was the **milling ratio** for wheat, sometimes too for rye: millers were legally obliged to use a certain minimum percentage of domestically-produced wheat in their grist. This device seems to have been invented by Norway in 1927; in 1929 both France and Germany adopted it; from 1930 onwards it became widespread in Europe and was applied in some non-European countries as well. It continued to be used up to the Second World War in many cases, and it was re-introduced by several countries after the war.

The most important of the new devices was the **import quota**. The first country to use quotas on a large scale as a means of protection was France: applied first in 1931 as an emergency measure to a few agricultural products, the system was extended in subsequent years to cover practically all agricultural products except wheat, and a number of manufactured goods as well; import quotas gradually became an integral part of French commercial policy. They were taken up to varying extents by other countries: Belgium was one of the first to introduce legislation to this effect, though it did not make full use of the system till 1933. In numerous other countries, import quotas were adopted as an element in measures of market organisation: this was the case in Britain, Germany, the Netherlands and Italy.

iii) A further step—intervention in agricultural markets

Of all the measures adopted to deal with the crisis of the 1930s, that which had the most significance and the greatest influence on subsequent developments was the attempt to organise domestic agricultural markets. This intervention was usually coupled with regulations concerning imports and, in some cases, exports.

The progression from measures of import control to more far-reaching intervention was particularly clear in **France**. Output of wheat had been rising fairly steadily, and the initial measures of protection prevented the fall in world prices from discouraging this trend. A big harvest in 1932 saturated the market and import controls could no longer maintain the price. Various measures were taken from then on, involving in particular government purchase of part of the crop at fixed prices, and culminating in 1936 in the *Office National Interprofessionnel du Blé*, with the task of fixing the wheat price and ensuring that it was observed. The *Office* had monopolistic control over all foreign trade in wheat: it could regulate imports and subsidise exports. The other main commodity subjected to market organisation in France was wine: here too the necessity arose in part because a domestic surplus made import control ineffective. Measures of organisation began in 1931 and were reinforced in 1934; they sought in particular to control the amounts marketed by producers and the period of marketing.

In **Britain**, to avoid restricting imports from the Empire, protection for agriculture had to take the form of marketing schemes, designed to strengthen producers' bargaining power, and subsidies. For wheat and sugarbeet, assistance was given by subsidies alone; in the former case, the market was left free and the subsidy was given through "deficiency payments", reviving a device used in the First World War and destined to play an important role after the Second. Milk was supported by Milk Marketing Boards with the exclusive right to sell milk and fix prices. Imports of beef were regulated by agreement with the main exporting countries, including Empire ones. The markets for bacon, potatoes and hops were supported by marketing schemes together with import controls; that for eggs through voluntary restrictions by exporting countries.

Denmark too was compelled, by the difficulties encountered on export markets and the consequent fall in farmers' returns, to abandon liberal practices.

The special character of the measures taken reflects Denmark's situation as a large net exporter of the commodities in question. All cattle sold on the home market were subjected to a tax, and the proceeds were used to buy up low-quality cattle in order to raise prices. Taxes were imposed also on sales of butter for domestic consumption, and the proceeds were distributed among producers. A particularly far-reaching scheme, involving what was probably the first agricultural marketing quota in history, was devised for pigs.

The situation of the **Netherlands** was similar to that of Denmark. The Dutch government too was forced, partly by falling import prices but even more by the difficulties facing exports, to depart from tradition and, with the participation of the producers concerned, to organise the markets for pigs, dairy products, cattle and fruit and vegetables.

Switzerland was another country in which an attachment to liberal economic principles did not prevent recourse to a significant degree of agricultural market organisation, involving government purchase of domestic wheat and rye at guaranteed prices, control of imports of feed grains and other feedingstuffs, subsidies for milk production, and intervention on the pigmeat market.

Austria began in 1931 to regulate supplies to the cattle market, and imports were admitted only in so far as they did not endanger sales of home-bred animals. The milk market too was organised from 1931 on, and various measures were adopted for other products.

Norway began to organise its agricultural market even before the crisis, with a grain monopoly set up under a law of 1926; from 1929 onwards various measures were taken, based mainly on sales co-operatives for the major products.

Sweden in 1930 reinforced its milling ratio for wheat with government purchases to support prices; organisation of the dairy market and other measures were introduced in 1932.

Yet more far-reaching measures of intervention were adopted in Germany under National Socialism and in Italy under fascism. The Nazis came to power in **Germany** in 1933 with a clearly- defined philosophy as to the role of agriculture in the nation. This philosophy formed an integral part of National Socialist thinking: its essential features concerned the social and racial importance of the farm population, the need to ensure fair prices to farmers and the importance of national self-sufficiency in food. In a short time, German agriculture was organised in accordance with a prepared plan. The *Reichsnährstand* (State Food Corporation) was set up in September 1933 to organise all aspects of food production and distribution and to regulate markets and prices. Full control of the volume and prices of imports was vested in the *Reichsstellen* (State Boards) which were set up for all important commodities from April 1933 onwards: the *Reichsstellen* could also buy and sell on the domestic market and operate buffer stocks.

In fascist **Italy** too, economic policy came to involve a high degree of central planning in agriculture as in other sectors. Under Mussolini, an effort was made to lift Italian agriculture out of technical backwardness and economic depression.

Great emphasis was laid on the policy of *bonifica integrale* (integral land reclamation), initiated by a law of 1928 which ordered the improvement of all unused but cultivable land. The "Battle for Wheat" aimed to make the country more self-sufficient. To support the wheat price, a milling ratio was introduced in 1931. Later, a full State monopoly was instituted: growers were bound to deliver their wheat at fixed prices, and imports were directly controlled by organisations responsible to the Ministry of Agriculture.

iv) Some consequences

A striking outcome of intervention during this period was the divorce between the trends of world prices and those of prices received by producers in protected importing countries. As Figure 8.2 shows, the fall in the wheat world price in 1930 and 1931 was not at all reflected in the domestic price in France and Germany, and in Italy was reflected only in part.

Subsequently, the wheat price in France fell under the influence of large domestic harvests rather than of the low world price; it recovered in 1936 and by 1937 was slightly above the pre-crisis level. In Germany the price declined from 1931 to 1933; afterwards, the strict controls instituted by the Nazi regime enabled a stable price level to be maintained. In Italy the price recovered by 1937

Figure 8.2—Wheat prices, 1927–1938

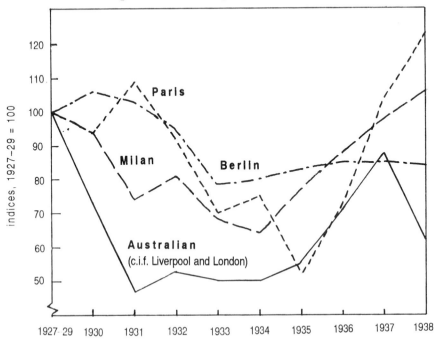

Source: International Institute of Agriculture, *International Yearbook of Agricultural Statistics*, Rome.

to nearly the pre-crisis level. When the world price suffered a further fall in 1938, the prices on these protected markets were unaffected.

As a result of protection and intervention, agricultural producers in most European countries, though they by no means escaped the crisis, were spared its worst effects. Farm output was not discouraged; rather the reverse. Production of most major commodities in Western Europe was higher in the period following 1929 than it had been previously; the expansion in wheat was particularly large. Numbers of livestock also rose. At a time when the general reduction in purchasing power was depressing consumption and when prices often were not allowed to fall sufficiently to offset this decline, the increasing trend in home production could only mean a cut in imports. Thus the fall in prices on the world market was accentuated and the volume of trade reduced. The value of world trade in foodstuffs as a whole was less by about a quarter after the crisis, in 1937, than in 1929.

The decline in the wheat trade mainly affected the United States and Canada; Argentina and Australia did not do so badly. Poland and the countries of south-eastern Europe managed to increase their exports of wheat and rye during and after the crisis, thanks in part to preferential treatment by France and, more important, to close commercial links established with Germany after 1933. Trade in barley and oats also declined; the only type of grain for which trade expanded was maize, this expansion being accounted for by imports into Britain (where no maize was grown). Trade in sugar fell, and the pattern shifted: the traditional exporters—Cuba and the Dutch East Indies—lost heavily, while the preferences for the dependencies of the United States—Philippines, Hawaii and Puerto Rico—and for countries of the British Empire enabled them to increase their trade.

Exports of livestock, of which cattle and pigs were the most important, suffered badly. Britain reduced its imports from the Irish Republic. Austria, which had been the world's largest importer of pigs, mainly from central and south-eastern Europe, cut its imports drastically; Germany too reduced its imports from Denmark and the Netherlands. South American supplies of beef and mutton to Britain were displaced by Australia and New Zealand as a result of preferential arrangements. Germany ceased to be a major beef importer. Trade in pigmeat suffered a decline, with reduced imports by France and Germany in particular: exports by Denmark and the Netherlands, especially the latter, were severely hit. On the other hand, Australia and New Zealand were able to increase their exports of pigmeat to Britain. For butter, Germany reduced its imports in 1934–38, while those of Britain increased, and as a result exports by Denmark and the Netherlands remained at about the same level while those of New Zealand and Australia more than doubled as compared with 1924–28. In cheese too, New Zealand and Australia gained at the expense of Denmark and the Netherlands.

Thus, in this period when trade in "temperate" foodstuffs in general was declining, the exporting countries which did least badly were those able to get preferential treatment from a major importing country: the American sugar-exporting colonies from the United States, to some extent south-eastern European countries from Germany and France, and above all the British Empire from Great Britain. France, Belgium and the Netherlands also gave preference to their overseas territories; this however—apart from wine and wheat from French North Africa—mostly concerned tropical and semi-tropical products. On the other hand, the agricultural exports of Denmark and the Netherlands suffered from increased protection in neighbouring countries and from discrimination against them in Britain; those of the United States suffered from the general slump in grains and from import restrictions both on grains and on pigmeat; and those of Argentina and other South American countries suffered from the preferential treatment given to Empire meat on the British market.

v) Reactions in agricultural exporting countries

Agricultural exporting countries were forced to take a number of measures to assist their farmers. Those which were adopted in Denmark and the Netherlands have already been described. The countries of central and south-eastern Europe were in a particularly difficult position. These were mostly poor countries where agriculture predominated; the peasant population was often living on a bare subsistence, and there was little possibility for public support. These countries made an attempt to co-ordinate their exports and to obtain preferential treatment from the countries of Western Europe; several conferences were held to this end, starting in July 1930. Other exporting countries, however, objected strongly to the idea of preferential treatment for their competitors and not much was obtained. During 1931 some preferential tariff agreements were negotiated, in particular by France with Hungary, Romania and Yugoslavia: these agreements provided for the reimbursement by France to the exporting countries of part of the duty on wheat. Germany also offered preferences on grain to Hungary and Romania, but this idea had to be given up because of the objections raised by countries entitled to "most favoured nation" treatment; however, at a later stage, the National Socialist regime entered into close trading links with south-eastern European countries, from which they derived a limited benefit.

The **United States** became extremely concerned at the prospects, especially for its wheat exports. Unlike most other agricultural exporting countries, the United States had the means to come to the rescue of its farmers. The emphasis was laid at first on government-financed stockpiling operations to relieve the market, but this effort proved largely unsuccessful. In the context of President Roosevelt's "New Deal", the Agricultural Adjustment Act of 1933 provided more effective and far-reaching legislation: it aimed to restore the balance between production and consumption and to give farmers "parity" prices. Payments were made to farmers for reducing their acreage of wheat, maize, cotton and tobacco; pigs in excess supply were purchased by the authorities and slaughtered. The Commodity Credit Corporation (CCC) was instituted to buy and sell agricultural commodities, making "loans" to farmers on the security of the commodities delivered. Surplus stocks were disposed of in various ways at home and abroad.

In **Canada** too, early efforts to help wheat growers consisted mainly of stock-piling operations. The Canadian Wheat Pool was founded in 1924, and received government support from 1929. As in the United States, the mounting burden of surplus stocks necessitated a change in policy: in 1935 the Wheat Board was established to buy grain from producers and to sell on world markets with the help of export subsidies.

Argentina and **Australia** lacked the means and the facilities for storing grain. The Argentine government bought a large part of the exportable surplus from producers and sold it on the world market, usually at a loss. In Australia, the Commonwealth government made grants to the individual States for distribution to farmers; it did not subsidise wheat exports directly till 1938.

Export subsidies became common in a number of other countries as well. **South Africa** began in 1931 to subsidise exports of processed foodstuffs and sugar and later extended subsidies to beef and mutton. The **Irish Republic** tried through export subsidies to counter the increased duties imposed by Britain. Even **New Zealand** began to subsidise its dairy exports in 1936.

International action, under the League of Nations and through agreements for wheat and for sugar, had little success in restoring balance to agricultural markets.

(c) Post 1945: Government guarantees and intervention

After 1945, in the immediate post-war period of food shortages, the aim was to expand agricultural production by all possible means, both to raise food supplies and to relieve balances of payment. For this purpose, income guarantees were given to farmers, price supports were introduced or reinforced, farm investments and improved farming methods were encouraged by credits and subsidies.

From about 1953 there was a change in emphasis as agricultural production caught up with demand. The aim was no longer to raise production at all costs, but to achieve selective expansion and to raise agricultural efficiency. At the same time, concern with the relatively low level of farm incomes was increasingly felt, and governments were placed in a quandary as the price guarantees they offered farmers tended to stimulate excess production. Policies tended to become increasingly complicated, and increasingly costly; attempts were made to limit expenditure and to restrain the growth of output of commodities in surplus. A few examples can be given.

In the **United Kingdom**, the Agriculture Act of 1947 committed the government to intervene on behalf of agriculture even in peacetime. The government undertook to buy, at guaranteed prices, the whole domestic output of major foodstuffs. Later, imports were practically freed from quantitative restrictions; duties were mostly low. Support to farmers was given mainly in the form of "deficiency payments", whereby the government, at the end of each marketing period, made up the difference between the average market price and the guaranteed price. With low market prices and rising domestic output, this system became a heavy burden on the national budget.

In **France**, a series of "Modernisation and Equipment Plans" aimed to raise agricultural production in order both to meet food shortages and to relieve the balance of payments. From 1950 onwards, surpluses made their appearance: exports of wheat and sugar had to be promoted by means of subsidies and surplus wine had to be distilled. The aim became one of "selective expansion". The markets of almost all important products were subjected to intervention in one form or another: the pre-war Wheat Board was enlarged to become the *Office National Interprofessionnel des Céréales* (ONIC), and new boards were introduced for dairy products, meat and livestock, oilseeds and other products. Domestic markets were virtually insulated from outside influences by strict controls over imports, exercised for most products through import licensing, but for grains and dairy products through State-controlled import monopolies. There was also an increasing degree of assistance to exports of products in surplus through direct export subsidies and other means. In the case of wheat, a means of restraining production existed in principle in the "quantum", under which the guaranteed price was applicable only to a standard quantity, any additional output receiving only the price realised on the export market: in fact this arrangement was not very effective in discouraging excess output. Efforts were made to deal with overproduction of wine.

In 1960, the *Loi d'Orientation* established the aim of "parity" with non-farm incomes demanded by the farm organisations but laid emphasis on improvements in productivity and in marketing and production structures. The various boards for supporting the markets of different commodities were merged in the *Fonds d'Orientation et de Régularisation des Marchés Agricoles* (FORMA). By now attention was increasingly turning to the prospects for French agriculture in the newly-formed European Economic Community, which appeared to offer a solution to the problems of French agriculture through increased outlets and higher prices.

In **Western Germany**, cut off from its traditional sources of food supply in Eastern Germany, a particularly serious situation was faced after the war. The Marshall Plan in 1948 permitted higher food imports, including feedingstuffs, making it possible to build up again the livestock sector. Still, when the Federal Republic was constituted in September 1949 shortages were the major problem. In 1950 and 1951, *Einfuhr- und Vorratsstellen* (Import and Storage Boards) were instituted for the main agricultural products, with the object of stabilising prices and maintaining them at levels consistent with the aims of agricultural policy: these boards controlled imports in a manner similar to the Nazi *Reichsstellen*, and could intervene on the domestic market by purchasing, selling and stockpiling. As the food situation eased and world prices declined, the Import and Storage Boards, together with other measures of import control, were used to maintain German prices at levels well above those on the world market. The Agriculture Act of 1955 laid a firm statutory basis for measures to assist agriculture.

Most of the other Western European countries also gave income or price guarantees to their farmers in the early post-war years, and later had to grapple with problems of surpluses while trying still to ensure adequate incomes to farmers. Thus **Switzerland** in 1947 inserted in its Constitution articles which provided a permanent legal basis for assistance to agriculture. These were implemented by the Agriculture Act of 1951, which "aimed to maintain a large peasant population to facilitate the supplies of the country by ensuring agricultural production and encouraging agriculture, having regard to the interests of the national economy". This Act provided the basis for subsequent legislation laying down detailed measures of support for various commodities.

Norway, like Switzerland, had the problem of reconciling the social and strategic objectives of a large agricultural population with difficult natural conditions. In 1947 its general objectives for agricultural policy were laid down, including that of ensuring the farm population of a standard of living comparable with other sectors.

Sweden also assured its farmers of a standard of living comparable with other sectors, with the special feature that food production was to cover no more than 90% of domestic requirements. The prices of the main agricultural products were maintained by a system of import monopolies and quantitative restrictions, and the difference between world prices and domestic prices was met by import levies.

Thus importing countries generally were able to maintain prices and support their farmers' income by restricting imports, up to the point where their own supply began to exceed demand. Agricultural exporting countries, however, did not have this possibility and moreover were harmed by the restrictions imposed by importing countries. **Denmark** had been the only country which dismantled its wartime apparatus of State control and returned to private trading. However, its exports of bacon, butter and eggs encountered increasing difficulties, and the net income of Danish agriculture declined. The result was to drive Denmark back into various forms of intervention.

Other agricultural exporting countries experienced similar difficulties. The **Netherlands**, after the war, continued its pre-war and wartime arrangements: the Agriculture Act of 1957 co-ordinated past legislation and introduced new provisions, and agricultural markets remained subject to intervention in various forms.

*   *   *

Thus, to implement the guarantees given to farmers in most countries after the Second World War, governments in Western Europe had provided price support in a variety of ways, in most cases intervening extensively in agricultural markets (the UK's deficiency payment system left the market free but entailed heavy public expenditure). Such action, however, meant that farmers had no incentive to adjust their supply. On the contrary, they were encouraged to continue increasing their production. Governments became more and more deeply involved, the cost of support rose and the degree of protection increased.

Nevertheless the farm income situation remained unsatisfactory. Incomes and living standards on farms did increase in absolute terms. Still, with overall demand for food rising less than proportionately to total consumer income, agriculture's share in national income was falling and the transfer of manpower from agriculture to other sectors, though substantial, was in most countries barely sufficient to avoid further widening of the gap in incomes per head between agriculture and the rest of the economy. As farmers' income expectations were increasingly geared to urban standards, their dissatisfaction grew.

Moreover, large disparities persisted within agriculture itself, between large farms and small, and between prosperous regions and less-favoured ones. Small farms, producing relatively little for the market, gained limited benefit from price support. "Structural policies" to deal with such problems began to be advocated, but by 1960 little action had been taken.

This was the unpromising background for the Common Agricultural Policy of the European Economic Community, which will be tackled in the next chapter. Developments in the United States and some other overseas countries will be considered in Chapter 12.

APPENDIX

1. Sources. This chapter is mainly a much shorter version of relevant parts of the author's *Government and Agriculture in Western Europe, 1880–1988*, already referred to. Detailed bibliographies will be found in that work.

For the late 19th-century developments, there are several works on individual countries, but no other comprehensive survey of agricultural developments, though the general background is well explained by W. Ashworth in *A Short History of the International Economy, 1850– 1950* (Longmans, London etc., 1952). For an alternative view, more favourable to protectionism, see Paul Bairoch's *Commerce extérieur et développement économique de l'Europe au XIXe siècle* (Mouton, Paris, 1976)—though as already indicated in the Appendix to Chapter 6, item 5, the present author remains unconvinced.

As regards protectionist policies during the 1930s, Margaret Gordon's *Barriers to World Trade* (Macmillan, New York, 1941) is particularly useful. The League of Nations report *Considerations on the present evolution of agricultural protectionism* (Geneva, 1935) was a penetrating analysis. Lamartine Yates, in *Food Production in Western Europe* (Longmans, London, 1940), provided the first comparative review of agricultural conditions and policies in the various European countries.

The most comprehensive sources for the early post-war period are five reports of the Paris-based Organisation for European Economic Co-operation (OEEC) from 1956 to 1961— *Agricultural Policies in Europe and North America*—which include chapters on each member country.

CHAPTER 9

THE COMMON AGRICULTURAL POLICY: MARKET ORGANISATION

Market organisation under the European Community's CAP has become highly complex. Its mechanisms are difficult to understand without some explanation as to how they came into being. This chapter will therefore begin with a brief account of the origins and development of the CAP, before studying the common market organisations for the various commodities as they stand at the time of writing (i.e. at the end of 1992).

This chapter deals only with market organisation, including measures affecting imports and exports. Structural measures and other aspects of the CAP will be considered in the next chapter.

(a) The evolution of the CAP

i) The initial stages

The Treaty of Rome, by which six countries set up the European Economic Community (EEC), and which entered into force on 1 January 1958, specifically included agriculture in the "common market", within which quantitative restrictions and customs duties on trade between Member States would be removed and a common external tariff established.

This in itself was an achievement: attempts to include agriculture in previous customs unions—between Belgium and Luxembourg, and later between these two and the Netherlands—had had limited success. Moreover, the United Kingdom had consistently refused to include agriculture in any common arrangement, and this was a major reason why the UK withdrew from the negotiations aimed at forming the EEC.

For France, the inclusion of agriculture was essential in order to provide an enlarged market for agricultural exports—especially as the advantage in the industrial field was expected to lie with Germany.

Agriculture remained a difficult subject for integration. As has been seen in the previous chapter, national agricultural policies in the countries concerned varied considerably in their methods and in the degree of support. The Treaty of Rome provided for the establishment of a Common Agricultural Policy (CAP): Article 39 (see Appendix, item 2) set out the aims of the CAP, involving a balance of interests between producers and consumers; Article 40 provided for common organisation of markets, while remaining vague as to the details; Article 43 laid down the procedures whereby regulations, directives and decisions relating to the CAP would be adopted by the Council of Ministers, on the basis of proposals by the Commission, and after consulting the European Parliament.

Annex II of the Treaty listed the agricultural products subject to the CAP: these included the products of "first-stage" processing—e.g. products of the milling industry, and dairy produce—but not those resulting from "second-stage" processing (though, as will be seen, trade in these "non-Annex II") products is also subject to CAP mechanisms).

Figure 9.1—Common market organisation: the basic model

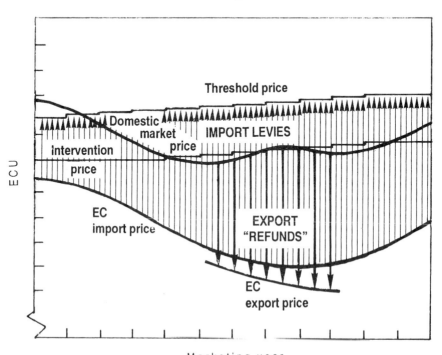

After much intensive negotiation, the Council of Ministers finally (in January 1962) decided on the basic methods of common market organisation (CMO) for cereals. Target prices would be established as a basis for determining both intervention prices at which public purchases could take place on the domestic market (through the various national boards now acting under EC legislation) and threshold prices at the common frontier. "Community preference" would be ensured by fixing the threshold price above the intervention price. Variable import levies would ensure that imports did not enter below the threshold prices; and export "refunds" could be granted where necessary to bring the price of exports down to price levels on export markets (see Figure 9.1). Levies and refunds also applied to the agricultural components of processed products—see Appendix, item 3.

Key elements in Figure 9.1 are:
* The **intervention price**, at which intervention agencies stand ready to buy produce and which therefore sets a floor to the domestic market.
* The **threshold price**, which is in effect a minimum import price.
* **Variable levies**, which bring the prices of imports up to the threshold price.
* **Export subsidies** (officially called "refunds), bringing the prices of exports down to prices on export markets.

Target prices have become, in practice, just a stage in the calculation and have been omitted in this diagram.

In the case of cereals, intervention and threshold prices are subject to monthly increments over part of the year, in order to give producers and traders an incentive to store produce themselves rather than put it all into intervention early in the season.

This diagram shows a hypothetical development over the marketing year. It has been supposed that the domestic market price is initially above the threshold price, but falls to the point where intervention occurs and sustains the price. Variations in the import price are fully offset, on a daily basis if necessary, by variations in the import levy. So long as the domestic price is below the threshold price, imports are unlikely except in so far as they have quality advantages (e.g. "hard" Canadian bread-making wheat).

While import levies are applicable throughout the year, export "refunds" are granted in the light of the market situation: it is supposed here that they operate only during the period of low domestic prices. Their amount is not automatic, but depends on the domestic market price and on the price that can be obtained on third country markets: it has been supposed here that this price is lower than the EC import price, but it can vary as between export destinations. Refunds are usually fixed on the basis of "tenders" from traders by weekly "Management Committee" decisions (see Appendix, item 4); export certificates giving entitlement to refunds are granted for stated quantities. There are also fixed (or "standing") refunds for exports to traditional EC customers. Export sales may also be made from intervention stocks at world prices.

In practice, for cereals and other products, the pressure of domestic supplies in recent years has meant that the domestic market price stays close to the intervention price most of the time; moreover, the element of "Community preference" has been increased by reducing the intervention price relatively to the threshold price. In 1992/93 the intervention price for soft wheat is 168 ECU per tonne and the threshold price 228 ECU; with prices on world markets around 80 ECU, export refunds up to 80 ECU have been required.

The cereals regime served as the model for several other CMOs. Those for the three "cereal-based" products—pigmeat, poultrymeat and eggs—were adopted at the same time as the cereals regulation. Other CMOs followed in the next few years. In most cases they incorporated the main features of the basic model—import levies, intervention and export refunds—though with variations depending on the nature of the product and the market: returns to producers were thus assured mainly through frontier protection and price support. For a few products—oilseeds, olive oil, durum wheat—support was given through direct payments, thus keeping down domestic market prices. The various CMOs will be more fully described later in this chapter.

Thus by the end of the 1960s, the EC had adopted for most products a system of protection and support which effectively insulated the internal market: the cost of support was borne mainly by consumers through prices above world market levels. This system was expected to provide a net revenue: the policy-makers did not take into account projections indicating that the cost of export "refunds" would come to exceed receipts from import levies.

A exception which proved to be significant concerns the whole area of **animal feedingstuffs**: in particular soya-based and other protein feeds, and what came to be called "cereal substitutes" (mainly cassava or manioc, and "maize gluten feed"—a by-product from the processing of maize into the sugar substitute "isoglucose"). These were subjected only to zero or low import duties, which in most cases were "bound" under GATT rules. This liberal import regime enabled these imported feeds to replace EC-grown feed grain and other fodder, and consequently the EC demand for "rebalancing" the protective system became a controversial issue in the GATT Uruguay Round (see Chapter 13).

The 1962 agreement also covered **financial provisions**. The Council adopted a regulation instituting a European Agricultural Guidance and Guarantee Fund (more commonly known under its French initials, FEOGA), to finance export refunds, market intervention and structural measures. The means by which the FEOGA itself was to be financed from the general Community budget were settled only in 1969.

Thus the three principles which were constantly evoked in subsequent discussions—**market unity, Community preference** and **financial solidarity**—were embodied in these early regulations, though not explicitly stated in these terms. The French in particular attached great significance to these principles.

The question remained as to what degree of support and protection should be aimed at. The large differences in prices between the Six made this an intractable problem. In particular, the German government was under strong pressure from its farmers to refuse any drastic cut in German farm prices. It was not till the end of 1964 that decisions were finally reached, whereby common prices for cereals would be introduced in 1967. The level was to be somewhat above the average for the Six, and well above world prices. Compensation for price reductions was to be given to farmers in Germany, Italy and Luxembourg.

ii) Trends in support prices

After common prices had initially been fixed, they were subject to annual determination by the Council of Ministers, on the basis of Commission proposals (see Chapter 14 on decision-making procedures).

The inflationary period which began with the oil crisis of 1973 (and which has already been discussed in Chapter 7) was the impetus for a series of substantial price increases (Figure 9.2). A more "prudent" policy was pursued in the late 1970s, but a further wave of price increases occurred in the early 1980s. By 1983, the problems of overproduction—which will be discussed further below—had become serious, and a "restrictive" policy had to be adopted. Since then, the common "institutional" prices in ECU have been frozen or reduced in "nominal" terms, implying a substantial fall in real terms. However, the "agri-monetary" arrangements to some extent offset this fall, as will be seen below.

iii) "Green rates" and MCAs

Throughout most of the 1960s, currency stability made it possible to fix common prices on the assumption that the relationships between the unit of account and the national currencies would remain unchanged.

From 1969 onwards, however, adjustments in exchange rates became frequent and substantial. Strict application of the rules for converting common prices into national currencies would have meant, for countries that had devalued (such as France), an increase in prices that would have run counter to their efforts to combat inflation. In countries that had revalued (such as Germany), the consequence would have been a cut in prices to producers.

The "agri-monetary" system that was developed to bypass this problem involved "green rates"—distinct from market exchange rates—for converting common prices into national currencies; and since this meant different price levels in trade between Member States, "monetary compensatory amounts" (MCAs) had to be applied at the frontiers, acting as a tax on exports from countries where farm prices were being kept low, and a subsidy on those where prices were being kept high. (The MCAs applied also to trade with third countries.)

In principle, the MCAs were to be phased out by gradually aligning the "green rates" on the market exchange rates. In practice, such phasing-out proved much easier when it involved *raising* prices to farmers than when it meant *reducing* them—largely because of continued opposition by German farmers to price cuts. This led in 1984 to the invention of the "green ECU" or "switch-over" mechanism, whereby an obligation on a strong-currency country to revalue its green rate (which would cut prices to its farmers in its national currency) was converted into an opportunity for weak-currency countries to devalue their green rates (thus raising prices to their farmers). The result was an upward drift of national prices that was not apparent from the ECU prices: the value of the "green ECU" moved upwards with the strong D-mark and exceeded that of the monetary ECU: between 1984/85 and 1992/93, the differential increased by about 14.5%, and the monetary realignments of September 1992 further increased the gap to 19.5%.

The agri-monetary arrangements were an unwelcome interference with free trade within the Community. MCAs caused uncertainties and complications for traders, and required checks at the internal frontiers of the Community. On the entry into force of the Single Market on 1 January 1993, green rates were aligned on monetary rates, leaving only small "monetary gaps", and MCAs were removed. Henceforth, following realignments within the ERM, green rates are to be adjusted immediately: at the most, a "monetary gap" of 2% can remain for up to twelve months. For floating currencies, adjustments can be made up to three times in each month, or immediately if the monetary gap exceeds 6% for three days running. These provisions mean that monetary changes will be quickly felt in prices, with greater uncertainty for farmers and traders (and also greater risks of speculation). However, the Agriculture Council refused to abolish the "switch-over" mechanism, as the Commission had proposed. Increases in national prices will thus tend to outweigh decreases: this is inconsistent with the aims of the "MacSharry"reform, and also adds to the budgetary cost of the CAP.

The viability of the new system appears to depend on a reasonable degree of monetary stability.

Figure 9.2—CAP "institutional" prices

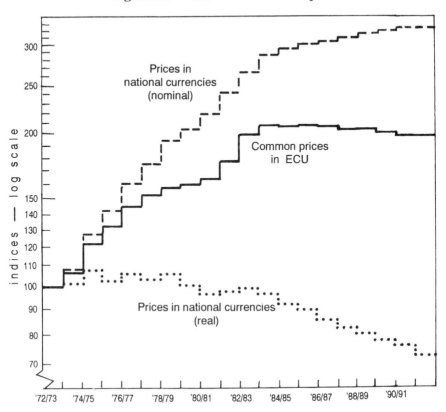

iv) Surpluses and budgetary costs

Agricultural output has continued to rise as a result of productivity growth, and was encouraged until the early 1980s by price increases. Consumption growth within the EC, on the other hand, has been comparatively limited, for the reasons already discussed in Chapter 4.

The inevitable result has been greater self-sufficiency: the volume of imports of most products competing with EC production has been reduced, and EC exports to third countries have increased. Table 9.1 gives data. From the first enlargement of the Community until shortly before the accession of Spain and Portugal (Greece is included in these data but does not substantially affect the results), self-sufficiency rose for almost all the products shown, especially cereals, sugar (in spite of the quota system—see below), and beef. Production of wine was held back by various restrictive measures; production of pigmeat, poultrymeat and eggs, being largely in the hand of big commercial operators and receiving relatively little price support, tended to adjust to market outlets. The Community remained a net importer only of fruit, vegetable oils, sheepmeat, and—not shown on this table because of the difficulty of comparing many different items—livestock feed.

The incorporation of Spain and Portugal modifies the absolute levels of self-sufficiency (these are deficit countries for cereals but net exporters of fruit, especially citrus, and wine). But the upward trend has continued.

Dairy products are not included in Table 9.1: as milk is mostly transformed into a variety of products, statistical problems arise. But here too, self-sufficiency has risen: in particular, the United Kingdom's former large imports of butter and cheese from New Zealand and other Commonwealth countries have virtually disappeared since accession to the EC. Of the EC's quota-controlled output of

Figure 9.2 relates to the key prices subject to annual determination by the Council of Ministers: intervention prices, or the nearest equivalent according to product. For some years, these data were published by the Commission in its annual *Agricultural Situation* report: data for recent years have been communicated directly by Commission services. The effect of "stabilisers" (see later in text) is included.

The common prices are first determined in ECU (data for earlier years in UA (units of account) or EUA (European Units of Account) have been converted in ECU equivalents).

They are then converted into national currencies, using not the monetary exchange rate but the "green rates" (see explanations in text). As these have been, on the whole, overvalued, the *average* of prices in national currencies increased faster than the common ECU prices. Variations between Member States have been considerable, with the biggest increases in the countries whose currencies have fallen most against the ECU. For the countries which acceded to the EC during this period, the alignment on common prices also partly accounts for the development shown.

National prices in "nominal" terms have been adjusted using the "GDP deflator" (i.e. the implicit price index of gross domestic product) to obtain the series in "real" terms.

Table 9.1—EC self-sufficiency in major foodstuffs
(production as percentage of domestic utilisation)

	EC 10		EC 12	
	>1973/74<	>1984/85<	>1985/86<	1989/90
Cereals (excl. rice)	91	118	110	120
Sugar	91	128	123	128
Fresh vegetables	94	101	107	106a
Fresh fruit (excl. citrus)	82	83	87	85a
Citrus fruit	47	50	75	70a
Wine	103	100	104	103b
Vegetable oils	..	47	56	65
	>1974<	>1984<	>1987<	1990
Beef and veal	96	108	107	108
Pigmeat	100	102	102	104
Poultrymeat	102	107	105	105
Sheep- and goatmeat	66	76	80	81
Eggs	100	102	..	103

a 1988/89   b 1990/91.

Source: Commission, *The Agricultural Situation in the Community* (various years and tables).

just under 100 million tonnes of milk per year in recent years, probably about 5 million tonnes per year have been surplus to domestic requirements and commercial exports. Besides subsidised exports (including food aid programmes), half or more of the production of skim milk powder has been sold within the EC for animal feed at subsidised prices; and a substantial proportion of butter production has been sold under special schemes, mainly to food processors.

Figure 9.3 shows costs of market support to the EC budget (through the FEOGA). In absolute terms, cereals and milk products are the biggest spenders, though in relation to the value of production, some other items—including olive oil, tobacco and some items not shown here such as cotton—are more expensive.

Export subsidies account for the greater part of expenditure on cereals and sugar, and about half in the case of dairy products and beef. The level of expenditure is dependent not only on the volume that has to be exported, but also on the world price level, over which the EC in most cases has only partial control. The trade issues involved will be considered in Chapter 13.

Intervention storage is also a big cost item for cereals, sugar, milk products and beef. At various points in time, the quantities of these products in public storage have reached unacceptable levels. This was particularly the case around 1985–87 in the case of butter and skim milk powder, in 1985–88 and again since 1991 for beef, in 1984–86 and again since 1990 for cereals. In the case of wine, large quantities of low-quality wine have been removed from the market through distillation, leading to substantial stocks of alcohol.

Figure 9.3—Market support for major products (1991 budget)

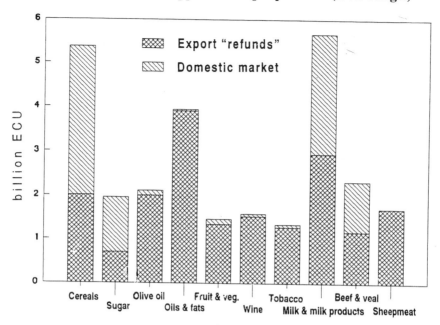

Source: Commission, *The Agricultural Situation in the Community, 1991 report* (Table 3.4.4).

There are various subsidies for disposal of butter and skim milk powder on the domestic market, besides intervention storage. Expenditure on fruit and vegetables consists partly of compensation to producer groups for withdrawing produce from the market, partly of subsidies for processing (especially of tomatoes). Direct aids are significant for durum wheat (included among "cereals"), olive oil, oilseeds (under "oils and fats"). In the case of "sheepmeat", support is given mostly in the form of "ewe premiums" (some support for "goat-meat" is included in this item). Expenditure on tobacco (which largely benefits Greece) consists mostly of "premiums" to purchasers to keep down the price. These various mechanisms will be further discussed below.

The level of spending on agriculture became a major problem for the Community budget. Table 9.2 shows the development. That the CAP should have accounted for the greater part of the total budget in the early stages was not surprising, since other policies had not been developed to the same extent; even subsequently, several Community policies do not require significant expenditure. However, there have been growing demands for increased spending on regional and structural develop-ment, especially in the southern regions of the Community, and for other purposes including development aid. As the total EC budget has been subject to certain "ceil-ings" (Appendix, item 5), there have been strong pressures to reduce the proportion required for agriculture. This has been the main factor promoting "CAP reform".

Table 9.2—EC budget expenditure on agriculture, 1991
(in billion UA/EUA/ECU)

	EC 9		EC 10	EC 12	
	1973	1980	1985	1986	1992
FEOGA "Guarantee" (market support, etc.)	3.8	11.3	19.7	22.1	32.9
FEOGA "Guidance" (structural measures)	0.2	0.5	0.7	0.8	2.9
FEOGA total	4.0	11.8	20.4	22.9	35.8
Total EC budget	4.9	16.0	27.5	34.9	61.1
FEOGA as % of total EC budget	82	74	74	66	59

Notes: For purposes of this table, changes in the unit of account can be ignored. For 1992, data are budget "appropriations", taking into account amending and supplementary budgets: not actual expenditure. All data refer to payments, not "commitments" (which may extend over several years).
Source: EC budgets (in *Official Journal*) and *Agricultural Situation* reports, various years (Table 3.4.1 in recent issues).

v) CAP reform

Market organisation for the various commodities has been subject to almost continual adjustment, but as the problems of surpluses and budget costs have intensified, increasingly far-reaching reforms have been required.

An important aspect of CAP reform has already been discussed: the freezing of support prices since 1984/85 (although, as was pointed out, the agri-monetary arrangements enabled some Member States to escape the full impact of this).

Reform can be said to have begun in earnest with the imposition of **milk delivery quotas** in 1984. It had become urgent to curb growing overproduction, and faced with the alternative of a drastic price cut or a quota system, the Ministers of Agriculture preferred the latter.

Then in 1988, with high spending on agricultural market support causing an overall EC budget crisis, **"stabilisers"** for several products were imposed. These operated in different ways depending on the commodity, as will be seen below, but generally provided for cuts in prices or subsidies if total EC production exceeded certain "maximum guaranteed quantities" (MGQs).

For almost all the products concerned, the MGQs were overrun in one or more of the subsequent years, and the penalties were applied. These stabiliser arrangements differ significantly from the individual quotas for milk: the MGQs apply to *global* EC output, and the system is thus subject to the so-called "free-rider" principle, in that any individual producer may expand output in the hope that others will contract.

A key element in the 1988 "stabilisers" package was the **"set-aside"** scheme. This was *voluntary*: producers who withdrew at least 20% of their arable land for at least five years were entitled to compensation. The response was relatively favourable in Germany and the Netherlands, where the rates of payment were high, but by the end of 1990/91 only some 2.5% of the total EC cereals area had come under the scheme. The impact on production would undoubtedly have been less than this, because of the well-known problems of "slippage", as farmers take out their least productive land and concentrate inputs such as fertiliser on the land remaining in cultivation.

The "cost-effectiveness" of the scheme was thus questionable: under such a voluntary programme, farmers have to be fully compensated for the revenue foregone. With the price support system providing a reasonably attractive alternative, the authorities were in a sense "bidding against themselves". Under US commodity programmes, as will be seen in Chapter 12, acreage reduction is a *condition* of obtaining price support. The "MacSharry Plan" moved the CAP further in that direction.

The **"MacSharry Plan"** (named after the current Commissioner responsible for agriculture) was put forward in the course of 1991 and agreed by the Council of Ministers—after difficult negotiations and with substantial modifications—in May–June 1992. Although the Council decisions were less drastic than the Commission had proposed, they nevertheless involved substantial price cuts for arable crops, with compensatory payments to producers *conditional* on set-aside.

Main features of the various common market organisations, taking into account these successive changes, are outlined in the following section.

(b) Common market organisations (CMOs)

It is not possible here to describe in detail all the features of the CMOs for all products: for this purpose, sources mentioned in the Appendix (item 1), including the relevant Regulations, should be referred to. Only the main points will be outlined below.

Implementation of a GATT "Uruguay Round" agreement along the lines of the bilateral US–EC agreement reached in November 1992 (see Chapter 13) would require cuts in the levels of protection and support: these however are not expected to exceed the cuts foreseen by the EC's own reform decisions (though for some commodities—sugar, wine, fruit and vegetables and olive oil—reform proposals still have to be made). Import levies would be transformed into *ad valorem* tariffs: however, reductions in import prices of more than 10% below the average of 1986–88 could still be offset by increased tariffs under the "special safeguard clause". Substantial "Community preference" would remain. But limits on quantities of subsidised exports and increased opportunities for imports could require a tightening of the restrictive measures—cereals set-aside, milk quotas, restrictions on beef intervention, etc.—discussed below. For oilseeds, the US–EC agreement requires a change in the EC's plans, as is explained below.

i) Crop products

Cereals

The basic elements of the CMO have already been described. Various adjustments have been made over the years, particularly under the 1988 "stabilisers", which by instituting a maximum guaranteed quantity (MGQ) of 160 million tonnes, somewhat reduced the effective intervention price whenever annual production exceeded this level. Under the "MacSharry Plan", which replaces the stabiliser scheme, intervention prices are to be substantially reduced. The Commission had proposed a cut of about one-third in effective price support, down to 100 ECU per tonne for the target price (which the Commission, perhaps optimistically, hoped would correspond to the world price). The Council agreed on cuts by stages over three years: starting from the 1993/94 marketing year (i.e. the 1993 harvest), the target price will come down by 1995/96 to 110 ECU, and the intervention price to 100 ECU. The threshold price will come down only to 155 ECU, thus maintaining substantial "Community preference" (the Commission had proposed 110 ECU). These prices apply to all cereals.

Compensation for the price cuts is to be paid, on a per hectare basis, on the basis of a rate rising to the equivalent of 45 ECU per tonne by 1995/96, adjusted according to average previous yields in each region. This compensation is available unconditionally under a "simplified" scheme for "small producers" (those who claim compensatory payment for an area of cereals, oilseeds and protein crops which, on the basis of the average regional yield, would produce not more than 92 tonnes of cereals).

Other—"professional"—producers get the compensation only if they **set aside** part of their land. According to the CAP reform decisions, the base area was to be the total used for cereals, oilseeds and protein crops (peas, beans etc.) in the three years 1989, 1990 and 1991: the US–EC agreement, however, requires a separate base area for oilseeds. Initially, the set-aside requirement is 15%. Compensation for set-aside is paid "at the level of the compensatory payment which would be paid from the marketing year 1995/96 for the same areas if cultivated with cereals".

The Commission had proposed to limit the compensation according to the crop area on each farm: on the basis of the average Community yield (stated to be 4.6 t./ha.), compensation would have been paid only up to 50 ha. per farm. This proposal encountered strong opposition from the countries with large arable farms—the UK, France, and Germany in view of the huge enterprises in the former East German *Länder*—and had to be dropped.

As regards the base area for calculating the percentage set-aside, Member States can opt either for individual base areas (as the Commission had proposed) or for *regional* bases: in the latter case, each producer requesting compensation must declare his total arable area as well as the percentage he proposes to set aside: if all the individual declarations add up to an amount which exceeds the regional total, the individual base areas are reduced proportionately, and in the following year, a percentage corresponding to the excess will have to be set aside with *no* compensation.

The set-aside land must be included in the rotation (to prevent the least fertile land being constantly taken out). Certain crops for non-food use can be planted on set-aside land provided the farmer has a contract with a processor: no area payments are granted in this case.

No time-limit is fixed for these new arrangements. The compensatory payments apply to "existing holdings"; the level of payment can be "reviewed periodically to take into account the development of productivity as well as expected developments on domestic and world markets". In an important concession to the EC, the US in November 1992 accepted that the payments, provided they are paid on a fixed base area and for a fixed yield, would not be subject to reduction in a Uruguay Round settlement (see Chapter 13).

Oilseeds

Community output was originally small in relation to imports, and the aim was to enable the products concerned to be traded within the EC at prices close to world levels. Imports were subjected only to small tariffs (maximum 15%)—which were "bound" in GATT—while subsidies (paid to "crushers") were intended to give domestic growers a return comparable with that from cereals. The subsidies proved to be high enough to induce a substantial growth in Ec output.

After a GATT panel had ruled that this system impaired the benefits of duty-free access for oilseeds granted in an EC–US deal in 1962 (see Chapter 13), the arrangements were changed, first through an interim scheme applicable to the 1992 harvest, then in the context of the "MacSharry" reform. Instead of aids to crushers of EC-grown oilseeds, "compensatory payments" would be made to producers on a per hectare basis. A "Community reference amount" is fixed at 384 ECU per hectare in 1992/93 and 359 ECU/ha. thereafter: on this basis, "projected regional reference amounts" are to be determined taking into account the average yield (the oilseed or the cereals yield can be chosen) in each region. A "projected reference price" of 163 ECU per tonne is also fixed, intended to represent a normal world price: to calculate the *final* payment, the projected regional reference amount is to be adjusted up or down by the extent to which the *observed* reference price (i.e. the world price) varies from the *projected* price (but taking no account of variations within 8% of the projected price).

As has been seen above, under the "MacSharry" decisions, the base area for arable crops was to include oilseeds. The US–EC agreement requires a separate base for oilseeds, of 5.1 million hectares from the 1995 crop onwards: this corresponds to the average area in 1989–91, i.e. the base used in the EC's own scheme. The EC undertook to maintain the set-aside requirement at a minimum of 10%.

It had already been foreseen that the oilseeds aid would be subject to "maximum guaranteed areas" for each type of oilseed: if the area planted exceeds the maximum, the payments are to be reduced by 1% for each 1% overshoot. This provision forms part of the US–EC agreement.

Durum wheat

Not to be confused with "hard wheat" (mostly imported from Canada and used for bread-making), "durum wheat is used for "pasta"and is produced in Southern Europe. It receives, in addition to the general support arrangements for cereals, a direct aid per hectare, to support production in "economically-disadvantaged" areas of traditional production in Southern Europe. Durum wheat too is included in the "MacSharry" compensation and set-aside provisions. Decisions taken previously required the alignment of its price on that for other cereals from 1993/94 on: to compensate for the bigger price reduction following the 1992 decisions, an additional aid of 297 ECU/ha. will be paid in the "traditional" production areas.

Olive oil

As with durum wheat, an important aim has been to ensure adequate incomes for farmers in the poorer regions of the EC where olives are mainly grown. Imports are subject only to a 20% duty, while "production aid" and "consumption aid" are paid to bridge the gap between producer returns and the lower market price. Under the "stabiliser" system, an MGQ of 1.35 million tonnes was set, any excess to result in proportionate changes in production aid; the stabiliser effect was later extended to the intervention price. Small producers, however, received increased production aid and were not subjected to the effects of the stabiliser.

Spain and Portugal, under their national regimes, had protected their olive oil producers by restricting imports of competing oils and fats: these restrictions had to be phased out by the end of 1990. A drastic fall in olive oil consumption in these countries would have upset market balance throughout the EC: consumption aid was therefore introduced in these countries at a level considered sufficient to prevent such a fall. No further change was made under the "MacSharry Plan".

Sugar

The regime includes the same basic elements as cereals (with intervention for refined sugar, and a derived "basic price" for sugarbeet), but also a production quota system. Each producer is entitled to the full guaranteed price only for a basic "A-quota" (subject to a 2% levy); for an additional "B-quota" a levy is applied (which can be up to 39.5%); while any further quantity ("C-sugar") is not eligible for support, so that its price depends on the export market—the cost of export subsidies ("refunds") being in principle financed from the levy on B-quota sugar. However, as the EC is committed to importing "preferential" sugar from the African, Caribbean and Pacific (ACP) countries—see Chapter 13—the cost of exporting the equivalent amount of EC sugar is held to be "aid" and is not charged to producers.

Despite the production quota system, production and export availabilities rose, and the cost of export subsidies was not covered by the levies. Under the 1988 "stabiliser" package, an "additional levy" can be charged, proportional to the total of the "normal" levies in each Member State, to clear the deficit arising in any year.

The sugar regime was not modified by the 1992 "MacSharry" reform but is due for review before the 1994/95 marketing year. The quota system has been severely criticised by the Court of Auditors for maintaining and even encouraging uneconomic production (see Appendix, item 1g); even Portugal, which before accession had no domestic sugarbeet production, was granted a quota.

Wine

Market organisation includes intervention arrangements (through distillation) and protection against third country imports, through customs duties and "countervailing charges" when prices fall below certain "reference prices". With the growth of surpluses, the distillation provisions have been reinforced (particularly under the 1988 "stabiliser" package), including a system of "preventive" distillation at low prices when the market is found to be in "serious imbalance". There are also subsidies for "grubbing-up" low-quality vineyards. However, in view of continued imbalance on the wine market, the CMO was due for another review.

Fruit and vegetables

The regime provides relatively flexible domestic support for fresh produce, since storage cannot be used to underpin the market for such perishable items. Producer groups can be authorised to withdraw produce from the market, with partial compensation, if prices fall below certain "buying-in" levels. Imports, on the other hand, are subjected to various controls: tariffs, quotas (generally applicable during periods of peak domestic production), and "reference prices": if import prices fall below these levels for a certain number of days, "countervailing charges" can be imposed on subsequent imports, until the price recovers.

For certain **processed fruit and vegetables**—sultanas and currants, dried figs, prunes, peaches and pears in syrup, and tomato products—processing aids are paid.

Under the 1988 "stabilisers", maximum guaranteed quantities were fixed for various fresh products—tomatoes, cauliflowers, apples, peaches, nectarines and citrus fruit—whereby withdrawal prices would be reduced in the year following any overrun. For several processed products—sultanas, currants, peaches in syrup and tomato products—the processing aids were also subjected to MGQs. Under the "MacSharry Plan", these stabilisers were considered to be working well enough and no change was made.

Tobacco

The CMO provides intervention prices and premiums. This regime became expensive in relation to the value of the product. Under the "MacSharry" reform, the numerous varieties are to be regrouped into a reduced number, and for each group of varieties a system of production quotas is to be applied, totalling 350,000 tonnes for the EC after 1994: no premiums will be paid for production beyond the quota levels. Intervention and export refunds are abolished.

Cotton

This is produced in Greece. Production aid will be cut under the "MacSharry" reform.

ii) Livestock products

Dairy products

The CMO uses basically the same methods of support as for cereals, but the target price for milk is implemented through intervention for butter and skim milk powder, and through threshold prices with variable import levies and export "refunds" for the various dairy products.

Growing surpluses necessitated the introduction of a production quota system in 1984. Overall national quotas are broken down into quantities for deliveries to dairies (plus some allowance for direct sales off farms). These can apply to individual producers, but in most cases they are administered through dairies, who can to some extent offset excesses against deficits among their suppliers. The penalty for overproduction is now 100% in both cases.

The quotas have been somewhat reduced through encouragement to farmers to give up milk production and through quota cuts, partly with compensation. On the other hand, quotas have been allocated to Spain and Portugal following their accession, and more recently to the former DDR *Länder*. The EC total in 1991/92 was 106.9 million tonnes (this includes direct sales from farms to consumers, and a "Community reserve").

Implementation of the system has proved difficult in some countries (especially in Italy). Still, together with limitations on the amounts of butter and skim milk powder that can be accepted into intervention, the system prevented the continued growth of milk deliveries which would otherwise have occurred, though it was still necessary—as has already been seen—to dispose of surplus butter and skim milk powder through various subsidised schemes and to subsidise exports.

Under the "MacSharry" reform, milk delivery quotas are to be further reduced, but by less than the Commission had proposed: a 2% reduction spread over the two marketing years 1993/94 and 1994/95. The butter price is to be reduced by 2.5% in each of these years (the Commission had proposed a 15% cut for butter and a 5% cut for skim milk powder, offset by a premium for the first 40 cows in each herd).

The scheme has proved quite acceptable to those farmers who have the benefit of a quota. One of the problems associated with any durable quota system, however, is how to reconcile it with the need for structural change. In December 1992, the Agricultural Council agreed to permit greater flexibility in the sale or leasing of quotas.

Beef and veal

The CMO was initially rather different from the basic cereals model, as this commodity was in short supply and expected to remain so: variable import levies (on top of customs duties) and export refunds were provided, and Member States were authorised to intervene on their domestic markets if prices should fall: provision for "permanent" intervention was not introduced until 1972 in order to stimulate production, and intervention did not become significant until 1974 when, contrary to expectations, the beef market became oversupplied.

During the 1980s, it became necessary to restrict intervention in various ways. Support buying was subjected to progressively tighter restrictions, as regards the conditions under which intervention can operate, the maximum quantity that can be sold into intervention, and other factors.

In the "MacSharry" reform, beef presented special difficulties: the cuts in cereals prices would give advantages to the grain-based meats—pigmeat and poultrymeat—as well as to intensive cattle units which, for environmental reasons, are no longer regarded as desirable. Further, it was agreed to reduce the intervention price by 15% over three years (down to 292 ECU/100 kg. carcass weight in 1995/96), and to reduce further the quantities that can be accepted into intervention (from 750,000 tonnes in 1993 down to 350,000 tonnes by 1997).

To compensate extensive beef producers, existing premiums for young male cattle and for "suckler cows" were increased (rising by 1995 to 90 ECU per animal for male cattle and to 120 ECU per cow), subject to "extensification criteria": the number of animals qualifying for these premiums is limited to certain "stocking densities". The limit falls from 3.5 "livestock units" (e.g. one cow) per hectare of forage area in 1993 to 2 LU per hectare from 1996 on. Further, the premiums can be increased by 30 ECU per animal on farms where the stocking density is less than 1.4 LU/ha.—a provision of particular interest to Ireland, with its extensive grass-based system of cattle-rearing. (As a result of this and other features, the net effect of the reforms on agricultural incomes in Ireland is likely to be *positive*.)

"Sheepmeat"

A CMO was introduced only after the UK had joined the EC: the EC import duty had been "bound" under GATT at 20%, and no import levy could be imposed. Under "voluntary restraint agreements", various exporting countries agreed to limit their exports in return for a reduction, and subsequently the suspension, of the duty. New Zealand remains the much the largest foreign supplier under these arrangements, though several Central and Eastern European countries have also entered into such agreements (which in 1992 were extended under the new agreements with the CSFR, Hungary and Poland—cf. Chapter 13).

Within the EC, a "basic price" determines the level of premiums paid per ewe and the level of intervention. Although the EC remains a net importer, output has been growing and the regime has become quite costly. Under the 1988 "stabiliser" arrangements, this basic price was subjected to a "maximum guaranteed quantity". In the "MacSharry Plan", the Commission tried to limit the costs of the "ewe premium" by fixing limits on the number of eligible ewes per flock. This encountered objections from the UK, where flocks are large in the hill areas of Scotland and Wales. Higher limits were finally agreed—1000 ewes in "less-favoured areas" and 500 elsewhere; beyond these limits the premium is still to be paid, but at half the basic rate.

Pigmeat, poultry and eggs

The CMOs for these three "cereal-based" products provide variable import levies (involving relatively complicated mechanisms) as the main means of support; for pigmeat, but not for poultry and eggs, internal market support can be provided, normally through aid for private storage and only exceptionally through public intervention. For all three products, export refunds can be granted. Budget expenditure has been limited, and the CMOs have not been significantly changed. (Note that under structural policy, EC investment aids cannot be granted to increase the number of pigs nor for any purpose to poultry and egg enterprises; moreover, the Commission does not authorise national aids for these purposes).

(c) A provisional assessment

The main features of the development and reform of the CAP market organisations have now been reviewed. Other aspects of the CAP will be considered in the following chapters.

It is however time to reflect briefly on the main implications of this and the previous chapter. The road since the inception of agricultural protectionism in the late 19th century has been long and tortuous. If governments in the developed market economies had restricted themselves to market stabilisation, smoothing out the inevitable fluctuations in market prices, the world-wide patterns of agricultural production and trade would undoubtedly look very different today. Western Europe would probably be importing much larger quantities of, for example, grain from North America, sugar from the Caribbean, dairy products from New Zealand, meat from Latin America and Eastern Europe. Producers in those regions, and European consumers, would benefit from lower prices.

However, governments have chosen to restrict these opportunities in the interests of their farming populations. How far these populations have actually benefited is a matter for debate: it is arguable that short-term income protection has encouraged farmers and their families to stay in farming when they might otherwise have moved to more profitable activities. As price support is proportional to output, it gives most benefit to the biggest producers; but the expectations of smaller producers too are raised, often unjustifiably. There is little doubt that the policies pursued have had the effect—as they were often meant to do—of keeping more people on the land, working a larger number of smaller farms, than would otherwise have been the case. The structural policies which might have countered such immobilities have been given relatively little attention, as will be seen in the next chapter.

In putting the emphasis on price support, governments overlooked the consequences of rising productivity on the one hand, and limited growth in food consumption on the other. Overproduction has been the inevitable consequence;

and governments delayed till the last minute taking action to deal with this problem. Even then, there has been great reluctance to reduce prices: other measures, of varying effectiveness, have been introduced in attempts to control the growth of supply.

Economists have for a long time advocated replacing price support with direct payments. Previous chapters have discussed some of the theoretical issues in the connection. Even if such payments involve increased *budgetary* cost, their *economic* cost should be less, as consumers benefit from lower prices, and the market can do its job of allocating resources and balancing supply and demand. It is however important that any system of direct payments should be both fair and not too complicated to administer: in practice, it is difficult to define the appropriate criteria. (A scheme of transitional income aids introduced in 1989, intended to compensate for losses due to CAP reform, to be implemented through programmes prepared by each Member State, was in fact applied only in five of them, the others finding it too complicated and expensive to administer, or simply unnecessary.)

The "MacSharry" reform is the most serious move in this direction to date, and as such deserves recognition. It greatly facilitates a Uruguay Round settlement, since the necessary cuts in protection and support are already largely contained within the EC's own reform: however, under a Uruguay Round agreement, the need to limit quantities of subsidised exports while admitting increased imports seems bound to require further restrictions.

The complexity of the new system is worrying. The link between compensatory payments and "set-aside" will require extensive administration and supervision, and the details are baffling for many farmers. It has taken the US many years to develop reasonably efficient systems to administer its acreage reduction programmes, and the EC, with numerous small and often fragmented farms, has a harder task. The "regionalisation" procedure, which aims to bypass the problems of administration at the individual farm level, will raise its own problems. The cost of compensation will be much higher than under the degressive system which the Commission had originally proposed.

Straightforward price cuts, with compensation on a per-person basis and limited in time, would have been preferable. But it must be recognised that, although price incentives have been largely responsible for the growth in production, it is not certain that price *cuts* would soon restore balance: for reasons pointed out in Chapter 2, production responds more quickly to price increases than to decreases. Drastic cuts would be needed to bring support prices down to market-clearing levels in the international context: politically and socially, this appears unacceptable. This means, however, that expenditure on export subsidies will continue, though it will have to be reduced under a Uruguay Round agreement.

In these circumstances, supply control through production quotas and set-aside may be a "second-best" solution. US experience suggests that, although the effectiveness of land withdrawal is doubtful, it may provide some flexibility in the management of supply. It also provides an answer to those who fear that Malthusian problems of hunger in the world will call for increased food production in Western Europe: in such cases, land set aside can be brought back into use.

Finally, it is by no means certain that the budgetary cost of the CAP can be maintained within the "guideline" (see Appendix, item 5). While much depends on world prices, which affect export subsidies, risks of increased costs arise, in particular, from possible underestimation of production growth, from the compensation arrangements and from the price-raising effects of the "switch-over" mechanism (see pp. 167–8) which the Agriculture Council has decided to maintain at least during 1993 and 1994.

In all this, it is difficult to recognise the "market economy". In agriculture, public intervention is far-reaching. That could, perhaps, have been avoided by different decisions at some time in the past: it is not easy to see how it can be avoided now.

APPENDIX

1. Sources:

a) **Agriculture in the early stages of European integration.** A useful study—broader than its title suggests—was by A.D. Robinson, *Dutch Organised Agriculture in International Politics, 1945–1960* (Nijhoff, The Hague: 1961). Another useful source is by the Forschungsinstitut der Deutschen Gesellschaft für Auswärtige Politik: *Die Europäische Zusammenarbeit auf dem Gebiet der Landwirtschaft* (Frankfurt: 1957).

b) **Origins of the CAP** are more fully described, with a detailed bibliography, in Chapter 12 of the author's *Government and Agriculture in Western Europe*. The problems for Germany in fixing common prices were discussed in a study by a group of well-known professors (the *Professorengutachten*): *Wirkungen einer Senkung der Agrarpreise im Rahmen einer gemeinsamen Agrarpolitik der EWG auf die Einkommensverhältnisse der Landwirtschaft in der Bundesrepublik Deutschland* (also in French, published by the Commission in *Etudes— Série agriculture*, No. 11 1962.)

c) **Current sources on the CAP** include the annual Commission report, *The Agricultural Situation in the Community*: this includes a large statistical section. The *Green Europe Newsletter* contains major Commission proposals and Council decisions, as well as special items. The *European Documentation* series sometimes contains a useful issue on the CAP. These are publications available through Community sales agents in various countries, or from the Office for Official Publications in Luxembourg.

Useful "CAP Working Notes", obtainable from the Documentation Centre of the Directorate-General for Agriculture of the Commission, provide reasonably up-to-date information on market organisation for major commodities. The *Official Journal of the European Communities* (OJ) contains Council and Commission regulations, including the annual budget.

Commercial sources include publications by the "Agra Europe" group: in particular the weekly *Agra Europe* (in several languages, not identical), and the English-language *CAP Monitor*, a loose-leaf publication with detailed information on CMOs, kept regularly up-to-date. These are expensive, but indispensable for those needing regular and accurate information.

d) Analytical works. Academic books and journal articles tend to lag behind events: they may be useful for background and analysis, but should not be relied upon for up-to-date information. (This applies also to the present work.) However, the CAP has spawned a vast academic literature: features such as the agri-monetary problems, milk quotas and set-aside have attracted particular attention, and the 1992 reform decisions will no doubt stimulate many more studies.

A general study of supply controls and direct income aids was published by OECD (Paris) in 1990: *Reforming agricultural policies: quantitative restrictions on production; direct income support.* This contains useful bibliographies.

e) Agri-monetary reform. The Commission's proposal for the post–1992 situation, which included a useful assessment of the current system, was contained in document COM(92)275 final. The Council decision (Regulation 3813/92), together with the implementing Commission regulation, appears in OJ L387 of 21.12.92.

f) The "MacSharry" reform. The Commission's proposals were published as Supplement 5/91 to the *Bulletin of the European Communities.* The Council decisions appear in a number of Regulations, in particular:
* No. 1765 on arable crops (OJ L181 of 1.7.92): this includes the compensatory and set-aside provisions). As regards oilseeds, this partly replaces Regulation 3766/91 (OJ L356 of 24.12.92). See also Commission Regulation 2293/92 (OJ L221 of 6.8.92) on detailed rules for set-aside.
* No. 1766 on cereals (also OJ L181 of 1.7.92): this becomes the new "basic" Regulation and includes the prices fixed from 1993/94 through 1995/96. (The 1992/93 prices appear in Regulation 1739/92, OJ L180 of 1.7.92).
* No. 2066/92 on beef and veal (OJ L215 of 30.6.92).
* No. 2069/92 on sheepmeat and goatmeat (also OJ L215 of 30.6.92).

g) Sugar. The Court of Auditors special report appeared in OJ C290 of 7.11.91; further comments were made in Chapter 4.2 of the Court's annual report for 1990 in OJ C324 of 13.12.91. See also a study by the Australian Bureau of Agricultural and Resource Economics (ABARE), *Domestic and world market effects of EC sugar policies* (Canberra: 1991).

2. Aims of the CAP. Article 39 of the Treaty of Rome defined these as follows:
(a) to increase agricultural productivity by promoting technical progress and by ensuring the rational development of agricultural production and the optimum utilisation of the factors of production, in particular labour;
(b) thus to ensure a fair standard of living for the agricultural community, in particular by increasing the individual earnings of persons engaged in agriculture;
(c) to stabilise markets;
(d) to assure the availability of supplies;
(e) to ensure that supplies reach consumers at reasonable prices.
It is important to note that these aims do *not* constitute an unqualified commitment to support farm incomes, although they have often been interpreted in this way (the vital word *"thus"* in point (b) is often omitted).

3. Processed products. For first-stage processed products listed in Annex II of the Rome Treaty, import levies or export refunds are applied in a manner similar to that for basic products. For non-Annex II products, under Regulation 3033/80 (as amended), complex rules apply: these aim to protect the EC's processing industries and to enable them to export at competitive prices, despite higher material costs due to the CAP. *Import* charges include a "fixed component"—i.e. a percentage tariff—and a "variable component" which reflects the quantities of the basic products used and the difference between EC and world prices for those products: adjustments are made at three-month intervals. For export refunds, the rules are very complex, and in practice the Commission has considerable flexibility.

4. Management Committee procedure. The general rules as laid down in the basic cereals regulation (now in Articles 22–24 of Council Regulation 1766/92) apply also to other CMOs. Implementing measures under the CMOs, such as rules relating to import levies (though not the daily rates, which are fixed directly by the Commission), the rates of export refunds and various other matters are referred to the Management Committee. This is chaired by the Commission, and consists of representatives of Member States (i.e. in practice, mostly from Ministries of Agriculture or their delegates in Brussels). Decisions are taken by the same "qualified majority" procedure as is laid down for the Council (see Chapter 14, Appendix item 2).

The Commission usually gets a majority for its intended action, sometimes by making adjustments. If the Committee does disagree, the Commission can still adopt the measures it thinks necessary, though it must then submit the matter to the Council, which can take a different decision, by qualified majority, within one month. This has rarely happened.

5. The EC budget "ceiling". Under a "Decision" of 1970, the Community's "own resources"—i.e. sums going automatically to the EC budget—consisted of the revenue from customs duties, import levies on agricultural products, and the levy on sugar producers: and in addition, contributions from Member States which however could not exceed 1% of their "VAT base"—i.e. the total value of goods and services subject to value-added tax (not the *amount* of tax: the definition of the *base* had been harmonised, but not the rates of taxation). In 1986, with the accession of Portugal and Spain, this limit was raised to 1.4%. With effect from 1988, a new "resource" was introduced, related to GNP, with an overall limit on "own resources" of 1.4% of GNP.

High expenditure on agriculture periodically pushed total spending close to the ceiling. A "guideline" for agricultural spending was agreed in 1984: for the period 1988–92, the growth of expenditure on agricultural market support was limited to 74% of GNP growth in the EC. Following the December 1991 agreement in the European Council on the "Maastricht" Treaty, the Commission proposed further increases in the budgetary ceiling (the so-called "Delors II" package). At its December 1992 session in Edinburgh, the European Council took a number of important budgetary decisions:

* The total EC budget will be frozen at 1.2% of Community GDP for two years, then rise to reach 1.27% by 1999: this implies an increase (at 1992 prices) from 69.2 billion ECU in 1993 to 84.1 billion by 1999.
* Total "structural" spending will rise from 21.3 billion ECU in 1993 to 30 billion in 1999: most of this is an increase in the three structural Funds (see next chapter), which rise to 27.4 billion in 1999. In addition, the new "Cohesion Fund" created by the Maastricht Treaty will channel 15.15 billion ECU over the seven-year period to the four poorest Member States: Greece, Portugal, Spain and Ireland.
* The budgetary "rebate" to the UK (see Chapter 14) is continued.
* The limit on the growth of spending on the CAP is maintained: this can rise from 35.2 billion ECU in 1993 to 38.4 billion in 1999. However, in a concession to France, it was agreed that increased costs arising from exchange rate movements could be taken into account: the text in question is unclear—especially as to whether it refers only to "recent" movements (i.e. in the last quarter of 1992) or also to future monetary changes—and may prove controversial. Note that the Agriculture Council's refusal to abolish the "switchover" mechanism (see pp. 167–8) is likely to lead to increased costs in the event of further re-alignments.

CHAPTER 10

STRUCTURAL, RURAL DEVELOPMENT AND ENVIRONMENT POLICY (EC)

It has already been pointed out that agricultural policies have been primarily concerned with price support, and that structural reform has had relatively little attention. Nevertheless, with growing realisation that the basic problems of agriculture cannot be solved by price support, measures aimed at assisting the process whereby small farms disappear and larger, more viable farms are created were developed in several Western European countries, and have been pursued under the EC's Common Agricultural Policy; the improvement of processing and marketing structures has also been promoted.

In the EC, the emphasis has gradually shifted to rural development, largely as a result of the needs of the Southern European countries, and in the context of the general reform of the EC Structural Funds in order to promote "cohesion" among the Member States. Most of the expenditure on agricultural structures, under the "Guidance Section" of FEOGA, now goes through regional programmes rather than "horizontal" measures.

Structural policies have also been adjusted to take account of growing concerns at the negative impact of intensive modern farming methods on the environment.

(a) Antecedents

In several countries of continental Western Europe, fragmentation of farms into small separate plots, as well as small overall farm size, have remained serious problems. Around 1960, holdings in Germany consisted on average of eleven separate plots, each less than a hectare: the problem of small size and fragmentation being particularly severe in the south of the country. In Belgium there were on average six plots per holding, in the Netherlands four. The problem was known to be serious also in parts of France, Italy, Spain and Portugal, and was widespread in Switzerland and in Austria.

Until the 1960s, structural measures had been mainly limited to attempts to consolidate fragmented holdings. Thus in **Germany**, consolidation had begun in some areas already in the early nineteenth century, but in many regions inheritance practices, whereby farms were split up at each generation, continually aggravated the problem. After the constitution of the Federal Republic in 1949, efforts were made to speed up the process of consolidation. But consolidation schemes—usually accompanied by new roads, drainage systems, etc., and sometimes by removing farmsteads from congested villages to the consolidated farmland—still proved costly and extremely slow to implement.

Consolidation measures have continued under national schemes in the EC Member States: in Germany around 1990, consolidation was still taking place at a rate of about 120,000 hectares each year.

More far-reaching measures of structural reform have been gradually developed. In **France**, a new departure took place on the basis of the *Loi d'Orientation* of 1960 and especially the *Loi complémentaire* of 1962 : public bodies—*Sociétés d'Aménagement Foncier et d'Etablissement Rural* (SAFER)—were established to buy and resell farmland with the aim of improving structures, and special retirement aids were granted to elderly farmers.

In **Sweden**, relatively far-reaching intervention began already in the 1950s, as County Agricultural Boards were given extensive powers to promote restructuring, through intervention on the land market, provision of State-guaranteed loans, advisory work, etc.

The **Netherlands** tended to concentrate efforts on designated areas, combining land consolidation, improved water management, re-allocation of farmland, compensation to farmers who gave up their farms, and retraining facilities.

Some of this experience was absorbed into EC structural policy. It was however necessary to innovate in important respects.

(b) From structural to rural development policies

A common structural policy in the EC was not initiated until well after the common market organisations had begun to function. The impetus was provided not just by the unsatisfactory state of production and marketing structures, but by the appearance of market imbalances: soon the Community of Six was well above self-sufficiency in several commodities. This motivated the Commission to produce in December 1968 its "Memorandum on the Reform of Agriculture", which became generally known—after the name of the Commissioner for Agriculture—as the "Mansholt Plan".

i) The Mansholt Plan and the 1972 Directives

The Mansholt Plan broke new ground. The problems of over-supply and the need for basic adjustments were recognised. A long-term programme—

"Agriculture 1980"—would contain a new approach to price policy, under which prices were again to play their true role of guiding production. Structural policy—which the Community had so far failed to develop—would aim to create "modern production units" through selective investment aids: such farms should reach 80–120 hectares of cropland, or 40–60 cows, with similarly high targets in other lines of production. About five million people should be helped to leave agriculture during the 1970s by early retirement schemes or by retraining. The land thus released would be made available for amalgamating holdings or for afforestation. Since the creation of the "modern production units" would accelerate production growth, the agricultural area in the Community (of Six) should be reduced by at least 5 million hectares in the period 1970–80 (it amounted to about 70 million hectares in 1968). The Community dairy herd should be reduced by about three million cows by 1976, by slaughter and by encouraging a shift to beef production.

The Plan provoked violent opposition among farming circles throughout the Community. The proposals for reducing labour and land were particularly controversial. In France, in particular, there was bitter reaction, as the debate took place against a background of concern about the prospects for the farm community, faced by acute problems of transition from a peasant-type, small-scale farming pattern to larger-scale, mechanised and capital-intensive units.

To a large extent, the aims of the Plan corresponded to trends which were occurring in any case and were bound to continue. The Commission's error lay partly in presenting the targets for farm size and for reductions in land and labour as if they were *plans* to be imposed by Community and national authorities. The debate made clear that such a planned approach to Community agriculture was unacceptable.

The outcome was modest: in 1972 the Council of Ministers adopted three "Directives":

* Directive 72/159 provided aid for **investments on farms** considered "suitable for development" and able to reach an income comparable with other occupations for "one or two" labour units.
* Directive 72/160 offered **payments to outgoers** in the form of annuities or lump sums to elderly farmers, or premiums to younger ones.
* Directive 72/161 sought to provide **socio-economic guidance and training**.

These schemes did not achieve their aims. Conceived in a period of economic growth and expanding employment, they were put into effect during the economic recession from 1973 on. Not surprisingly, there were few applicants for the outgoers' scheme, and in so far as some land was released, little of it went to farmers who had submitted modernisation plans under Directive 72/159. Consequently, modernisation on these farms took the form largely of intensification on the existing area. By about 1980, the Commission was having to point out that this brought the scheme into conflict with the aim of holding down supply.

Another criticism which was increasingly levelled by some Member States at Directive 72/159 related to the selectivity principle which from the start had governed this scheme. In particular, the "comparable income" criterion excluded—as it was meant to do—the majority of small farms. Justifiable in a context of economic growth and expanding employment opportunities, this approach seemed over-restrictive when employment opportunities off the farm were limited, and when there was increasing concern at the need to maintain rural communities, particularly in the less-favoured areas. The number of beneficiaries under Directive 159 was nowhere very large, but in Italy and the new Member States in Southern Europe, the proportion of farms which could meet the criteria was very limited indeed.

So in 1985 the basic directives were replaced by Regulation 797/85, under which investment aids could be provided to practically any low-income farmer who put forward an improvement plan: the lower limit of eligibility disappeared, and instead an *upper* limit was introduced stipulating that the improvement plan should not raise income *above* 120% of a "reference income". An attempt was made to create a stronger link with market policy by providing that the investments should improve quality and adjust production in line with market requirements, or should reduce costs, save energy and improve the environment and living conditions.

Various other amendments and additions have been made in recent years, and Regulation 797/85 was replaced by Regulation 2328/91 (see Appendix, item 2). With the overall reform of the structural Funds in 1988, the whole emphasis has changed, as will be seen below.

ii) The development of regional measures

Directive 75/268 on **"less-favoured areas"** was the first measure in favour of specified regions, providing "compensatory allowances"—based usually on the number of livestock per farm—to farmers in mountain, hill and other less-favoured areas: it was taken up quite extensively in such areas. The number and extent of areas classified as "less-favoured" has constantly increased, and now covers almost half the total agricultural area in the EC. By 1990 there just over 1.2 million beneficiaries, including over 200,000 each in Germany, Spain and Greece (but only 92,000 in Italy). This scheme (now incorporated in Regulation 2328/91) remains essentially a social instrument rather than a means of structural adjustment: Germany in particular seems to have used it as an additional means of compensating farmers for price cuts.

From 1978 onwards, a series of measures was adopted in favour of **Mediterranean regions** in particular. Dissatisfaction by Italy at the distribution of benefits under the CAP was initially the main driving-force. Aids were provided for irrigation, infrastructure improvement, afforestation, inshore fisheries and other items. Besides Italy, southern regions of France benefited from some of these measures, and on the accession of Greece in 1981 similar measures were extended to this country, followed in 1982 by a more general programme to accelerate agricultural development.

Ireland was able to take advantage of this trend, obtaining programmes for agricultural development in the west of the country, for drainage and so on. This in turn led to British demands for similar assistance for Northern Ireland. Before long almost every Member State had obtained FEOGA "Guidance" aid for regional schemes of one kind or another.

In 1981 three small **"integrated programmes"** were adopted, for the Western Isles of Scotland, the Lozère in France and the Belgian Ardennes, the intention being that development in the rural areas concerned should include sectors other than agriculture, and that the Regional and Social Funds (see below) should contribute. More ambitious **"Integrated Mediterranean Programmes"** were introduced in 1985 to help the southern regions of the Community of Ten to face up to competition from the new Member States (Spain in particular). A programme for the development of Portuguese agriculture was begun even before Portugal had joined the Community; a similar programme for less-favoured areas in Spain was adopted in 1988.

iii) Action under the reformed structural Funds

The "integrated" approach was carried further with the important reform of the Structural Funds agreed in 1988, following political agreement to double spending on structural action from 7 billion ECU in 1989 to 14 billion by 1993. The Funds in question are primarily the European Regional Development Fund, the European Social Fund and the Guidance Section of FEOGA. Five priority objectives were defined, among which the following are relevant here:

* **Objective 1:** development and structural adjustment of regions whose development is lagging behind. These regions were defined as those in which per capita GDP was less than 75% of the Community average in the previous three years: as they cover the whole of Greece, Portugal and Ireland, most of Spain, the south of Italy, Sardinia, Corsica and the French overseas *départements*, many rural areas are included (see map).

In Objective 1 regions, FEOGA Guidance can finance improvements in rural infrastructures, irrigation, etc.; the Regional Fund contributes to investments for job creation, infrastructure, support for local development initiatives, etc.; and the Social Fund mainly supports training activities. In practice, in rural areas, direct involvement has come mostly from FEOGA Guidance: the contributions of the other Funds have been relatively indirect.

"Community Support Frameworks" (CSFs) were prepared within each region, and after approval by the Commission became the framework for action, normally under "Operational Programmes". About 80 such Programmes involving FEOGA Guidance are under way.

A special aid programme for the five *Länder* of the former DDR was also established. There are three major priorities for agriculture and rural development: horizontal structural measures (with emphasis on processing and marketing), improvement of living and working conditions, and protection of the environment (pollution being a major problem). The total contribution in these

categories is 850 million ECU for three years, of which 650 million from
FEOGA Guidance.

* **Objective 5b:** promoting the development of rural areas. The criteria for defin-
ing these areas included a high share of agricultural employment, a low level
of agricultural income, and a low level of socio-economic development (assessed on the basis of GDP per inhabitant). In fact, the criteria were flexible,
and for mainly political reasons, every Member State not covered by Objective
1 obtained a "5b" region—see map.

In these areas, the three Funds can contribute along the same lines as in Objective 1 regions, also on the basis of Community Support Frameworks. Within
the relatively limited amount of money available, priority is being given to
diversification of agricultural production, development of small- and medium-
sized enterprises, tourism, protection of the environment, and training related
to such measures. About 74 Operational Programmes are being implemented.

* **Objective 5a.** This is *not* a regional approach, but regroups various measures,
mostly taken over from legislation existing before the reform of the Structural
Funds: the general aim is now described as that of "speeding up the adjustment
of agricultural structures, with a view in particular to the reform of the common
agricultural policy". Only FEOGA Guidance is involved. The measures in
question (other than the aids for farmers in less-favoured areas) are applicable
anywhere in the Community. In Objective 1 areas, they are implemented
through the Operational Programmes.

There is a long list of somewhat heterogeneous measures, as indicated below
(see also Table 10.2); some of these are of minor importance. The classification
is the author's and does not necessarily correspond to any official grouping.

Improvements on farms:

—Investment aids (already discussed above). Since 1990, aid can be granted
   also for diversification of activities, in particular by tourism or craft activities, or by direct sales of farm produce.
—Aids for young farmers (under 40) to begin farming. This has been of particular interest to France.
—Aids for technical and economic training for farmers who are benefiting from
   the investment aids, and for farmers under the age of 40.
—Aids to encourage the keeping of farm accounts.
—Aids to groups of farmers for mutual assistance, relief services and management services.

Social assistance to farmers:

—Compensatory allowances for farmers in less-favoured areas (the former
   Directive 75/268, already described above).
—Incentives for early retirement. Although the 1972 scheme had little effect,
   a similar measure was re-introduced in 1988, and reinforced in 1992 in the
   context of the "MacSharry" package. EC finance for this new scheme will
   come not from FEOGA Guidance but from FEOGA Guarantee, ostensibly
   on the grounds that it accompanies the changes in market organisation.

Improvements in marketing and processing:
—Aids for the improvement of processing and marketing structures. This has
   been the most successful scheme in terms of uptake since its introduction in
   1977: marketing co-operatives and smallish enterprises are the main
   beneficiaries. It is continued, but in the context of "sectoral plans", to be
   prepared by Member States and approved by the Commission.
—Aids for the launching of **producer groups** to improve marketing are available for all products in Greece, Spain, Italy and Portugal, and for a more
   limited range of products (but including in particular fruit and vegetables)
   in other Member States.

Improvement of market balance:
—Structural measures aimed at improving market balance in specific sectors
   have been in existence for some time: these include aids for restructuring
   wine, olive oil and citrus fruit production.

Priority areas for Structural Funds

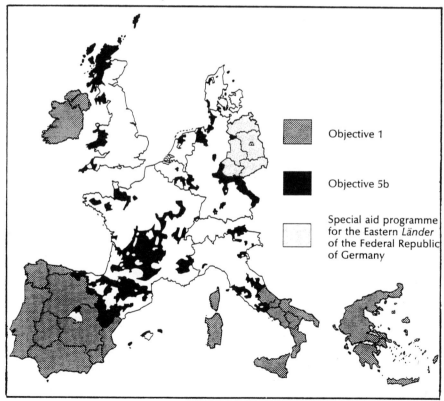

Objective 1

Objective 5b

Special aid programme
for the Eastern *Länder*
of the Federal Republic
of Germany

Note: Objective 1 also covers the Canary Islands (Spain), the Azores and Madeira (Portugal), and the French overseas *départements* (Caribbean islands and Guyana).

—**Set-aside.** The initial scheme in force up to 1992 (already discussed in the previous chapter) was partly financed from the "Guidance" section and was contained in the Structures Regulation. The set-aside programme adopted in 1992 in the "MacSharry Plan" context, however, forms part of the "arable crops" Regulation and will be financed by FEOGA Guarantee.

The Structures Regulation also contained provisions for "extensification" and "conversion"—i.e. a reduction in output per hectare of surplus crops, of conversion to "non-surplus" products—but in fact little use was made of extensification, while the necessary list of non-surplus products could not be agreed.

The development of a common **forestry** policy had been resisted by some Member States, using the argument that forestry falls outside the scope of agricultural policy as defined in the Treaty of Rome. However, under decisions taken in 1989 and reinforced in the "MacSharry" package of 1992, EC aid can be given to farmers for afforestation as "an alternative use of agricultural land" and for the development of forestry activities on farms (Regulation 2080/92). Other schemes provide for afforestation and the improvement of woodland "with a view to improving the agricultural situation" (Regulation 1610/89), and for protecting forests against atmospheric pollution and against fire (Regulation 1613/89). Forestry measures can also be included under the regional development programmes discussed below. The processing and marketing aids referred to above can also be granted for forestry products.

iv) Funding

Structural policy, unlike market organisation, is only partly financed by the Community budget, the rest being paid for, depending on the scheme, by Member States or by the beneficiaries. The standard rate of Community finance was formerly 25% for the "horizontal" measures, with higher rates in certain areas. Regulation 2052/88 on the reform of the Structural Funds provided that rates of Community assistance should be differentiated in the light of the seriousness of the problems, the financial capacity of the Member State concerned, and other factors, subject to maxima of 75% of the total cost in the case of Objective 1 regions and 50% in other regions. Subsequently, the Commission fixed the rates for Objective 5a measures at 50–65% in Objective 1 regions and 25–50% elsewhere.

Table 10.1 shows the projected distribution of finance over the period 1989–93 covered by present legislation, as between the priority Objectives and the three Funds; Figures 10.1a and b show the projected five-year distribution between Member States of Community expenditure under Objectives 1 and 5b respectively (note that although the pie-charts have been drawn the same size, the total amount is far greater for Objective 1 than for 5b). Objective 5a finance is not allocated in advance, and may be spent in any region.

Table 10.1—Projected finance under EC structural Funds, 1989–93
(in billion ECU)

	All sources	Regional Fund	Social Fund	FEOGA "Guidance"
Total *of which:*	60.3	..	..	..
Objective 1	36.2	21.0	9.8	5.4
Objective 5a	3.4	–	–	3.4
Objective 5b	2.6	1.1	0.4	1.1

Note: The total includes 3.8 billion ECU under "Community initiatives", of which 2.1 bn. for Objective 1 and 0.2 bn. for Objective 5b; the allocation between the Funds is not determined.
Source: Commission, *Annual report on the implementation of the reform of the structural Funds, 1989*, COM(90)516 final (Annex I-2).

Figure 10.1—EC Structural Funds: projected distribution of finance, 1989–93

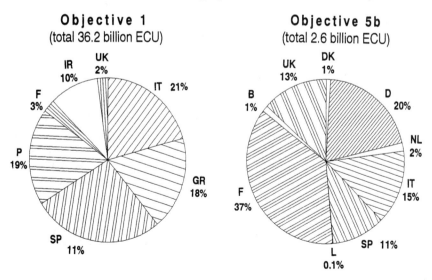

Objective 1
(total 36.2 billion ECU)

Objective 5b
(total 2.6 billion ECU)

Source: As Table 10.1 (Annexes I-3 and I-6).

Table 10.2—FEOGA "Guidance": 1991 commitments
(in million ECU)

	Through Obj. 1	Through Obj. 5b	Horizontal	Total
"Operational programmes"	454	221	n.a.	675
Other rural development	412	30	n.a.	443
Less-favoured areas (compensatory allowances etc.)	242	n.a.	232	475
Marketing and processing	106	n.a.	98	203
Investment aids	120	n.a.	139	260
Aids for young farmers	25	n.a.	133	158
Early retirement	15	n.a.	0	15
Adjustment of production	43	2	5	50
Set-aside	n.a.	n.a.	26	26
Other	25	6	25	57
TOTAL	1444	260	657	2361

n.a.—not applicable.
Source: Direct Commission communication. Some transitional measures have been omitted.

Table 10.2 shows the planned use of FEOGA Guidance money in the single year 1991, as between types of aid. The greater part of the money now goes to regionalised programmes, either the new Operational Programmes under Objective 1 or 5b, or programmes begun before the reform of the Structural Funds in Portugal, Spain, Greece, etc. A substantial part of expenditure on the specific measures also goes through Objective 1 programmes. (In the "5b" regions, these measures are implemented independently of the Operational Programmes.

v) Future development

As has been seen, the early "horizontal" measures did little to promote structural improvement, though they were presumably helpful to the individual beneficiaries. The effectiveness of many of the early regional schemes is also open to doubt: many of these were introduced in response to a political need, with little prior analysis, little or no consultation at the regional level, little or no appraisal of environmental effects, and subsequently hardly any objective analysis of the results. (See however Appendix, item 4.)

However, the 1988 reform of the structural Funds has brought important changes. The greater part of EC spending now goes through Operational Programmes in the designated "Objective 1" and "Objective 5b" regions, aiming in most cases at an "integrated" approach, with contributions from the various Funds, and covering a period of between three and five years. Although horizontal measures are retained, in the Objective 1 areas these are now mainly implemented through the Operational Programmes: this, it is hoped, will avoid dispersion and permit a more effective use of the money. "Partnership" has become a key word, particularly in the preparation and implementation of the programmes.

This new approach reflects the limitations of structural policy if it attempts to resolve problems within the farm sector in isolation. Adjustment in farm structures and improvement in farm incomes require a favourable economic environment, and an integrated approach to development is particularly necessary in regions which are economically backward.

Procedures for monitoring and assessment are laid down in the basic Regulation on the Structural Funds (Regulation 2052/88). *Ex ante* assessments of the Operational Programmes (i.e. soon after their establishment) have been carried out by teams of independent consultants, and appear generally positive: the main criticisms in some areas relate to cumbersome procedures, imprecise definition of aims, insufficient integration of the various Funds and inadequate involvement of the local populations. Though these reports cannot alter the programmes already drawn up, they will be taken into account by the Commission in preparing the legislation upon which the second round of programmes will be based.

The "Maastricht Treaty" reinforces the aim of "economic and social cohesion" in the EC, adding a new article to the Treaty of Rome declaring that "the Community shall aim at reducing disparities between the levels of development of the various regions and the backwardness of the least favoured regions, *including rural areas*" (author's italics) and providing for a new "Cohesion Fund". The so-called "Delors II package" (the Commission document setting out the necessary follow-up to the Maastricht Treaty), proposed additional funding for rural development and declared:

Ominous trends are threatening the future in a large part of the Community: the steady decline in agricultural employment, the widening gap between town and country..., the flight of the young people from the land, the absence of factors to attract business, the damage caused to the environment by intensive cultivation and desertification. This situation could endanger the survival of the rural world, one of the pillars of the European development model...

Rural development policy must generate prospects for the future which will allow sufficient farmers to stay on the land, diversify employment in rural areas, contribute to better planning, step up the effort in favour of local development, and preserve the countryside.

The Edinburgh session of the European Council in December 1992 achieved a compromise between the attempts of the UK and other Northern countries to restrain the growth in EC finances and the demands of the Southern European countries, led by Spain, for increased spending on programmes of interest to them: as part of the overall budgetary deal, spending on the existing structural Funds and on the new Cohesion Fund will increase over the period 1993–1999 (see Appendix to Chapter 9, item 5).

(c) **Environmental measures**

In several of the northern EC Member States, the environmental effects of modern farming methods have generated increasing public concern: water and air pollution by chemicals and intensive livestock units, destruction of wildlife habitats, changes in the appearance of the countryside, etc. Some countries—in particular Denmark and the Netherlands—have introduced stringent environmental controls on their farmers, particularly since the mid-1980s.

At the Community level, apart from technical rules such as the prohibition of certain agrochemicals, a number of measures have been introduced in recent years. A general legal basis was provided by the Single European Act of 1986, which added to the Treaty of Rome a new "Title" on the environment (see Appendix, item 5). Action relating to agriculture so far includes the following:

* The **"Nitrates Directive"** no. 91/676 aims to reduce water pollution caused by nitrates from agricultural sources— both chemical fertilisers and animal manure. It requires Member States, in the first place, to establish a "code of good agricultural practice, to be implemented by farmers on a voluntary basis"; and in the second place, to designate "vulnerable zones" in which to implement "action programmes" under which certain measures become *mandatory*. These include rules relating to:
  —periods when the application of certain types of fertilisers is prohibited;
  —storage capacity for livestock manure;
  —limitation of the application of fertilisers depending on soil characteristics, climate, etc., and based on a balance between the nitrogen requirements of crops and the supply from the soil and from fertilisation.
  It will take several years before such action programmes are implemented.
* Regulation 2092/91 on **organic farming** specifies the cultivation practices (non-use of chemicals, etc.) required for produce to be classified and labelled as "organic"; an EC inspection service will be set up. Only plant products are covered so far.
* Steps have also been taken in the context of structural policy to encourage "environment-friendly" farming practices. As has been mentioned above, the types of **investments on farms** eligible for aid now include protection and improvement of the environment.
* In response to a British request, reflecting growing public concern in the UK about effects of modern farming on the countryside, authorisation for Member States to introduce special aids in **"environmentally sensitive areas"** (ESAs) was included in Regulation 797/85 (now in Regulation 2328/91). Subsequently, Community finance was made available for this scheme, though it remains optional for Member States. Aid is granted to farmers who, as part of a programme for each sensitive area, undertake to follow production practices which are compatible with requirements for protecting the environment and landscape, and to apply these practices for at least five years. Examples of practices to be *avoided* include ploughing up permanent pasture or draining

wetlands. By the end of 1990, the scheme was being applied in six Member States: most of the individual beneficiaries were in Germany, but the average area per beneficiary was much bigger in the UK.

* The "MacSharry" package adopted by the Council in May–June 1992 includes a further environmental scheme, under which aids can be granted to farmers who undertake, for a minimum of five years, to adopt or maintain practices which reduce pollution (such as reduced use of agrochemicals and extensification of crop and livestock production) and which contribute to protecting the countryside; aid can also be paid to farmers who set aside farmland for at least twenty years for environmental purposes, such as "biotope reserves", natural parks or "the protection of hydrological systems" (Regulation 2078/92). Member States have to implement this scheme through "multiannual zonal programmes".

Despite these measures, EC legislation on agriculture and the environment is currently lagging behind public opinion. In the general context of "green" issues, environmental damage due to intensive modern farming causes widespread concern. Further, in view of surplus farm production, farmers are seen not just as providers of food but also as "guardians of nature": and there may now be more willingness to subsidise farmers for conserving the countryside than for producing surplus food. Most farmers, and their organisations, continue to resist this development, but the pressures are increasing. Undoubtedly, there will be more national and EC legislation in this field in the years ahead.

APPENDIX

1. The "Mansholt Plan"—officially the "Memorandum on the Reform of Agriculture in the European Economic Community"—was published as a Supplement to the *Bulletin of the European Communities*, no 1, 1969.

2. "Directives" and "Regulations". Community "socio-structural" policy was initially contained mainly in "Directives", which require implementation through national legislation and were thus regarded as more flexible than "Regulations", which are directly applicable. However, problems arose in Italy as legislation was required in each region. More recent measures have taken the form of Regulations, but scope has been left for variations in national implementation, and even, in some cases, for Member States to opt out entirely. The reform of the structural Funds is contained in Regulation 2052/88 (*Official Journal* L185 of 15.7.88). The basic "consolidated" Regulation on the "horizontal" measures, replacing no. 797/85 which had undergone numerous amendments, is no. 2328/91 (*Official Journal* L218 of 6.8.1991, p.1). The measures relating to processing and marketing, replacing Regulation 355/77, are contained in Regulations nos. 866/90 and 867/90 (*Official Journal* L91 of 6.4.90). The 1992 "accompanying measures" in the "MacSharry Plan" context are contained in Regulation 2078/92 (environmental measures, including long-term set-aside), 2079/92 (early retirement) and 2080/92 (afforestation on farms), all in *Official Journal* L215 of 30.7.92.

3. Reports. The Commission's new approach to rural issues was outlined in "The Future of Rural Society", *Bulletin of the European Communities, Supplement 4/88* (this is often referred to as the "Rural World" report). A useful *Vade Mecum* on "Agriculture and the

Reform of the Structural Funds" was issued by the Commission in the *Green Europe Newsletter* series, no. 5/90: this however is already out-of-date in certain respects. There is an annual report on "the implementation of the reform of the structural Funds". A more useful document is the "mid-term review", which also discusses implications of the Maastricht Treaty: "Community structural policies: assessment and outlook" (COM(92)84 final).

The Commission's annual *Agricultural Situation* report includes a chapter on "Rural Development", and some relevant statistics. The annual *Financial Report on the European Agricultural Guidance and Guarantee Fund, Guidance Section* contains only financial data. For many structural measures, information on implementation does not reach the Commission until well after money has been spent and claims for FEOGA reimbursement are submitted by Member States.

The "Delors II package" is contained in COM(92)2000 final ("From the Single Act to Maastricht and beyond: the means to match our ambitions") and COM(92)2001 final ("The Community's finances between now and 1997").

4. Analysis. The Commission itself has rarely made any deep analysis of the results of structural policy: the reports mentioned above are usually limited to financial data on amounts paid out. It has tended to blame this situation on Member States, who do not provide required information. This leaves a suspicion that much of the money spent, particularly on the earlier regional schemes, has had limited effect.

To some extent this gap has been filled by the Court of Auditors. It made critical assessments of the investment aids on farms (Chapter 6 of its annual report for 1989 in *Official Journal* C313 of 12.12.90); of the Integrated Mediterranean Programmes (Special Report no. 4/90 in *Official Journal* C298 of 28.11.90); and of the compensatory allowances in less-favoured areas (Chapter 9 in its report for 1990 in *Official Journal* C324 of 13.12.91).

However, as indicated in the text, monitoring and assessment is required by the basic Regulation on the Structural Funds, so this situation should improve.

By comparison with issues of price policy, there has been relatively little academic analysis of structural policy. The extensive survey of farm households carried out in several EC regions by the Arkleton Trust confirmed that the use of "horizontal" structural measures in 1987–91 remained low. Compensation measures in less-favoured areas were the most widely-used. As regards investment aids, the relaxation of eligibility criteria has caused some reduction in use in regions of large-scale farming, but significant increases in Greece, Spain and southern Italy. The main results of this study are contained in the final report by the Arkleton Trust to the Commission, entitled *Rural Change in Europe* (publication forthcoming).

The role of aids to young farmers in promoting installation and modernisation is considered, though not very conclusively, in *Farm take-over and farm entrance within the EC* (Commission, 1991). (The poor quality of the English text makes this difficult to read.)

5. Agriculture and the environment. Article 130R of the Single European Act establishes the following aims:
(i) to preserve, protect and improve the quality of the environment;
(ii) to contribute towards protecting human health;
(iii) to ensure a prudent and rational utilization of natural resources.
It specifies that *"preventive action should be taken, that environmental damage should as a priority be rectified at source, and that the polluter should pay"*; also that *"environmental protection requirements shall be a component of the Community's other policies"*.

Application to farming of the "polluter pays principle" has so far proved difficult: the tendency is rather to pay farmers for practices considered desirable...

Environmental issues have received considerable attention in recent years. Most of these studies relate to particular countries. A useful review of the evolution of environmental policy in Denmark is given by A. Dubgaard in *The Danish Nitrate Policy in the 1980s* (Institute of Agricultural Economics, Copenhagen: 1991). General reports have been made by the London-based Institute for European Environmental Policy and by the World Wildlife Fund; Agra Europe (London) published in 1991 an (expensive) special report entitled *Agriculture and the Environment: How will the EC resolve the conflict?*. These sources will no doubt continue to produce studies in this field.

CHAPTER 11

FOOD POLICY AND THE SINGLE MARKET

There is no clear definition of "Food Policy". An OECD report of 1981 with this as its title listed its major characteristics as dealing with the food economy *as a whole*, recognising the "systematic character" of the food chain and its links with the rest of the economy. In 1990 another OECD report on *Agriculture and the Consumer* stressed the need for "coherent demand-oriented food policies" and gave a long list of objectives, in particular:

* Encouraging an efficient, competitive and environmentally sound farming industry;
* Providing a wide choice of foods at reasonable prices to consumers;
* Full recognition and balancing of producer and consumer interests in all elements of policy.

Food safety, informative labelling, consumer participation in policy decisions, education and information programmes on food, nutrition and health were among the other items. (See Appendix, item 1).

Such targets are partly covered by those of agricultural policy: the aims of the CAP set out in Article 39 of the Treaty of Rome refer to assuring "the availability of supplies" and ensuring "that supplies reach consumers at reasonable prices". The products directly subject to the CAP (in Annex II of the Treaty) include farm produce and the results of *"first-stage"* processing (such as flour, sugar and dairy produce): but measures taken under common market organisation affect the entire food chain. In most countries the relevant government department is a "Ministry of Agriculture and Food". In the EC Commission, the Directorate-General for Agriculture (DG VI) is in principle responsible for implementing all the aims of the CAP, but food legislation is handled by DG III

(Internal Market): differences of view can arise. DG IV is responsible for Competition.

Whatever the administrative structure, it is undeniable that in national agricultural policies and under the CAP, farmer-oriented aims have predominated. Consumer representation in policy-making has been weak where it comes in conflict with farming interests: it plays a greater role in the more technical aspects of food legislation.

The topics discussed in this chapter are disparate: in fact, there is really no consistent "food policy" but rather a collection of different types of action. Among the subjects discussed here, competition policy and the EC's "Single Market" are in fact policies in themselves, whose scope extends well beyond their impact on the food sector.

The EC's involvement in food law arises primarily from the aim of achieving free movement of produce between the Member States: "harmonisation" of legislation is therefore discussed here, including measures relating to plant and animal health.

(a) Food subsidies

When prices are supported above market-clearing levels, consumers are subsidising farmers, though this may not be obvious. "Deficiency payments", or direct income support to farmers, have advantages over market support: besides permitting market signals to guide production, they shift the burden of support from consumers to taxpayers, through national (or EC) budgets. As taxation is to some extent "progressive", bearing more heavily on the higher incomes, this is in principle a more equitable system than price support which, by raising the unit cost of food, is proportionately a heavier burden on low-income households. In the CAP, there are product-based direct payments for some products; direct income payments, so far limited, will become more important under the "Mac-Sharry" reforms, while prices will be reduced. In the US, deficiency payments are important for major crops (cf. Chapter 12).

In some cases, the cost of food, having been raised through price support to farmers, is then reduced to consumers through subsidies. Such subsidies have been introduced not so much in the consumer interest as in order to dispose of surpluses. Various EC subsidies on butter and skim milk powder, and occasionally beef, are cases in point. In no case do EC subsidies come near to compensating for the whole increase in food costs to the consumer arising from price support to the farm sector.

Likewise, though the EC has a programme of subsidies for "school milk", and though various schemes exist at the level of the Member States, there are no welfare *food* subsidies comparable in scope to the "Food Stamp" programme in the United States (see Chapter 12). Western European governments apparently take the view that overall social welfare programmes are a better way to deal with problems that arise among poor people.

(b) Nutritional guidelines

In several countries, particularly in North-Western Europe and North America, the health authorities have issued dietary advice, aimed primarily at reducing obesity, heart disease and cancer. Although this has been based on many expert studies, none of it is entirely uncontroversial. The main recommendations may be summarised as follows:

* Overall food intake should not be greater than is needed for energy expenditure.
* As fat is a concentrated energy source, total fat intake should be decreased; because of suspected links with coronary heart disease, "saturated" fat (mostly animal fats) should be partially replaced by "polyunsaturated".
* Sugar is also a concentrated energy source, and a cause of tooth decay: excess consumption should be avoided.
* Dietary fibre helps to prevent certain gastro-intestinal diseases: its intake should be increased.
* Excess salt can contribute to diseases of the circulatory system: its intake should be reduced.

As individual needs vary, such recommendations have generally stopped short of specifying precise intake levels. Some recent reports have been particularly cautious, such as that published by the British Department of Health in 1991, which avoided any mention of "recommendations" and preferred to speak of "reference values" (see Appendix, item 2).

At the EC level, there was an attempt in a Council of Health Ministers in 1990 to establish an "action programme" on nutrition: nothing came of it, and it is now unlikely that this will be pursued.

Official guidelines have to some extent influenced the public's eating habits, and health-conscious consumers are numerous enough to make it worthwhile for food stores to offer foods such as low-fat dairy produce, "low-cholesterol" margarine based on sunflower oil, wholemeal bread or unhusked rice, etc., quite apart from the offerings of specialised "health food" shops. On the other hand, there is increased consumption—especially among young people—of "junk foods" eaten on the move rather than at meals, such as potato crisps (which are high in both fat and salt) and sweetened soft drinks.

(c) Competition policy

Chapter 3 has discussed the trend towards concentration in the food industry and the need to protect consumers against monopolistic practices. Competition policy raises complex legal and economic issues, which cannot easily be treated in a short space. Issues involved relate to acquisitions and mergers, but also to various practices which may be held to interfere with competition. Most countries with market economies have developed legislation and institutions, taking a variety of forms, intended to preserve the public interest in such matters.

i) The United States

In the US, "anti-trust" legislation has a particularly long history, with the Sherman Act of 1890 providing a vital legal basis. The Clayton Act of 1914 outlawed mergers which might substantially lessen competition. The Robinson-Patman Act, passed in 1936 during the Great Depression, was designed to protect small businesses: its main provision, making it unlawful for firms to discriminate in price between different purchasers if the effect was to lessen competition, has been the basis for many subsequent legal actions. This body of legislation has probably helped to prevent the emergence of outright monopolies or of abusive monopolistic practices, although under the Republican administrations of the 1980s, the climate seems to have been more permissive with regard to some very large mergers.

In the absence of outright monopoly, a small number of firms may through joint conduct behave similarly to a single dominant firm. The US anti-trust laws did not provide an adequate safeguard against such practices. The concept of "shared monopoly" was developed to close this gap, and was first applied in 1972 in the "Kellogg case", when the Federal Trade Commission charged the three largest manufacturers of breakfast cereals with obtaining enormous monopoly profits through tacit collusion, involving massive advertising (12% of sales), the production of an undue number of brands, and agreements to allocate shelf space in retail shops. The accusations, however, could not be proved: US law seems to remain inadequate in this respect.

ii) Western European countries

The **United Kingdom** has a relatively high degree of concentration in the food industry. An important step in ensuring competition was the passing in 1964 of the Resale Prices Act, which prevented food manufacturers from imposing prices on retailers. Under the Fair Trading Act of 1973, proposed mergers can, upon the advice of the Office of Fair Trading, be referred to the Monopolies and Mergers Commission (MMC) for consideration of the impact on the public interest. A merger qualifies for investigation if the gross assets acquired are £30 million or more, or if, as a result of the merger, the enterprises will together account for 25% or more of the supply or acquisition of particular goods or services in the UK. The ultimate decision, however, is political, lying with the Secretary of State for Trade and Industry.

In practice, only a small proportion of mergers which fall within this qualification are referred to the MMC—less than 5% over the years. Outright refusals by the MMC have been rare: an important case, however, was that of a proposed merger between Tate & Lyle and British Sugar which would have resulted in a single company refining and distributing about 95% of sugar supplied to the UK market.

A major reason why many mergers between UK food and drink manufacturers have *not* been referred has been the buying-power of the major retailers. By developing their own brands, as has been described in Chapter 3, the big food chains can put pressure on their usual suppliers, often obtaining large discounts. The Office of Fair Trading has concluded that competition between retailers has caused the benefits of special discounts and similar practices to be passed on to consumers. It is recognised, however, that the issue of retailers' power must be kept under review.

Among other EC Member States, legislation varies in extent and effectiveness. **Germany** has quite far-reaching provisions under the Cartel Act of 1980, which imposes a general ban on restrictive practices; dominant firms are supervised to prevent abuse; and mergers can be forbidden if they seem likely to bring about a dominant position. In **France**, concerted practices liable to restrict competition may be forbidden, and the activities of dominant companies or groups can be prohibited if they inhibit the normal functioning of the market.

iii) The European Community

With the growth in cross-border activities, the need for action at the Community level has become increasingly evident. Several food industries—confectionery, chocolate, flour and "pasta"—have been identified as being among those where rationalisation and European-scale mergers in the Single Market context could bring economies of scale, but also risks of reduced competition.

The Treaty of Rome provided a basis for action. **Article 85** prohibits agreements between undertakings which may affect trade between Member States and which affect competition. This provision can be applied to "horizontal" arrangements whereby different firms engaged in the same type of enterprise restrict competition. Such cartels—possibly disguised—are more likely to arise where a homogeneous product is concerned, and at first-stage processing, than for the branded and differentiated goods which make up the greater part of the food trade: in the early stages of the EC, this legislation was invoked against sugar refineries. Article 85 may also be applied to "vertical" arrangements, whereby a supplier attempts to commit his retail channels to sell his product only: a case in 1992 related to the sale of ice-cream in Germany (see Appendix, item 3).

Article 86 of the Treaty aims to prevent the abuse of a "dominant position" in any product market. This text provided an insufficient basis for the control of mergers, but with the prospect of the "Single Market" (see below), more far-reaching legislation was adopted in 1989. The Mergers Regulation recognises that the dismantling of internal frontiers is causing increased concentration: it accepts that such development can promote "dynamic competition", but aims to prevent "lasting damage to competition". "Concentrations" are defined to cover both mergers and acquisitions, but not "co-ordination of competitive behaviour" (including "joint ventures"), which however may require investigation under the Article 85 procedure. Proposed concentrations must be notified to the Commission if they have a "Community dimension": i.e. a world-wide turnover exceeding 5 billion ECU and an EC turnover exceeding 250 million ECU. Cases where each of the parties concerned has two-thirds or more of its turnover within a single Member State are *excluded* from Commission competence.

The main case relating to the food industry requiring detailed examination concerned the take-over in 1992 of Perrier, the French producer of mineral water, by the Swiss food group Nestlé. As both Perrier and Nestlé already owned several other French mineral waters, Nestlé together with BSN, the other major producer, would have had a "duopoly" in the French market. The Commission agreed to the acquisition only on condition that Nestlé should sell off some of its mineral water brands, amounting to about 20% of the market, to a "third force". Even after this sale, Nestlé and BSN will have about two-thirds of the French market.

Also in 1992, the Commission considered a proposed joint venture by the Danish company Carlsberg and the British firm Allied Lyons to combine their brewing interests in the UK (where the five biggest brewers already controlled 80% of the market). This was accepted, but on condition that Allied's retail outlets (the "pubs") should have greater freedom to purchase from other brewers.

The existence of the Mergers Regulation should have a deterrent effect, quite apart from cases actually referred. In general, the Commission has taken the view that competition in the food sector remains sufficiently strong, but that the continuing process of concentration calls for vigilance.

An important guarantee of the consumer interest is provided by free trade: international competition makes monopolistic power and restrictive practices more difficult. Within the European Community, although the traditional protectionist measures—customs duties and quantitative restrictions—have been abolished, "non-tariff barriers" have remained significant for foodstuffs and for some agricultural inputs. Attempts to remove such barriers, especially in the 1992 "Single Market" context, are thus significant.

(d) "The Single Market"

A White Paper issued by the Commission in 1985 set out the aim of completing a "fully unified internal market" by 1992: an aim which implied "the abolition of barriers of all kinds, harmonisation of rules, approximation of legislation and tax structures, strengthening of monetary cooperation and the necessary flanking measures to encourage European firms to work together".

The **Single European Act** of 1986 modified the Treaty of Rome in a number of respects, strengthening the role of the European Parliament, reinforcing cooperation in monetary policy, adding the aim of "economic and social cohesion" (in favour of the poorer Member States), adding new provisions on promoting research and technological development and on environment policy; it also provided for "European cooperation in the sphere of foreign policy". (See Appendix, item 4).

The Act laid down the aim of "progressively establishing the internal market over a period expiring on 31 December 1992", declaring that "the internal market shall comprise an area without internal frontiers in which the free movement of goods, persons, services and capital is ensured".

The persistence of barriers to intra-EC trade, and the potential benefits from their removal, were stressed in a report produced in 1988 at the request of the

Commission on *The Cost of Non-Europe* (the "Cecchini Report"), one volume of which concerned the foodstuffs sector. It found that in just ten product sectors, there remained over 200 non-tariff barriers. Typical barriers included the following:

* Rules prohibiting the sale of a product containing specific ingredients.
* Rules preventing a producer from using a generic name unless its product conforms to certain requirements as to content.
* Rules as to how goods are packaged and labelled.
* Taxes which discriminate against imported produce.
* Various procedures which complicate imports, including import licenses, health registration requirements, border inspections, etc.

The Cecchini Report found that such barriers had been increasing in number in previous years. Sometimes when the Commission had ruled against a national regulation, the Member State concerned had side-stepped by replacing the regulation with another having similar effect.

Direct and quantifiable benefits from removing such trade barriers would arise from the use of less expensive ingredients, reductions in labelling and packaging costs, and elimination of bureaucratic "red tape". The Cecchini Report estimated such benefits, for the ten product sectors studied, at some 500–1000 million ECU, or 2–3% of value-added in the industry. Much of this would come from the removal of just a few barriers. Top of the list were restrictions in Germany, France, Luxembourg and Greece on the use of vegetable fat in ice-cream; laws in Italy, France and Greece regulating the content of *pasta*; laws in Italy, Spain and Greece on saccharimetric content in beer; restrictions in Italy on the use of plastic containers for mineral waters and soft drinks.

The most profound impact could come from *indirect* benefits: widening of consumer choice, increase of trade, increased efficiency in manufacturing. Consolidation of the German beer industry was given as a particular example of the latter: there were still about 1200 separate breweries in Germany, and the report considered that consolidation, and a move to national rather than locally-brewed brands, would produce economies of scale.

Finally, the Cecchini Report stressed the pace of world-wide change in the food industry, and concluded that restructuring in the single market would improve the competitiveness of EC firms.

The removal of non-tariff barriers within the EC is dependent on harmonisation of legislation: this will be discussed next.

(e) "Harmonisation"

The *Codex Alimentarius*, established in 1962 by the World Health Organization and the Food and Agriculture Organization, provides a set of food standards which are widely accepted internationally, with the aim of protecting consumer health and ensuring fair practices in the food trade. These standards define the composition of a wide range of commodities and set out recommended technological practices.

As between EC Member States, however, national standards differed widely, and often constituted serious barriers to trade. The Commission initially sought to harmonise standards on the basis of Article 100 of the Treaty of Rome, which provides for "Directives for the approximation of such provisions... in Member States as directly affect the establishment or functioning of the common market". The first item of legislation in this field, in 1962, substantially reduced the number of permitted food colourings. In 1969, the Commission put forward a long list of foodstuffs for harmonisation. But in some Member States (particularly the UK), the whole concept of "Euro-standards" imposed by Brussels became very unpopular. Moreover, unanimity in the Council of Ministers was required to adopt the proposed Directives: progress was very slow. By 1985 only two-fifths of the programme originally planned for 1969–73, and later extended in time, had been implemented.

Rulings by the European Court of Justice played a key role in subsequent developments. The most significant ruling, in 1979, concerned the French blackcurrant liqueur known as *Cassis de Dijon*. Germany was prohibiting its import, as its alcohol content was less than that required by German laws. On the basis of Article 30 of the Treaty of Rome, which prohibits "quantitative restrictions on imports and *all measures having equivalent effect*" as between Member States, the Court ruled that the import ban must be removed. Although Article 36 of the Treaty permits restrictions on certain grounds including "protection of health and life of humans, animals or plants", this condition was not satisfied in the *Cassis de Dijon* case.

The principle of **"mutual recognition"** was thus established, implying that products that have been "lawfully produced and marketed" in one Member State must be accepted if exported to another Member State. Although in the *Cassis de Dijon* case reference was made to an item "produced and marketed", and this is the phrase usually quoted, it follows from basic EC legislation that the principle of mutual recognition must apply also to produce that has been imported from a non- EC country, if it complies with the rules existing in the importing Member State: such produce is then in "free circulation" within the Community. (See Appendix, item 5.)

In judging whether a reference to Article 36 of the Treaty justifies a restriction, an important criterion is that of **"proportionality"**: national measures restricting imports should be limited to what is necessary to attain the legitimate aim of protecting health (the Court has pointed out that proper labelling may be sufficient). In 1988 the Court upheld a challenge to the German beer laws (*Reinheitsgebot*), which were preventing imports, as the German authorities had failed to prove that there was a risk to health sufficient to justify this measure.

Many of the barriers to intra-EC trade arising from differing national regulations should thus disappear as traders take advantage of the principle of mutual recognition.

With this background, a "new approach" to harmonisation of national laws became possible. The Commission's 1985 White Paper on the Internal Market

was accompanied by a Communication on foodstuffs, which stated that further proposals would be limited to those justified by the need to:
* promote public health;
* provide consumers with information and protection in matters other than health;
* ensure fair trading;
* provide for the necessary public controls.
In a further Communication, in 1989, the Commission explained that its strategy "essentially consists in combining the adoption of harmonised rules at Community level, which are applicable to all foodstuffs marketed in the Community, with the principle of mutual recognition of national regulations and standards for matters which do not require the adoption of Community legislative measures".

The chances of adoption of Commission proposals were reinforced by a new Article 100A added to the Treaty of Rome by the Single European Act: this substituted "qualified majority" voting in the Council for the unanimity rule. This Article also specified that Commission proposals "concerning health, safety, environmental protection and consumer protection, will take as a base a high level of protection."

About twenty "horizontal" harmonisation measures in the food and drink sector (some of which amend previous legislation), were proposed under the new approach, in the context of the aim to complete the "Single Market" by the end of 1992. Besides legislation in the food sector, there is also a substantial programme of harmonisation related to animal and plant health. The measures are too numerous to be described in detail: only the main categories are outlined below (see however Appendix, item 6). In most cases, the recent measures are not entirely new but reinforce earlier legislation.

i) Food safety laws

"Horizontal" measures include the following:
* **Labelling, presentation and advertising.** The scope of previous legislation has been extended to restaurants and other catering establishments. Labels on foodstuffs should indicate the quantities of the main ingredients; perishable products should have a durability ("use by...") date; treatment by irradiation must be indicated.
* **Additives.** For the various types of additive (colourings, emulsifiers, preservatives, sweeteners, etc.), a "positive list" of accepted additives is established, any others being illegal. The general principle is that additives can be approved only if they correspond to a "reasonable technological need" and "present no hazard to the health of the consumer".
* **Materials in contact with foodstuffs.** The aim is to avoid any contamination of foodstuffs by the packaging material which could endanger human health. The framework Directive is backed up by specific Commission measures relating to particular materials.

* **Foods "for particular nutritional uses".** Such foods must fulfil the nutritional requirements of persons with special needs, or of infants and young children; they must be suitable for their claimed purpose. Foodstuffs for normal consumption must not be advertised as "dietary".
* **Official control.** The purpose here is to establish equivalence between the various systems of enforcement in the Member States.

Besides these horizontal measures, and despite the reluctance of the Commission's DG III to propose vertical harmonisation, legislation has continued to be applied to some particular types of product: this has concerned the labelling and content of alcoholic drinks (e.g. the definitions of "gin", "rum", "whisky" etc.), of coffee extracts, fruit juices and jams.

ii) Food quality

This is a more recent and even more controversial field of legislation than food safety. Legislation in this field, initiated by DG VI, appears to have been motivated more by concern for producers than consumers: the first significant Commission reference to promoting food quality occurred in its 1988 document *A Future for Rural Society*, which—in the context of CAP reform—sought to reassure the farming community. Pressure for legislation arose mainly from French interests, bearing in mind France's experience with the *appellation contrôlée* system for wine and cheese; and was supported mainly by the Southern European countries.

The multiplicity of national quality labels and symbols, and the risk of fraudulent advertisement of produce possessing no particular quality, suggests a need for denominations that can be applied and recognised Community-wide.

On the other hand, there is a substantial body of opinion, particularly in the food industry and in the northern Member States, and shared by the BEUC (*Bureau européen des unions de consommateurs*, which tends to represent a northern point of view), to the effect that *quality* is not an appropriate subject for legislation. It is held to be a subjective concept, which cannot be objectively defined; provided foods are clearly and accurately labelled, market forces will give a premium to the produce which consumers like best.

Nevertheless, Commission proposals were finally adopted in July 1992, and provide for the following:

* **Geographical indications.** Two types of geographical description are instituted: "protected designation of origin" (PDO) and "protected geographical indication" (PGI). In the former case, the quality or characteristics of the product must be "essentially or exclusively" due to a particular geographic environment; in the latter case, they need only be "attributable" to the geographic origin. (The distinction, which is not clear, seems to arise from existing practices in some Member States.)
* **Certificates of "special character".** This should enable producer groups to register a product as having a specific character which distinguishes it clearly from other similar products belonging to the same category.

This legislation remains controversial. A difficult problem arises as regards produce whose name originally referred to a geographic area, but which has come to be produced much more widely and to be recognised by the public as designating the name of the product rather than its place of origin. There are many examples. "Cheddar" cheese began in a region of England, but the name is now used in many countries; a more recent case is that of "*feta*" cheese, a traditional Greek product which Denmark has begun to manufacture and export. The Regulation on geographical indications provides that "names that have become generic may not be registered", and attempts to define criteria in this respect: the Commission is to draw up an "indicative" list of generic products, but this will not be easy.

iii) Veterinary controls

In its 1985 White Paper on the completion of the internal market, the Commission stated that in order to abolish the health checks of animal products at the internal borders of the Community, the necessary controls would have to be limited to the places of dispatch only, apart from spot checks on arrival or in transit. Conditions for placing produce from third countries on the EC market, whilst ensuring a "high level" of consumer protection, should be equivalent to those applied to EC produce.

To this end, since 1985, previous legislation has been reinforced; final decisions by the Agriculture Council in December 1992 enabled all remaining intra-EC frontier controls to be removed with entry into force of the Single Market on 1 January 1993. The following fields are covered:

* **Veterinary checks in intra-EC trade.** Directive 89/662 aims to ensure that necessary checks are carried out at the place of dispatch. This measure applies to most products of animal origin (listed in an Annex to the Directive). Another Directive lays down the principles for veterinary checks on products entering the EC from third countries.
* **Animal health.** Numerous measures have been adopted to control various livestock diseases, in particular brucellosis and tuberculosis in cattle, and swine fever.
* **Public health.** This includes "horizontal" measures establishing minimum hygiene conditions to be met by slaughter-houses etc., providing for the control of chemical residues in livestock products, banning the use in livestock farming of growth- promoting hormones, and other measures. There are also numerous "vertical" measures applying to particular product groups: these include rules on milk products, meat preparations, poultrymeat, game and rabbit meat, and fishery products.

iv) Plant health controls

Legislation aims to ensure that food from plants is safe for consumers and to prevent the introduction or spreading of harmful organisms. As with veterinary controls, harmonisation should avoid the need for border controls, by carrying out controls only at the place of departure; imported produce should be checked only on arrival in EC territory. Since 1985, former legislation has been reinforced particularly in the following respects:

* **Protection against the introduction and spread of organisms harmful to plants.** To this effect, a framework Directive adopted in 1991 established plant health standards for trade within the EC and to imports from third countries. Subsequent legislation has listed harmful organisms, laid down specific protection measures, etc.

* **Plant protection substances.** Only substances on "positive" lists are authorised. To allow free trade in plant products, maximum levels of pesticide residues have been fixed for cereals, fruit and vegetables, foodstuffs of animal origin and animal feed.

* Rules on the production, control and labelling of **organic foodstuffs** (already referred to in Chapter 10). At present, this relates only to the vegetable sector, but the Commission is working on a proposal to include products of animal origin. Rules have been adopted for granting third country products the status of organic products.

*　　*　　*

Despite the Commission's "new approach" since 1985, harmonisation remains a sensitive issue in public opinion: the earlier "Euro-recipe" controversies have not been forgotten, and some such legislation remains in force. The benefits of accurate labelling, or of the various controls which are less obvious to consumers, are rarely associated with the EC. Some recent initiatives have been misunderstood (often deliberately misrepresented by the media).

The controversy provoked during 1992 over ratification of the "Maastricht" Treaty, which has resulted in efforts to curb the power of "Brussels" and to promote the principle of "subsidiarity" (i.e., legislating at the EC level only when national legislation does not suffice) now makes the Commission prudent as regards further harmonisation. In fact, the "1992" programme has any case been completed, barring just a few exceptions. Major new initiatives in this field seem unlikely for some time to come, the accent now being placed on enforcement and management of existing legislation.

APPENDIX

1. Food policy. The OECD reports referred to are: *Food Policy* (Paris, 1981) and *Agriculture and the Consumer* (Paris, 1990). Both these are rather general and vague.

2. Nutritional standards: A convenient review is given by T.R. Gormley *et al.*, "Food, Health and the Consumer", in *Prospects for the European Food System*, ed. B. Traill (Elsevier, London and New York, 1989).

The report by the British Department of Health is *Dietary Reference Values for Food Energy and Nutrients for the United Kingdom* (HMSO, London: 1991). This indicated, for instance, energy needs at 2550 kcal./day for adult males and 1,940 kcal./day for adult females as *average* requirements, on the grounds that excess intake can be harmful by causing over-weight. For all other nutrients (e.g. protein at 55 gr./day for adult males and 45 gr./day for adult females), "reference nutrient intakes" were set at the *upper* end of the range of require-ments, because an intake moderately in excess has no adverse effects but reduces the risk of deficiency. The report stresses that none of its "reference values" are necessarily valid for a particular individual.

3. EC competition policy. A general review of *national* legislation was given in the Commission's "Studies Collection", Commerce and Distribution Series no.10, *Measures taken in the field of commerce by the Member States of the European Communities* (1985). The Treaty of Rome includes a section containing "rules applying to undertakings", the operative provisions being those of Article 85 on restrictive practices and Article 86 on "abuse of dominant positions". The "Mergers Regulation" no. 4064/89 on "the control of concentrations between undertakings" is published in the *Official Journal of the European Communities*, no. L395 of 30.12.89 (pp.1-13). A "Commission Notice" clarifying the dis-tinction between concentrations and "co-operative" situations, in particular "joint ventures", was published in the *Official Journal*, no. C203 of 14.8.90 (pp.11-15).

An analysis covering various industrial sectors appears in A. Jacquemin *et al.*, "Horizontal mergers and competition policy in the European Community", *European Economy* no. 40, May 1989.

The Commission publishes an annual report, *Competition Policy*, which includes the food industry.

Under Article 85 of the Rome Treaty, the Commission took "interim measures" in March 1992 to prevent the two main German ice-cream producers—Langnese Iglo (part of the Unilever group) and Schöller—from enforcing contracts whereby retailers accepting their products were obliged to buy exclusively from them. The case had been brought by Mars, on the grounds that these contracts damaged the sales of its own ice-cream chocolate bars. Under another restrictive practice, manufacturers provide retailers with freezing cabinets which may only be used for these manufacturers' products.

4. The Single Market. The Single European Act is available as Supplement 2/86 to the Commission's *Bulletin of the European Communities*. In the *European Documentation* series, a 1991 report discusses "Consumer Policy in the Single Market", with brief reference to foodstuffs. A short but useful account of the Single Market aims was provided in another Commission brochure *Opening up the Internal Market*: this was completed in June 1991, but will no doubt be followed by similar publications.

The "Cecchini Report" is officially called *Research on the "Cost of Non-Europe"* (Com-mission, 1988). This includes several volumes: see especially the "Executive Summary" on the foodstuffs industry in Volume 1 ("Basic Findings").

5. Mutual recognition. The most relevant European Court cases are:
—Judgement of 20 February 1979 in Case 120/79 (Cassis de Dijon): [1979] ECR 649;
—Judgement of 14 July 1983 in Case 174/82 (Sandoz): [1983] ECR 2445;
—Judgement of 12 March 1987 in Cases 176/84 and 178/84 (Beer): [1987] ECR 1213 and 1262.
(ECR stands for "European Court Reporter".)

As regards third countries: the *Cassis de Dijon* case concerned an item produced and market-ing in an EC Member State; the Sandoz case confirmed the application of the mutual recog-nition principle to an item containing ingredients imported from a third country (Switzerland). Previously, in the Donckerwolke case (no. 41/76 [1976] ECR 1921), the Court had stated that *"according to Article 9(2) [of the Treaty of Rome] the provisions adopted for the liberalisation of intra-Community trade apply in identical fashion to products originating in member-States and to products coming from non-member countries which are in "free circulation" in the Community".*

6. Harmonisation. Note that the English text of Article 100 of the Treaty of Rome refers to "approximation", an incorrect translation of *"rapprochement"* in French or *"Angleichung"* in German. This misuse has passed into secondary legislation.

On the evolution of EC food law, see P. Gray, "Food law and the internal market", *Food Policy*, April 1990. The Commission's 1989 "Communication on the free movement of foodstuffs within the Community" appears in the *Official Journal* no. C271 of 24.1.89.

There is background material also in International Business Intelligence, *1992—Planning for the Food Industry* (Butterworths, London etc.: 1989).

The state of implementation of the Single Market provisions is documented annually in detail in a set of Commission reports under the general title *Completing the Internal Market*: volume 4 includes foodstuffs, and volume 5 deals with veterinary and plant health controls. On-line consultation of the "INFO 92" data-base provides up-to-date information. As there are numerous Council acts, as well as Commission implementing measures, these sources should be referred to if a complete list is needed. Most of the relevant Directives and Regulations have been subject to successive amendments: however, the Commission is due to publish "consolidated" texts. References to former texts will therefore not be given here.

Two monthly publications by Agra Europe (London), though expensive, are valuable to those who have to keep regularly in touch with this area: *Eurofood* and *EC Food Law*. A special Agra Europe report—*A Single Market in the E.C.: Implications for the international food and agribusiness industries* (1992)—is expensive and aimed mainly at agribusiness firms.

The "Club de Bruxelles" (run by specialised journalists) has published two reports by Jacqueline Smith: *The Community Agri-Food Industry in the Single Market* (1990), and *The Quality of Agri-Food Products in Europe* (1992): these too are expensive (academic discounts are available), but the second in particular is the best available account of recent legislation.

CHAPTER 12

OTHER DEVELOPED MARKET ECONOMIES

The previous chapters have mainly concerned the European Economic Community. Other countries will be discussed in this chapter, most very briefly, but more attention will be given to the United States.

To give a general view of the extent of government intervention, Figure 12.1 shows calculations made by the OECD of "producer subsidy equivalents". The PSE measures "the value of the monetary transfers to farmers from consumers of agricultural products and from taxpayers resulting from agricultural policy". Market price support—including "administered prices", tariffs and levies on imports, import quotas—is the main component in most countries; direct payments may also be an element (particularly in the US in view of the role of "deficiency payments" there—see below).

(a) EFTA countries

The European Free Trade Association, unlike the EC, has not attempted to create a common market in agriculture nor to set up a common agricultural policy; nor does the 1992 agreement on the European Economic Area covering EFTA and the EC. As has been seen in Chapter 8, most of the countries now in EFTA have a long history of agricultural protectionism, and in most cases, their levels of price support are higher than those in the EC. They have been faced with the same problems of oversupply, and have also introduced production quotas and other measures in an attempt to restore market balance.

Austria provides price supports; imports of main products are regulated by commodity boards; exports are subsidised. There are production quotas for milk, sugarbeet and wheat. Mountain farming receives special subsidies.

Switzerland likewise supports prices, restricts imports and subsidises export of some products. Supply controls are in force for milk, rapeseed and sugar.

Figure 12.1—Producer Subsidy Equivalents
(as percentages of the value of production, 1990)

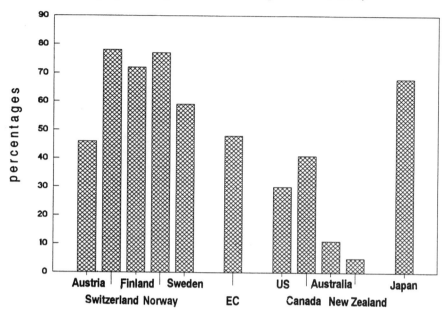

Notes and source: see Appendix, item 2.

Direct payments are used to supplement farm incomes, principally in the mountain regions.

Finland maintains a very high price level through export subsidies and strict border measures including quantitative restrictions, variable import levies and import licensing. Supply controls include a short-term land retirement programme and milk production quotas.

Norway supports prices to producers, partly by deficiency payments; strict border measures include tariffs and quantitative restrictions; exports are subsidised. Milk production is subject to quotas.

Sweden supports prices, with variable import levies and export subsidies. A fallowing scheme to discourage cereal production has been in operation. In 1990 it was decided to phase out price supports over a five-year period, and export subsidies over three years, compensating farmers through direct income payments, while changes in border protection would be subject to an overall agreement in the GATT Uruguay Round. Measures to protect the rural environment are significant.

The above countries (Iceland and Liechtenstein are the other EFTA members) have submitted applications to join the EC, though the Swiss position is uncertain following the referendum in December in which membership of the EEA was rejected. Those countries which join will have to accept the CAP as it stands when they join—including the implications of the 1992 reform decisions. Sweden will have to re-introduce market intervention mechanisms for cereals and other products, and apply the EC system of withdrawals for fruit and vegetables. The other countries will have to reduce their degree of protection. Switzerland and Austria have long traditions of intervention on behalf of their farmers, partly to ensure self-sufficiency in food for security reasons, partly because of a widely-held belief in the social value of the farming community, especially in the mountain regions. In the case of Norway and Finland, important aims have been to maintain population in the northern and eastern areas close to the former Soviet Union. These aims will not be easy to reconcile with the more market-oriented adjustments taking place under the CAP: the role and scope of compensatory payments will be a crucial consideration.

(b) The United States

Developments in the **United States** need more attention, partly because the EC is now adopting mechanisms similar to those of US agricultural policy, and especially because of the leading role played by the US in trade negotiations.

i) Evolution

As was pointed out in Chapter 8, intervention began during the 1930s in the context of the "New Deal". In 1948 the Commodity Credit Corporation (CCC) was given the task of "stabilising, supporting and protecting farm incomes and prices, of assisting in the maintenance of balanced and adequate supplies of agricultural commodities... and of facilitating the orderly distribution of agricultural commodities".

Price support for most major commodities was "mandatory", and the level of price support was related to the concept of "parity"—originally defined in terms of the relationship between prices paid and received in 1910–14 (regarded as a favourable period). So-called "non-recourse loans" were the main instrument of price support (see below).

When surplus problems re-appeared, an initial response was the "Soil Bank" of 1956. This had two components. An "Acreage Reserve" provided for one-year contracts under which farmers received compensation for taking land out of use: this proved extremely costly in relation to the results obtained, and was discontinued after the 1958 crop. The "Conservation Reserve" provided for longer-term diversion of land into permanent grass, trees, water storage or wildlife encouragement: similar provisions have been continued under subsequent legislation.

More effective supply controls were required. In the 1960s, together with a reduction in price supports, "acreage diversion payments" were offered to encourage farmers to take land out of feed grain, wheat and cotton: but "mandatory" supply controls were rejected by producers in a referendum in 1963. From 1964 on, farmers were offered benefits if they complied with *voluntary* acreage controls: this, however, was expensive and not very effective. In 1970 a "set-aside" programme was introduced whereby farmers were required to take a percentage of land out of grain and cotton *as a condition* of eligibility for price support. However, the 1970s were a period of expanding exports, including exports to the USSR, with high world prices, and efforts at supply control were relaxed.

After 1981, with renewed difficulties on export markets, farm incomes declined. The 1981 "Agriculture and Food Act" instituted minimum target prices, to increase by about 6% annually in line with expected inflation. But in fact, the rate of inflation declined, while surplus stocks increased, and the costs of support began to escalate. The "Food Security Act" (FSA) of 1985 marked a shift towards a more "market-oriented" policy (though the legislation adopted by Congress was less drastic than the Reagan administration had proposed). Under the FSA, price supports were to be progressively reduced, and acreage reduction was made a condition for support. Partly because of these policy changes, partly because of severe drought in 1988, costs of support, after hitting a peak of nearly $26 billion in 1986, came down to $6.5 billion by 1990, as expenditure on price-support "loans" was virtually eliminated (see Figure 12.2).

Figure 12.2—US: costs of commodity support programmes (fiscal years)

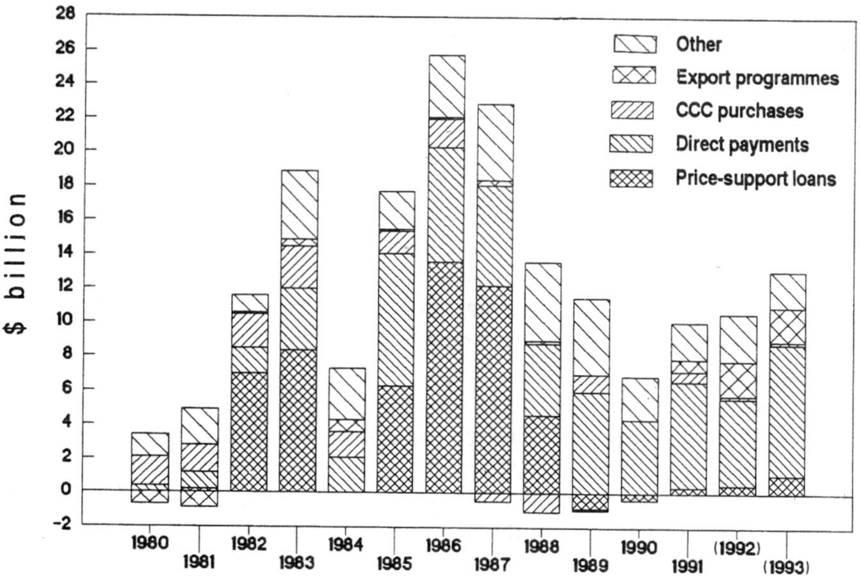

Source: USDA, *Agricultural Outlook*, October 1992. Data are for "fiscal" years, i.e. ending on 30 June of the year indicated. 1992 and 1993 data are estimates in the President's Budget for fiscal 1993, based on November 1991 supply and demand estimates.
"Conservation" programmes, rural development and consumer services such as the Food Stamp programme are not included.

The 1990 "Food, Agriculture, Conservation and Trade Act" (FACT) relaxed some of restrictions on price support (see below), while giving farmers greater flexibility in planting to respond to market forces. Budget preoccupations remained, however, and were reflected in the "Omnibus Budget Reconciliation Act" (OBRA), adopted by Congress at the same time as FACT: this amended some provisions of FACT so as to reduce total programme costs by some $13 billion from the original estimate of $54 billion over the five years 1991–95.

ii) Main commodity programmes

The price support systems are complex. The following is a brief and simplified account (see sources in the Appendix, item 1, for further details).

Cereals and cotton

The main elements are as follows (see also Table 12.1):
* **"Target prices"**: these were reduced during the 1980s. Under FACT, they are frozen during 1991–95.
* **"Loan rates"**: i.e. prices at which producers can hand their produce over to the Commodity Credit Corporation, obtaining "non-recourse loans", with the option of reclaiming the produce later if prices improve. Loan rates thus act as a "floor" under the market. They are determined annually on the basis of 85% of the average market prices of the previous five years, excluding the highest and the lowest, subject however to adjustment by reference to the ratio of stocks to utilisation. After reductions before 1990, this formula has subsequently led to increases, and higher expenditure on "loans" is expected in "fiscal" 1993 (i.e. 1992/93—cf. Figure 12.2).
  For cotton, rice, and since 1990 for soyabeans, there are "marketing loans", under which non-recourse loans can be repaid at world market prices if these are lower than market prices: in effect, these are export subsidies.
* **"Deficiency payments"**: these are paid to eligible farmers to make up the difference between the market price (or the loan rate, if this should be higher) and the target price. Deficiency payments have become the main item in support costs (Figure 12.2). However, an upwards drift in rates of payment is avoided by referring to "program yields", which have been frozen, rather than actual yields.
* The benefit of loan rates and deficiency payments is available only to farmers who comply with specified **acreage reductions**: the land in question cannot be used for other crops and must usually be devoted to approved conservation practices. The size of the reduction is determined annually on the basis of the ratio of stocks to total use in the previous crop year. In 1992, as stocks had been substantially drawn down, the requirement was reduced, and there is no acreage reduction for the 1993 wheat crop; but for maize, following a record harvest in 1992 and rising stocks, the reduction goes back up (Table 12.1).
  There is no payment for the minimum acreage reduction, but farmers can opt for additional paid diversion. The "base" area for wheat and feed grains is the five-year moving average of land "considered planted" to the crop (this

Table 12.1—US: Price supports and acreage reductions

	Target price		Loan rate		Deficiency payment		Acreage reduction	
	Wheat	Maize	Wheat	Maize	Wheat	Maize	Wheat	Maize
	$ per bushel						*per cent*	
1987	4.38	3.03	2.28	1.82	1.81	1.09	27.5	20
1988	4.23	2.93	2.21	1.77	0.69	0.36	27.5	20
1989	4.10	2.84	2.06	1.65	0.32	0.58	10	10
1990	4.00	2.75	1.95	1.57	1.28	0.51	5	10
1991	4.00	2.75	2.04	1.62	1.35*	0.41	15	7.5
1992	4.00	2.75	2.21	1.72	0.65*	0.48*	5	5
1993	4.00	2.75	2.45	1.72	..	..	0	10
	$ per tonne							
1992	145	108	81	68	24*	19*		

Notes: The years indicated are those in which the crop is harvested: the prices apply over the following marketing year. Loan rates are the effective, not the basic rates. Acreage reductions are the minimum required for entitlement to programme benefits.
Source: USDA, *Agricultural Outlook*, November 1992 (Table 19).

includes land put into an approved conserving use); for rice and cotton, the average of previous three years is taken.

Partly to reduce budget costs, partly to permit greater flexibility, the FACT introduced the "triple base", whereby on 15% of each producer's base area he can grow any crop and is entitled to the loan rate if he chooses a crop to which loan rates apply; the OBRA however removed entitlement to deficiency payment on this 15% share. (The three elements of the "base" are the permitted area, on which the programme crop is planted and deficiency payments may be paid; the area which must be idled under the acreage reduction rules; and the 15% area on which flexibility is allowed. The total remains as the producer's "base" for subsequent years.) There is provision for additional flexibility between crops on 10% of the base, but without giving entitlement to programme benefits.

Over the years, an extensive system of supervision has been built up to check on compliance with acreage restrictions. Among other methods, aerial photography is used in combination with detailed information on land ownership and use.

Sugar

Production is protected by restrictive import quotas: in 1992, to bypass an adverse GATT ruling, these were transformed into "tariff quotas" with the same effect. Under the North American Free Trade Agreement (NAFTA), the US has generally granted to Mexico either immediate tariff-free entry for agricultural commodities or the conversion of non-tariff measures into tariffs and their gradual phasing-out: but for sugar, the US will use the full transitional period of fifteen years, and any increases in imports from Mexico will be at the expense of other sugar importers.

Milk

Production is supported by a minimum price, implemented mainly through CCC purchases of butter, milk powder and Cheddar cheese (these account for almost all the "purchases" item in Figure 12.2), and by import restrictions. The support price can be adjusted depending on the level of government purchases, but under the FACT cannot be less than a specified amount. The OBRA however imposed "assessments" (levies) on dairy producers at a rate of about 1% of the minimum price: these can be repaid to those who do not increase their deliveries. Producers can also be "assessed" the amount needed to reimburse the government for purchases of dairy products above a certain amount: in 1992, it is not expected that this amount will be reached.

Payment limitations

The large amounts of government payments collected by some individual farmers has caused public outcry, and led to the introduction of limits. Under the 1990 legislation, several limits are imposed, the most significant of which is a maximum of $50,000 per farmer on deficiency payments. Farmers can however get around these restrictions by dividing their farm into supposedly separate enterprises in which relatives take a share.

iii) Longer-term land retirement

The former Conservation Reserve Program (CRP) has been incorporated, under the 1990 FACT, in an "Environmental Conservation Acreage Reserve Program" (ECARP). This includes, besides the CRP, a new "Wetlands Reserve Program" (WRP).

Under the CRP, farmers who undertake, for ten years, not to cultivate land which is subject to erosion but to put it to grass or trees, can receive an annual payment (averaging around $156 per hectare in 1992) and an initial payment towards the cost of establishing vegetative cover. The aim is to extend the area concerned to some 16-18 million ha. by the end of 1995, about 10% of the total US cropland. Amendments to the scheme aim to make the CRP more cost-effective. Under the WRP, land must be kept permanently as wetland: the goal is to reach about 0.4 million ha. by 1995.

iv) Domestic food programmes

Several domestic food assistance programmes exist particularly to promote child nutrition through school meals, etc. Much the biggest scheme is the "Food Stamp Program", established in 1964. With these "stamps", low-income households can buy food of their choice through normal market channels. The number of beneficiaries in 1990 was around 20 million, with an average benefit per person of around $60 per month. By no means all this benefit represents extra spending on food (probably less than a quarter): some of the income that would otherwise be spent on food is spent instead on non-food items. As a means of reducing agricultural surpluses, therefore, this is not a cost-effective scheme.

It is however significant in welfare terms, and has received considerable political support. In the 1985 and 1990 farm bills, the benefits were expanded and eligibility broadened. With the recession of recent years, the cost of the Food Stamp programme has been rising steeply, and is expected to reach around $23 billion in 1992 and 1993; "child nutrition" and other food programmes add a further $11 billion. The total of $34 billion represents more than half the total budget for the US Department of Agriculture, and is considerably more than the current cost of commodity support programmes, estimated at $10.6 billion in "fiscal" 1992 and $13.1 billion in 1993.

v) Export policy

In relation to exports, US policy in recent years has been overtly aggressive. The 1985 Act included an "Export Enhancement Program", which was continued and reinforced by the 1990 Act. Besides export credit guarantees already available from the CCC, provision was made under the "Targetted Export Assistance Program", renamed in 1990 the "Marketing Promotion Program", for export subsidies (paid "in kind", i.e. in terms of the product concerned), targeted on markets where US exports are considered to suffer from "unfair" foreign competition, including China, the former USSR and North Africa (mostly for wheat).

The 1990 Act, with a view to putting pressure on other countries in the "Uruguay Round", included the so-called "GATT trigger": if there was no agreement by end-June 1992, funding for export promotion would be increased and acreage restrictions could be removed. If by end-June 1993 there is still no agreement, the Secretary for Agriculture is entitled to waive all the cuts required in agricultural spending to meet "deficit-reduction" targets. Export subsidies were in fact sharply increased in 1992, and there is no acreage reduction requirement for the 1993 wheat crop.

Food aid to developing countries has been granted under "Public Law 480" of 1954. This was originally a means of surplus disposal, and has played an important role in relieving disaster situations, but there has been a shift towards using the food provided, through sales for local currency, to finance development projects in the recipient countries. The annual budget for PL480 is around $1.5 billion; food aid represents only a few per cent of total agricultural exports.

*   *   *

The above is a greatly simplified account of a number of very complex and often controversial programmes. Over the years, US legislators have sought— with varying success—to reconcile price support with supply control. Annual restrictions on the area planted have played a central role, and have provided flexibility: thus there were no restrictions in 1979–81, but in 1983, to deal with surplus problems, a total of 12 million ha. (20% of cropland) was withdrawn. Now, long-term withdrawal under the CRP and WRP is planned to take out 18 million ha. by 1995.

Experience has been gained in dealing with technical problems such as establishing each producer's "base" acreage and verifying compliance with the various acreage reduction programmes. The problem of "slippage" is well-known: the reduction in output will never be in the same proportion as the reduction in area, as farmers idle the least productive land and intensify output on the remainder.

There have always been pressures for a more market-oriented system: "Get the government out of agriculture" has been a slogan advanced even by some farming organisations (the Farm Bureau in particular), representing the most efficient and competitive producers. On the other hand, existing programmes create vested interests—in agribusiness as well as in the farm sector—which try to hold on to their privileges. Chapter 14 will discuss further the various influences on policy-making.

Since 1985, under Republican administration (constrained however by the Democrat majority in Congress), policy has on the whole moved in a more market-oriented direction. However, the attempts to maintain income support while cutting support costs have made the programmes for crops increasingly complex. Moreover, a high degree of support and protection remains for some products, notably dairy products and sugar: the producers and agribusiness enterprises concerned are opposed to the trade liberalisation which the US has been seeking through the GATT Uruguay Round.

The Democratic Party has in the past leaned more towards support and intervention. However, agricultural policy was not a major issue in the 1992 Presidential election: domestic agricultural policy does not seem likely to change significantly following the election of Bill Clinton. The Vice-President, Al Gore, is reported likely to push for more environmental measures. As regards trade policy, while in general the new Administration may be more protectionist, there was no indication by end 1992 that it might want to go back on the bilateral US–EC deal of November 1992.

For the main crops, with the domestic market price underpinned at relatively low levels but with farm incomes supported through deficiency payments, the US can export at prices far below those prevailing within the EC. Thus the 1992/93 "loan rate" for wheat of $81 per tonne is less than half the EC intervention price: the various export programmes enable the US to sell even below this level. As has already been seen, the EC can compete on world markets only by granting very high export subsidies. The conflicts to which this situation gives rise will be discussed in the next chapter.

(c) Other overseas exporters

i) Canada

With its vast land resources and with huge, highly-capitalised farms in the Western Provinces, Canada is efficient in several branches of agriculture, particularly grain and the extensive rearing of beef cattle. For these products, Canadian exports are very competitive. On the other hand, these branches of production are vulnerable to fluctuations on world markets. Weather variations, which can be extreme, are also a problem for Canadian agriculture.

Hence, "stabilisation" has been an enduring theme of agricultural policy. For most commodities, the emphasis of the Federal government has been to stabilise prices and incomes around market-oriented levels, as part of a general commitment to provide "fair returns" to farmers.

The Agricultural Stabilization Act (originally passed in 1958, subsequently amended) provides "floor prices" to producers of beef cattle, pigs, sheep, wool, "industrial" milk and cream, maize and soybeans, and for cereals grown outside the Prairie Provinces (which come under the responsibility of the Canadian Wheat Board). The minimum floor prices for these products are set at not less than 90% of the average market price of the previous five years, with some adjustment for changes in production costs; annual deficiency payments are used to make up the difference if average market prices during the year are below the floor price.

Additional programmes are operated by the Provinces, over which the Federal government has little control. These vary greatly by commodity and between Provinces: the most generous schemes guarantee prices to producers based on full costs. Some "tripartite" stabilisation schemes have been established, involving contributions to a stabilisation fund by producers, Provincial and Federal authorities.

For wheat, barley and oats in the Prairie Provinces of Manitoba, Alberta and Saskatchewan (the main grain-growing area), the Canadian Wheat Board (CWB), in consultation with the Federal government, establishes each year "initial prices" based on expected market conditions: this price is paid to producers for their deliveries. If the average price realised over the year is below the initial price, the Federal government makes up the shortfall: in several years since 1986/87, substantial Federal subsidies have been required.

The Federal Western Grains Stabilization Act assures growers of grains and oilseeds in the CWB area of an aggregate net cash flow not less than the average of the five previous years: if necessary, a payment is made equal to the shortfall. Producers contribute to the stabilisation fund, but here too, public payments have been substantial in several recent years.

Besides these ongoing programmes, there has been special Federal or Provincial assistance to the grain and oilseed sectors in years of low prices, and for drought relief.

Large and growing expenditure by the Federal government has also been incurred through its long-standing commitment to subsidise the storage and transport of grain and oilseeds from the Prairie Provinces to the points of export on the Western and Eastern sea-boards—in effect, an export subsidy.

Some important commodities are subject to relatively far-reaching intervention. This is above all the case for milk, where most output comes from relatively small farms in the Eastern Provinces (Ontario and Quebec): the delicate political issues concerning Quebec's relationship with the Federation largely account for the degree of support. All fluid milk must pass through producers' marketing boards at the Provincial level, which set the milk price on the basis of full costs of production: aggregate output is then limited by individual producer quotas to the amount that is demanded at that price. Milk for manufacturing receives a target price, implemented through public subsidy. Liquid milk may not be imported from the United States; imports of butter and cheese are subject to tariffs and quotas, and imports of milk powder to a tariff.

For "feather products" (eggs, chickens, turkeys), there are price support and supply control schemes similar to that for fluid milk. Supply management applies also to tobacco.

Thus intervention in Canadian agricultural markets has become extensive, incurring large public expenditure in some years. Nevertheless, Canada's strong interest in the export market for its grain has put it in the "liberal" camp in international trade negotiations: Canada joined the Cairns Group in the Uruguay Round context (see Chapter 13). However, as the implications of trade liberalisation for Canada's own protected sectors have become clearer, Canada's attitude has appeared increasingly ambiguous.

Under the North American Free Trade Agreement (NAFTA), Canada will immediately eliminate or phase out its tariff and non-tariff import barriers, *except* for those in the dairy, poultry, egg and sugar sectors.

ii) Australia

Like Canada, Australia has extensive land resources that permit low-cost production and exports of grain, beef, sheepmeat and wool. Although some agricultural products are supported or protected, the overall degree of support is low, and Australia is a rare case of a developed country where protection on manufactures exceeds that on agricultural products.

In agricultural policy, the emphasis has been on measures to reduce price uncertainty. Thus the Australian Wheat Board (AWB), which has a monopoly on exports, and formerly also controlled domestic marketing, used to set domestic prices and guaranteed public assistance to producers, though the level of public assistance has been very low; in 1990, this "underwriting" of returns to wheat producers was replaced by a gradually declining government guarantee of borrowings by the AWB. For beef, there is no domestic price support.

For several other products, statutory marketing boards, at both the Commonwealth and the State levels, administer a variety of "home consumption price schemes", whereby domestic and export prices are kept separate and producers are paid a weighted-average (or "equalised") price for sales in the two markets. For most products, support is limited. However, the dairy sector receives quite substantial assistance, and in most States milk production is limited by quotas. Sugar production is also restricted through quotas, and imports (banned until 1989) are subject to a tariff, although Australia is a net exporter.

On export markets, Australia is generally a "price-taker" (except perhaps for wool): its exports of grain, sugar, beef and sheepmeat suffer from protectionism in importing countries and from export subsidies by the US and the EC. Australia has therefore adopted an aggressive stance with regard to agricultural trade liberalisation in the Uruguay Round, and took the initiative in forming the "Cairns Group" of "fair-trading" nations.

iii) New Zealand

New Zealand has a climate which permits cattle and sheep to be grazed on pasture throughout the year, and large, efficient farms. The export of meat, dairy products and wool has played a vital role in the country's overall economic development.

This export orientation, however, has made agriculture vulnerable to changes on export markets; in particular, the absorption of the United Kingdom, formerly New Zealand's biggest customer, into the CAP mechanisms in 1973 was a severe blow, which was partly overcome by product diversification and by developing markets in Japan, the Middle East and Australia.

Producer boards play an important role in organising exports; but given the importance of agriculture in the total economy, the scope for public assistance to the sector is limited. In 1978, in response to falling farm incomes, the government began to supplement the minimum prices offered by the producer boards, but this led to an increased government deficit. In 1985 a new government severely reduced the level of assistance, as part of a liberalisation programme affecting all economic sectors.

New Zealand has enthusiastically supported the aim of agricultural trade liberalisation in the Uruguay Round, but as a small country, its individual negotiating strength is limited: it has therefore played a leading role in the Cairns Group.

(d) Japan

Japan is a densely-populated island with limited land resources: it is inevitably dependent on food imports. The "food security" argument for supporting domestic production, formerly significant in several Western European countries, continues to be evoked in Japan. But farms are extremely small, and mostly operated on a spare-time basis by people with other main sources of income: labour productivity is low and not easily improved.

Structural adjustment is seen as vital, but has been hindered partly by a high rice price, which gives an incentive to the maintenance of small plots growing rice even in built-up areas, and by traditional obstacles to the renting of land. However, legislation has been passed to facilitate renting; and as many farmers are now in the older age groups, some acceleration of structural change may occur.

Rice is the mainstay of farming income. In the early years after World War II, government intervention on the rice market aimed mainly to ensure supplies to consumers: subsequently, it became the main policy instrument for raising farm incomes. Imports are strictly controlled, and in practice are virtually nil. The domestic market too is controlled: the price paid to producers has risen to eight times the international level, while rice is resold at somewhat lower prices to consumers, entailing large government deficits. The high producer price encouraged surplus production and the build-up of public stocks; an acreage control programme was introduced in an effort to limit production.

On the other hand, Japan has become a major importer of feed grain, oilseeds, sugar, meat and some dairy products. With its large and prosperous population, and with consumption patterns shifting to some extent towards Western-style diets, would-be exporters see great potential in the Japanese market. As a result of strong international pressure, Japan began in 1988 to phase out its import quotas on beef, dairy products, oranges and other fruit, and other items. In the Uruguay Round, Japan has been required to accept further liberalisation, with rice the most controversial item.

Rice raises very sensitive political issues in Japan. The support—including financial support—of farmers is important to the governing Liberal-Democratic party. However, the US–EC deal of November 1992 put the Japanese government under still stronger pressure to find a solution, which seemed likely to involve replacing import control by a very high tariff, together with some form of compensation to farmers.

APPENDIX

1. Sources. Reports by the OECD (Organisation for Economic Cooperation and Development, Paris) are a useful source for the member countries, covering Western Europe, North America, Oceania and Japan, and some non-member countries. A series of country studies were published in 1987 under the general heading *National Policies and Agricultural Trade*; subsequently, annual reports entitled *Agricultural Policies, Markets and Trade—Monitoring and Outlook* provide regular updates (probably too detailed for most readers).
Agricultural Protectionism in the Industrialised World, edited by F.H. Sanderson (Resources for the Future, Washington D.C., 1990), contains excellent studies on Canada, Australia, New Zealand and Japan (those on the EC and the US are somewhat overtaken by events).
For the United States, the US Department of Agriculture (USDA) publishes a wealth of regular reports as well as special studies. The monthly *Agricultural Outlook* is particularly useful. Papers on various aspects of US policy were contained in *Agricultural–Food Policy Review*, published by USDA in 1989; this precedes the 1990 Farm Act but gives useful background. There is also a vast academic literature: see for example *Agricultural and Food Policy: Issues and Alternatives for the 1990s*, edited by R.G.F. Spitze (University of Illinois, 1990). A good study of acreage controls is given by D. Ervin, "Some lessons about the political-economic effects of set-aside: the United States experience", in *Set-Aside*, ed. J Clarke (British Crop Protection Council: 1992).
On Australia, see also D. MacLaren, "The political economy of agricultural policy", *Journal of Agricultural Economics* (UK), 43.3, Sept. 1992 (pp.424–439).

2. PSEs. These were developed by the OECD to provide a general measure of intervention in food and agriculture that could be used in the GATT Uruguay Round context. The OECD reports referred to above explain in detail the methodology and the results. They have been widely accepted, despite inevitable methodological problems. It should be noted in particular that they do *not* necessarily measure the benefit to farmers of support measures, but only the cost to consumers and/or taxpayers; they do not measure the extent of trade distortion (some measures are more trade-distorting than others); they are affected by movements in world prices, even if there has been no change in domestic policies; and they do not adequately allow for the effects of supply control, either direct measures such as production quotas or payments linked to supply control measures, such as US deficiency payments. This last problem will become more acute with the EC's move to compensatory payments conditional on set-aside.

The EC supported an Aggregate Measure of Support (AMS), which would be based on a *fixed* external reference price and would measure only *trade-distorting* measures; being an aggregate measure, it could enable big concessions on some products to offset smaller concessions on others.

"Consumer subsidy equivalents" (CSEs) are also calculated by OECD: they consist of the market transfers due to market price support net of any consumer subsidies connected with agricultural policy (they do not take account of welfare food schemes such as the US Food Stamp programme, except in so far as consumption is thereby increased). They might be better called "consumer tax equivalents", as they always have a negative sign. They have not been shown here, as they differ from PSEs mainly in so far as deficiency payments or direct payments, being financed from taxation and not through market support, are not counted.

These issues are discussed by H. de Gorter and D.R. Harvey in *Agricultural Policies and the GATT: Reconciling Protection, Support and Distortion*, Working Paper 90–6 of the International Agricultural Trade Research Consortium (available from Dr. Gorter, Department of Agricultural Economics, Cornell University, Ithaca, NY 14853).

CHAPTER 13

AGRICULTURAL TRADE ISSUES

The developments discussed in previous chapters all combine to create tensions in agricultural trade. The growth of supply—made possible by technological progress but over-encouraged by public support—and the relatively slow growth in demand causes traditional exporting countries to lose markets in former importing countries. On world markets, exporters find themselves in increasingly keen competition. From time to time, the tension is relieved by substantial import demand from sources such as the former USSR and some less-developed regions of the world. But usually, lack of purchasing-power holds back such demand; food aid programmes, though helpful in times of famine, have their limits.

Trade disputes between the EC and the US have been recurrent since the beginnings of the CAP. The economic provisions of international commodity agreements on wheat and on sugar, under which world market stabilisation had been attempted in the early post-1945 era, broke down. Multilateral attempts under the General Agreement on Tariffs and Trade (GATT) to liberalise world trade met with little success: in the latest "Uruguay Round", agriculture was a major stumbling-block, and the bilateral EC–US agreement of November 1992, which provides a basis for an overall settlement, was reached only with great difficulty.

Numerous studies have been made of the effects of trade liberalisation. Some aspects of this work are open to question (see item 3 in the Appendix to Chapter 6, and item 1 in the Appendix to the present chapter). Nevertheless, the general thrust is clear. Trade liberalisation, by reducing prices in protectionist countries, would stimulate consumption and reduce production in these countries; the increase in import demand would raise world prices, particularly if *multilateral* liberalisation is achieved. Exporters would benefit, as would consumers and taxpayers in formerly protectionist importing countries (effects on *developing* countries are more controversial). Producers in these countries would lose, though the rise in world prices would soften the impact. However, the overall increase in economic welfare would enable producers to be compensated through direct payments and still leave a net benefit.

However, such arguments make little political impact in importing countries. While the negative impact on producers would be very clear, the benefits to consumers would be diffuse and not so much noticed. The concept of compensation to losers from gainers raises theoretical and practical difficulties which have been discussed at several points in previous chapters. Farmers' organisations in protectionist countries continue to oppose price cuts, and dislike any substitution of direct payments for price support through the market. Their governments usually remain attentive to their demands, despite the reduced numbers of the farm population. This is a paradox which requires explanation: Chapter 14 will consider more fully the political issues involved.

(a) EC trade

In the early years of the Community, agricultural trade between the first six Member States expanded rapidly in value—much more so than imports from third countries (Table 13.1). After 1973, with near-saturation of the domestic market despite the extra outlet in the UK, growth in EC output spilled over onto export markets, while imports from third countries rose relatively little. The inclusion of Portugal and, especially, Spain in the 1986 data causes a statistical increase in "intra-EC" trade and a corresponding fall in trade with third countries: since 1986, intra-EC trade and exports to third countries have continued to rise, while imports from third countries have been relatively stagnant in value (with a fall in the *volume* of imports of several commodities).

Table 13.1—Trends in EC trade in agricultural products

		Intra-EC trade	Imports from third countries	Exports to third countries
		billion UA		
EC 6	1963	2.5	9.4	2.5
	1972	9.4	14.0	4.7
		billion ECU		
EC 10	1973	15.8	24.5	7.4
	1984	57.8	58.3	31.2
EC 12	1986	70.1	52.8	28.8
	1991	98.0	56.9	36.0
		indices		
	1963–1972	378	148	127
	1973–1984	365	238	423
	1986–1991	140	108	125

Notes and source: See Appendix, item 12.

i) Internal EC trade

An important question is whether the growth of internal EC trade corresponds to the comparative advantages of the various countries and regions. This subject cannot easily be dealt with in a short space (but see sources mentioned in Appendix, item 2).

The "common market" has not been allowed to function freely in agriculture. The development of production and trade has been influenced by CAP support measures of various kinds, by supply controls (in particular milk quotas since 1985), and by monetary compensatory amounts (MCAs). Still, specialisation has occurred as efficient producers have taken advantage of the wider market.

Much the fastest growth in output has been in the **Netherlands**, as a result of expansion in highly-efficient production of pigmeat and poultrymeat, vegetables and flowers. **Denmark** and **Ireland** profited from their accession in 1973: Ireland particularly in beef and milk, with its strong natural advantage in grass-based production. Denmark did best in pigs and poultry. The **United Kingdom's** advantage in large farm size is reflected in an expansion of cereals and especially oilseeds.

France has *not* been the main beneficiary of the common market. Its best developments have been in cereals and especially oilseeds, output of which comes mostly from the big farms of the Paris basin, and in poultrymeat (mainly in Brittany, with easy access to imported feed). But cattle and dairy production have been held back by unfavourable market developments and by poor production and marketing structures in many regions; pig-farming has suffered from Dutch competition.

Overall growth in farm output has been relatively slow in **Germany** and **Luxembourg**, where farm structures are deficient, costs are high and farmers have been particularly subject to a cost-price squeeze. Nevertheless, with the help of MCAs (acting as subsidies in this case), Germany has been able to increase its agricultural exports, particularly of dairy products to Italy.

Perhaps the most disappointing result is that of **Italy**, which should have taken greater advantage of its climate in the production of fruit and vegetables: but deficient production and marketing structures, and sometimes poor-quality produce, held back the development. Much of the wine output was formerly of low quality and had to be cut back. **Greece**, after accession to the EC in 1981, had difficulty in maintaining some of its traditional exports, such as wine, which had formerly been subsidised, while Denmark and the Netherlands were able to expand sales of pigmeat and dairy products on the Greek market. The experience of **Spain** and **Portugal** since 1986 is relatively short, especially as they do not obtain entirely free access for their main export products until after 1995: however, for some fruits and vegetables, relatively efficient Spanish marketing is proving effective.

The general impression is that good structures and efficiency in production and marketing have been even more important than geographic advantages.

ii) External EC trade

Figure 13.1 shows the pattern of EC imports and exports of agricultural products, by region, in 1990. This includes tropical and semi-tropical products, as well as feed for livestock: in these terms, the EC is a net importer, although it is a net exporter of "temperate-zone" foodstuffs. The main food and feed items traded by the EC are as follows:

* **North America:** the EC imports feedingstuffs (soya, maize, maize gluten feed), some Canadian hard wheat for bread-making. The EC exports a considerable variety of processed foods, including dairy products, processed meat and cereal preparations, wine and spirits (especially whisky).
* **EFTA** (European Free Trade Association, i.e. Iceland, Finland, Norway, Sweden, Austria, Switzerland, Liechtenstein): the EC imports fish, some dairy produce and meat. EC exports are mainly fruit, vegetables, flowers and plants, wines and spirits.
* **Eastern and Central Europe (including Yugoslavia):** the EC imports pig-meat and poultry products, cattle and meat, fruit and vegetables, wine (more detail in later section). EC agricultural exports go mainly to the Republics of

Figure 13.1—EC agricultural trade in 1990

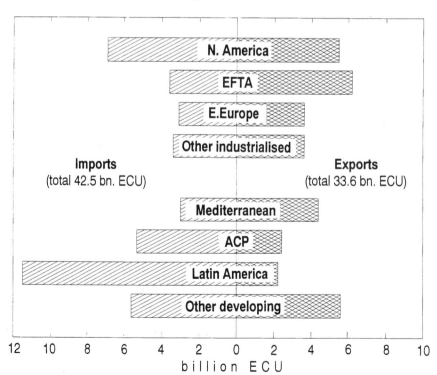

Notes and source: See Appendix, item 12.

the former USSR, especially cereals, meat and butter (much of this consisting of produce from intervention stores).
* **"Other developed" countries:** the EC imports some meat from Australia and New Zealand, some butter from New Zealand (though much less than before UK accession), fruit from South Africa, etc.
* **Mediterranean countries:** the EC imports fruit and vegetables (especially citrus fruit and tomatoes) from most of these countries, wine and olive oil from the three Maghreb countries (Algeria, Morocco, Tunisia). EC exports include cereals, sugar and dairy products.
* **ACP (African, Caribbean and Pacific) countries:** the EC imports sugar, some beef, fruit and vegetables, coffee, tea and cocoa. EC exports include cereals, dairy products, sugar.
* **Latin America:** the EC imports bananas and other fruit, soya from Brazil, some beef (though much less than in the past) from Argentina and Uruguay, coffee, etc. The EC exports various processed foods, including milk powder.
* **Other developing countries:** the EC imports a wide range of tropical and semi-tropical products, and exports grain, sugar, dairy products, meat (some of this under food aid programmes—see Appendix, item 3).

(b) Special EC import arrangements

The general basis for EC trade policy lies in Article 110 of the Treaty of Rome, which states that "by establishing a customs union between themselves Member States aim to contribute, in the common interest, to the harmonious development of world trade, the progressive abolition of restrictions on international trade and the lowering of customs barriers".

This aim has often been in conflict with the CAP. However, the EC has granted import concessions on specific agricultural products to some countries or groups of countries. These will be considered in some cases by groups of beneficiary countries, in other cases by commodity.

i) The generalised system of preferences (GSP)

The GSP was launched under UNCTAD (United Nations Conference on Trade and Development) in 1968. Under this scheme, the EC grants reduced tariffs to all countries designated by the United Nations as "developing", and to a number of other countries which asked for the same benefits, such as China (see Appendix, item 4). The list of potential beneficiaries now covers some 130 countries. However, as Mediterranean or ACP countries can usually gain more favourable concessions under their respective schemes (see below), the GSP is used mainly by Asian and Latin American countries.

Some Eastern European countries have been among the beneficiaries for certain products. However, bilateral agreements between these countries and the EC (see below) give greater advantages.

The preferences cover industrial and agricultural products. As regards the latter, the EC concessions now apply to around 400 agricultural products, mostly processed, with an import value over 2 billion ECU. Customs duties may be reduced or removed, with limits on the volume of preferential imports for some products. No duties are applied to preferential agricultural products from countries classified as "least-developed".

As most of the GSP beneficiaries are in tropical or semi-tropical regions, their agricultural exports do not as a rule compete directly with EC produce, and the GSP has not raised major issues in relation to the CAP.

ii) ACP sugar

Conflicts of interest can be acute in the case of sugar, which is produced from sugar-cane in tropical climates and from beet in Europe. Before the CAP, several of the overseas producers had preferences—arising from former colonial links—with France and the UK: as members of the African, Caribbean and Pacific (ACP) group (see Appendix, item 5), these countries were able to press their claims after the formation of the EC.

The EC undertook to purchase free of duty from these ACP countries a total of about 1.3 million tonnes of raw sugar annually. For these quantities, the EC guarantees a price to be fixed each year "within the price range obtaining in the Community". The precise interpretation of this provision has caused difficulty, but it gives the ACP producers a very considerable advantage over the relatively low and fluctuating world price.

While EC sugar production has grown, despite the production quota system, to exceed domestic needs, this commitment to ACP countries has been maintained: the result is to increase the amount which the EC must export to the world market.

iii) Mediterranean countries

Under its "global Mediterranean policy", announced in 1972, the Community granted tariff reductions, mostly ranging from 20% to 80%, for agricultural products, mainly fruit and vegetables and wine, to the various Mediterranean countries (see Appendix, item 6).

The items in question are sensitive, competing with the EC's own production in its southern regions. Hence, in many cases, the concessions are limited to specific quantities and periods (off-peak periods for EC production). Moreover, they do not affect the "reference prices" and "countervailing charges" (see Chapter 9), which are often a more significant means of protection than tariffs.

In 1992, as part of a "new" policy involving financial and technical co-operation for ten Mediterranean countries, and to take account of the advantages gained by Spain and Portugal through their accession to the EC, the EC granted further trade concession: customs duties on agricultural products are to be abolished in two equal stages—on 1 January 1992 and 1 January 1993—subject to the existing tariff quotas and timetables. The tariff quotas are however increased in four equal stages of 5% each year from 1992 to 1995 (but only by 3% per year for some sensitive products, such as new potatoes, tomatoes and wine).

Turkey has had an Association Agreement with the EC since 1964, which provided for the step-by-step formation of a customs union, with full membership as the final target. Turkey has obtained tariff concessions for most of its agricultural exports, including tobacco, raisins, citrus fruit, etc.

The EC had an agreement with Yugoslavia (classified as a "Mediterranean" country), giving concessions on various agricultural products, including cherries, wine, plum brandy, tobacco and "baby beef".

iv) Meat

In 1974, the Community **beef** market suddenly and unexpectedly came into surplus: imports—mainly from South America but also from Eastern Europe— were drastically restricted, and fell further in subsequent years. The variable import levy system, on top of a 20% tariff, effectively precluded any imports other than those benefiting from preferential arrangements. Some such arrangements, granting cuts in the levy or tariff, or both, have been negotiated under GATT; others are granted by the EC autonomously and on an annual basis. Some concessions are open to any third country, others to specific countries (the most recent relate to CEECs—see later section). Several types of cattle and beef are involved. Details are given in the Appendix, item 7.

In the case of **mutton and lamb**, where there is no import levy and only a 20% import duty, the large traditional imports by the UK from New Zealand, Australia and Argentina caused imbalances on the EC market. As the duty was "bound" under GATT, exporting countries were asked to accept "voluntary" export restraint, in return for reduction or abolition of the duty. Agreements were reached with most suppliers, including, besides the exporters mentioned above, Hungary, Poland, Yugoslavia and Bulgaria.

v) Dairy products

As with beef, the system of threshold prices and import levies constitutes a barrier to imports which is very difficult for third countries to overcome. The accession of the United Kingdom to the Community in 1973 led to a big reduction in imports of dairy products, which the UK had formerly obtained from Commonwealth countries. As a "temporary" derogation from CAP rules (which has however continued), the UK was authorised to import annually from New Zealand, at a reduced import levy, a specified quantity of butter (55,000 tonnes in 1992, down from 166,000 tonnes in 1973). Limited quantities of cheese continue to be imported under reduced-levy agreements negotiated in GATT with several third countries, including New Zealand, Australia, Canada, Switzerland and Austria.

vi) "Cereal substitutes"

Big increases have occurred in EC imports of items for which no significant protection existed because the EC had conceded low or zero rates of duty at an early stage, and these—being "bound" under GATT rules—could not be unilaterally changed. This was the case for "cereal substitutes"—manioc (or cassava) was subject only to a 6% duty, and Community imports rose very fast—from 3.8 million tonnes in 1977 to a peak of 8.1 million tonnes in 1982.

An agreement was then reached whereby Thailand—the main supplier—would limit its exports to 5.5 million tonnes annually, the Community undertaking in return to help rural development and diversification in the areas of manioc cultivation in Thailand. Agreements were also reached limiting imports from Indonesia, Brazil and China. The current agreement with Thailand provides for total exports of 21 million tonnes over the years 1991–94.

vii) EFTA and EEA

The European Free Trade Association does not provide for free trade in agricultural products, nor for a common agricultural policy. Likewise, the Treaty on the European Economic Area (EEA) signed in May 1992, which establishes the general principle of free trade between the EFTA countries and the EC, specifically excludes agricultural products from the free trade provisions, apart from maintaining some existing bilateral concessions. It declares only that the Contracting Parties will "examine difficulties", "seek appropriate solutions", etc.

Under the EEA, however, the EFTA countries will apply the "harmonisation" rules established by the EC (see Chapter 11).

Any EFTA country which becomes a member of the EC will have to accept all EC legislation and policies, including the CAP (the so-called *acquis communautaire*): as with previous enlargements, only temporary derogations are allowed to new Member States.

viii) Central and Eastern Europe

Table 13.2 shows the pattern of EC agricultural imports from Central and Eastern European countries (including the former Yugoslavia). Relatively important currents of trade included pigs, pigmeat and poultrymeat from Poland and Hungary; live cattle and meat from Yugoslavia; fruit and vegetables from these three countries; rapeseed from Poland; wine from Hungary, Yugoslavia and Bulgaria; tobacco from Yugoslavia and Bulgaria.

Hungarian exports of cattle to Germany and Italy, once an important item of trade, had been virtually excluded by EC import levies.

The quantities traded are subject to substantial variations (the data shown are averages for the three years 1988–90, which is also the period taken as a basis for the concessions negotiated under the agreements discussed below). In particular, exports by Romania of dairy products, meat and cereals were sharply reduced in 1990 by shortages and export restrictions.

The **"Europe Agreements"** establishing associations between the EC on the one hand and the Czech and Slovak Federal Republic (CSFR), Hungary and Poland on the other were signed in December 1991. Pending ratification, their trade provisions are being applied on the basis of "interim agreements". An agreement has also been reached with Romania, though details are not currently available; negotiations with Bulgaria, at the time of writing, are held up largely by difficulties over agricultural trade.

Table 13.2—EC agricultural imports from Central and Eastern Europe, 1988–90
(in million ECU)

	PL	CS	H	R	BG	YU	AL	USSR
Live animals, meat	282	76	309	28	31	248	1.5	10
Preparations of meat and fish	42	4	43	8	1	14	–	51
Dairy products, eggs	21	23	18	12	9	3	–	8
Fresh vegetables	112	6	60	5	7	75	1.7	3
Fresh fruit and nuts	71	9	27	6	5	62	0.6	3
Preparations of fruit, vegetables and nuts	51	9	39	1	11	27	0.1	8
Cereals, flour and cereal preparations	3	7	26	6	0	5	–	1
Oilseeds, fats and oils	104	30	57	3	13	32	6.4	22
Beverages and spirits	8	13	14	6	22	35	0.2	25
Tobacco	1	0	2	1	13	7	0.4	–
Other food and feed	75	13	92	7	15	77	1.5	20
TOTAL	770	190	687	83	127	585	12.4	151

Notes and source: See Appendix, item 12.

The Agreements provide in general for the establishment of free trade areas over a ten-year period. EC duties on imports of most manufactured products are immediately removed.

The EC's willingness to open its market for agricultural products was limited in view of the oversupply of most of the products concerned on the EC market. However, on the basis of the average volumes of trade in 1988–90, concessions were made, relating in some cases to the import levy, in others to the customs duty. Most of these concessions are subject to quantitative limits: any imports above these limits remain subject to levy and/or duty.

The concessions are complex, and fall into several categories. Table 13.3 covers some of these.

* **"Levy products—ex-GSP"**. Products in this list already benefited from tariff cuts under the Generalised System of Preferences. The *levy* is reduced by 50% from the outset of the Agreement, subject to maximum quantities which rise above the base period by 10% per year for five years. This list includes some high-value products, of considerable interest to the countries concerned: the main items are shown under A in Table 13.3.
* **"Duty products—ex-GSP."** These too already had preferential duty rates under the GSP: but GSP concessions are renegotiated annually. Under the Agreements, the preferential rates (zero in several cases) are *consolidated*. These products are not subject to levy. There are no quantitative limits. The lists are long: they include meat from "non-domestic swine" (i.e. wild boar),

Table 13.3—Main EC concessions on agricultural products under "Europe Agreements" (in tonnes)

	CSFR		HUNGARY		POLAND	
	Year 1	Year 5	Year 1	Year 5	Year 1	Year 5
A. Levy reduction: 50%						
Ducks and duckmeat	275	375	1400	1940	950	1300
Geese and goosemeat	1100	1500	12600	17300	12600	17200
Pigmeat: salted	–	–	1100	1500	2200	3000
preserved	–	–	220	300	7000	9600
Sausages	–	–	4400	6000	1650	2250
B. Levy reductions: 20% – 40% – 60%						
Beef*	3000	4000	5000	6600	4000	5600
Sheep and sheepmeat*	2000	2500	11200	13000	6600	9000
Live pigs	–	–	–	–	1000	1400
Pigmeat	4700	6400	22000	30000	7000	9800
Hams	500	700	–	–	–	–
Chickens	–	–	–	–	2500	3500
Chickenmeat	5300	7300	23350	31450	3500	4900
Turkeymeat	500	700	3000	4100	1000	1400
Milk powder	2500	3400	–	–	3000	4100
Butter	1000	1400	–	–	1000	1400
Cheese	1000	1400	1000	1400	2000	2800
Eggs in shell	5350	7300	1050	1450	1100	1500
Wheat	–	–	170000	232000	–	–
Wheat flour	20000	27000	–	–	–	–
Buckwheat	–	–	–	–	3200	4350
Barley for malting	30000	41000	–	–	–	–
Malt	35000	45000	–	–	–	–
C. Duty reductions: 20% – 40% – 60%						
Potatoes	–	–	–	–	3190	4400
Onions	–	–	42700	58300	108310	147290
Peppers	–	–	10000	13636	120	160
Frozen vegetables	–	–	24600	33550	41550	55300
Preserved cucumbers	–	–	14800	20200	–	–
Mushrooms	–	–	–	–	28840	33880
Fruit juices	–	–	1000	1350	1000	1350
Hops	4500	6150	–	–	–	–

* See text. NB: These lists—especially list C—do not show all the commodities concerned.
Source: Interim Agreements, in *Official Journal* L114, L115 and L116 of 30.4.92.

some poultry products, and various fruits and vegetables. For soft fruit for processing—raspberries, black-currants, red-currants, strawberries, gooseberries—minimum import prices must be observed (these are products with a short production season during which EC producers are very sensitive to competition from imports).

* **"Levy products—new concessions."** Import levies are subject to reductions of 20% in the first year, 40% in the second year and 60% in the third year, within quantities which rise above the base period by 10% per year for five years. This category includes many important commodities: the main ones are listed under B in Table 13.3. Duties, where applicable, are also reduced at the same rate: this concerns only beef and sheepmeat, for which the duty is normally 20%. For sheepmeat, however, these countries already benefit from suspension of duty for quantities defined under "voluntary restraint agreements": these quantities are increased as indicated in the Table.
* **"Duty products—new concessions."** The duty is reduced according to the same calendar as levies under the previous category, for a long list of products in the case of Hungary and Poland: only some examples are included under C in Table 13.3. There is no corresponding list for the CSFR.
* **Young male cattle for slaughter or fattening** (an important item for the partner countries but particularly sensitive for the EC in view of oversupply). Under the "balance-sheet" procedure (see Appendix, item 7), a reduced levy is granted for an amount that is decided annually, taking into account expected EC supplies: this used to come mostly from Yugoslavia, but special preference (a 75% cut in the levy) is now granted to the CSFR, Hungary and Poland. Further, under the new Agreements, additional quantities can be imported from these countries on a "first-come-first-served" basis, also with a 75% levy cut. These extra quantities are determined annually by calculating the difference between the annual "balance-sheet" quantity (currently 198,000 head) and "reference quantities" which rise from 217,800 head in 1992 to 297,000 head in 1996.
* **Processed agricultural products.** These products were already eligible for tariff reductions under the GSP. The EC phases out—usually in one or two years—the "non-agricultural component" (i.e. the duty), while the "variable component" applicable to these "non-Annex II products" (related to the levy applicable to the basic products—cf. Appendix to Chapter 9, item 3) is progressively reduced, subject to quantitative limits which increase by approximately 10% per annum over the five-year period.

Wine is not covered by these concessions, but separate bilateral negotiations are taking place.

Each Agreement contains a "safeguard clause" providing that in case of "serious disturbance" to the market, the two parties concerned shall consult to find an appropriate solution: "pending such solution, the Party concerned shall take the measures it deems necessary". A Joint Committee set up under each Agreement has the task of settling any disputes that may arise.

(c) GATT and the Uruguay Round

Though in principle the General Agreement on Tariffs and Trade (GATT) makes no distinction between agricultural and other products, in practice agriculture has always been a special case. The Agreement contained a general prohibition of quantitative import restrictions: nevertheless Article XI permitted import quotas on agricultural products if domestic production restrictions were in force; the United States obtained in 1955 a waiver going even beyond this provision to legalise its use of import quotas to protect domestic dairy producers (though its dairy programmes did not control supply).

The formation of the European Economic Community brought into application Article XXIV of the Agreement which, in sanctioning customs unions, stipulates that the common external duties must not on the whole be higher or more restrictive than the general incidence of duties collectively applied by individual member countries before forming the union. Negotiations between the Community and its trading partners in 1960–62 led to some reductions in duties and to "bindings" (i.e. an undertaking not to increase the duty in question without giving compensation). The US thus obtained duty-free entry (or nearly so) for soyabeans, soyabean meal, other oilseeds and cotton. EC imports of soya were at the time limited.

The "Kennedy Round" of trade negotiations which began in 1963 produced only modest results in agriculture. The "Tokyo Round" in 1973–79 was important for world trade in general: tariffs were cut by about a third on a world-wide basis. In the agricultural sector, however, tariff reductions were mainly limited to tropical products. The EC did make some of the specific concessions already discussed for beef and cheese.

In the years following the Tokyo Round, problems on world agricultural markets grew more acute, and there were successive conflicts between the EC and the US, provoking threats of "trade wars". A new GATT round was formally launched at a ministerial meeting in Punta del Este in Uruguay in September 1986. For the US, as for the group of fourteen "fair-trading" nations formed at a meeting at Cairns in Australia the previous August (see Appendix, item 11), progress in liberalising agricultural trade was an essential ingredient of the negotiations.

The US initially proposed to phase out over a ten-year period all agricultural import restrictions and all subsidies that directly or indirectly affect trade. This "zero option" was immediately denounced by the EC as being quite unrealistic. Differences were subsequently somewhat narrowed: still, the conference in Brussels in December 1990 which should have concluded the Uruguay Round collapsed, mainly because of continued disagreement over agriculture.

The conflict between the US and the EC was exacerbated by the issue of oilseeds, where the US—supported by the findings of two successive GATT panels—continued to attack the EC support system, even after the change in this system decided in 1991 (see Chapter 9). In November 1992, the US threatened to impose prohibitive (200%) duties on white wine, rapeseed oil and wheat gluten from the EC, with a total value of some $300 million; a longer list of products for retaliation was held in reserve. In the atmosphere of crisis which this provoked, and in the aftermath of the US Presidential election, US and EC Commission negotiators reached an agreement covering oilseeds and the other main Uruguay Round issues.

On the basis of this US–EC agreement, and taking into account proposals previously made by the Secretary-General of GATT, Arthur Dunkel, the main features of a possible Uruguay Round agreement appeared as follows:

* **Access.** Border protection (e.g. EC import levies) would be changed into customs tariffs, which would then be reduced by 36%, as compared with the average of support in 1986–88, over the six years 1993–99. The reduction for any individual product must not be less than 15%. A "special safeguard clause" would permit an increase in the tariff if the import price falls by more than 10% below the average 1986–88 import price (expressed in national currency—ECU in the case of the EC).
  Minimum access opportunities would be granted, rising from 3% to 5% of domestic consumption over the six years. The EC Commission proposed to implement this undertaking through a reduced tariff (32% of the basic rate) for the necessary quantities. But interpretation remained unclear, particularly as to whether the commitment would relate to commodity groups (e.g. meat) or to individual products (e.g. beef or pigmeat).

* **Internal support** would be reduced by 20% by comparison with 1986–88, on average for all products together (by reference to the AMS—Aggregate Measure of Support). Credit would be given for reductions already made since 1986 (both the EC and the US considered that they had met this requirement through their respective policy changes).

* **Export subsidies.** There would be a 36% cut in budgetary expenditure combined with a 21% reduction in the subsidised export volume, product by product.

* **"Decoupled" income support.** The Dunkel proposals had envisaged that aids which are not related to the volume of production would not be subject to reduction (i.e. would fall within the "green box", as opposed to the "red box" of subsidies which would have to be reduced). It was vital for the EC to ensure that this exemption would apply to the compensatory payments introduced under the "MacSharry" reform. The US conceded this point: direct aids would not have to be reduced if they are within the framework of production-limiting programmes: to this effect, they must be made on a fixed base (area for crops, or number of animals) and fixed yield.

* **"Rebalancing"** had always been an essential claim by the EC. As has already been observed, imports of certain feedingstuffs—both protein feeds such as soya and "cereal substitutes" such as manioc and maize gluten feed—continued to be imported into the EC freely or subject only to low import duties. This reduced the market for EC-produced feed grains, and also caused a geographical imbalance with feed-based pig and poultry enterprises concentrating near the northern ports. The EC had therefore insisted that its agreement to other elements in the package would be conditional on acceptance by other parties of some increase in protection for the items in question. But for the US and the Cairns Group, this remained unacceptable. The US–EC agreement provided only that if EC imports of non-grain feed ingredients should increase to a level

which might undermine the implementation of CAP reform, the two sides would consult with a view to finding a mutually acceptable solution; it subsequently appeared that this undertaking applied only to maize gluten.

The EC–US conflict over oilseeds was resolved by an undertaking on the part of the EC to create a separate base area (under the "MacSharry" reform, oilseeds and cereals would have been alternative crops within the base area on each farm). This oilseeds base area—5.1 million hectares—corresponded to the average of 1989–91, though it is less than the 1992 area. "Set-aside" from this base must be at least 10%: if the actual area exceeds the amount thus calculated, compensatory payments will be reduced.

This agreement remained to be endorsed by all the other GATT participants, and by the EC Member States. EC rules (see Appendix, item 10) provide that the Commission negotiates in trade matters on behalf of the Community. Its "mandate" from the Council of Ministers, in this case, had been to remain within the bounds of the CAP reform decisions. The Commission declared that this condition had been respected, although it accepted that problems would arise in the beef sector, where subsidised exports would have to be substantially reduced; it also laid stress on a "peace clause" obtained from the US, which in its view recognised the CAP as being "compatible with GATT".

News of the US–EC deal, however, provoked large-scale farmer demonstrations with a strong anti-American flavour, especially in Strasbourg and Brussels, in which farmers from several EC countries—and even from Japan and South Korea—participated. Farmer opposition was particularly strong in France. The French government disputed the Commission's arguments as to the compatibility of the deal with the CAP reform programme, and threatened to block final Uruguay Round agreement; when the Commission nevertheless formally submitted its new position to GATT, France denounced this as "null and void". Other Member States too—especially Spain, Italy and Belgium—expressed their concern over the likely effects of the proposed deal; Ireland worried about effects on the beef sector. On the other hand, it was significant that the German government did not support France on this issue, while the UK, Denmark and the Netherlands insisted on the need for a successful outcome to the Uruguay Round. The following chapter will explore more fully the various national attitudes.

Still, it seemed unlikely that the agricultural agreement negotiated with the US could be overturned, when so much hung on the outcome. Apparently the French aim was to obtain adjustments and compensation where possible. Decisions by the Agriculture Council in December 1992 enabling more producers—especially in France—to benefit from the "suckler cow" premiums (cf. p. 179), and adding new regions in France where aids for durum wheat can be paid (p. 176), appeared to be steps in this direction. The French government was careful to stress that it would take a final position only when a complete GATT package became available: by that time, a change of government following elections due in March 1993 seemed inevitable.

APPENDIX

1. General sources. The Commission's annual report on the *Agricultural Situation in the Community* includes a chapter on external relations, but without much detail. Fuller information is provided, though not very systematically, in the *European Documentation* and *European File* series. *Europe: World Partner*, published in 1991, contains some general information on relations with various groups of third countries.

Developments in EC trade are discussed in various papers in *The Common Agricultural Policy and the World Economy*, ed. C. Ritson and D. Harvey (CAB International, Wallingford, UK: 1991).

A comprehensive analysis of the effects of reform in the EC and the US was made at the request of the Commission by a group of experts and published in 1988 under the title *Disharmonies in EC and US agricultural policy measures* (two volumes, the second very large).

Numerous econometric studies of the effects of trade liberalisation have also been made by American and Australian agencies and academic experts. See for example "Effects of gradual food policy reforms in the 1990s" by Kym Anderson and Rod Tyers, in *European Review of Agricultural Policy*, 19(1992) 1–24; also by Kym Anderson, "Analytical issues in the Uruguay Round negotiations on agriculture", *European Economic Review*, 36(1992) 519–526.

2. Intra-EC specialisation. An interesting series of studies is being made, under contract from the EC Commission, by J.P. Butault and colleagues at the *Institut National de Recherches Agronomiques* (INRA) in Nancy. See in particular J.-C. Bureau and J.-P. Butault, "Productivity gaps, price advantages and competitiveness in E.C. agriculture" *European Review of Agricultural Economics*, 19 (1992), pp.25–48; also *Generation and distribution of productivity increases in European agriculture, 1967–87*, Eurostat series 5D, 1991.

In Eurostat's *Production, prices and income in EC agriculture* (1991), tables A4.2–10 show the development of output of the various commodities in each EC country.

See also the contribution by Caroline Saunders, "The CAP and intra-EC trade", in the work edited by Ritson and Harvey mentioned above.

3. EC food aid. Quantities are decided annually in advance by the Commission. For 1992, these are:
* cereals: 1.4 million tonnes;
* milk powder etc.: up to 53,000 tonnes;
* butteroil: up to 6,800 tonnes;
* sugar: up to 11,540 tonnes;
* vegetable oil: 70,000 tonnes;
* other products: up to total value of 48 million ECU.

These quantities are a small proportion of total EC exports of the commodities in question: cereal exports, for example, have been above 30 million tonnes in recent years. However, food aid is also provided individually by some Member States, and additional EC supplies are sometimes sent in response to urgent needs.

4. The Generalised System of Preferences. *European File* no. 16/87 dealt briefly with this subject. Issues arising in relation to the review of the system were discussed by the Commission in "Generalized System of Preferences: Guidelines for the 1990s" (COM(90)329 final).

5. The ACP group. Trade, aid and co-operation relations between these countries and the EC are defined in the Lomé Convention, which first entered into force in 1975 (following a previous Convention with the original six EC Member States). The Lomé Convention has been updated on several occasions: the present Convention—the fourth—covers the period 1990–2000. The agreement on sugar takes the form of a Protocol attached to the Convention. Sixty-nine countries in Africa, the Caribbean and the Pacific belong to the group.

6. Mediterranean policy. The EC's trade concessions under its "global Mediterranean policy" were extended to Morocco, Algeria, Tunisia, Egypt, Israel, Jordan, Lebanon, Syria, Cyprus, Malta and Yugoslavia.

"The European Community and the Mediterranean", *European Documentation* 3–4/1985 was a useful study: unfortunately this has not been updated to take account of developments following the accession of Spain and Portugal.

The new Mediterranean policy is contained in three Regulations of 29 June 1992: Regulation 1764/92 in OJ L181 has the trade concessions.

7. Beef: the main preferential arrangements.
Quotas fixed under GATT:
* An annual quota—53,000 tonnes—of frozen beef and veal—levy-free but at the full 20% customs duty.
* Annual import quotas of cattle not intended for slaughter: 47,600 head of "mountain breeds" from Austria and Switzerland—levy-free and at 4% duty.
* An annual quota of 34,300 tonnes of "high-quality" cuts of beef (so-called "Hilton beef") from the US, Canada, Argentina, Uruguay and Australia)—free of levy and but subject to full duty. A further "autonomous" quota (decided by the EC) of high-quality cuts may be admitted free of levy and with 4% duty: in 1992, this applied to 11,430 tonnes from Argentina, Brazil, Uruguay, Australia and New Zealand.

"Balance-sheet" quotas (decided annually by EC):
* Frozen beef and veal for processing from any third country, at nil or reduced levy, full 20% duty: quantity nil in 1992.
* "Young male cattle" for further fattening, at reduced levy, full 16% duty: 198,000 head in 1992. Formerly, this trade consisted mostly of exports from Yugoslavia to Italy and Greece, but imports from Serbia and Montenegro were banned in 1992. The CSFR, Hungary and Poland currently benefit from a 75% levy reduction on the greater part of the total quantity; a smaller part, from any third country, gets a 65% cut.

CEECs:
* Additional quantities of live cattle and beef, at reduced rates of levy, the amounts being progressively increased (see text), from those CEECs with which the EC has concluded "Europe Agreements".
* A monthly quota for "baby beef" was formerly granted to Yugoslavia—reduced levy, subject to conditions relating to the EC price level, full 20% duty. As mentioned above, imports from Serbia and Montenegro are currently banned.

ACPs:
* An annual quota of beef from six African ACP countries— 49,600 tonnes in 1992—90% of the levy paid as an export charge in the exporting country, free of duty.
Agra Europe's *CAP Monitor* includes further details.

8. Central and Eastern Europe. The first three Interim Agreements were published in in the *Official Journal* of 30.4.92, respectively nos. L114 (Poland), L115 (CSFR), and L116 (Hungary) The detailed concessions appear in various annexes and Protocols.

9. The Uruguay Round. For keeping in touch with ongoing negotiations, there is no substitute for the serious daily press such as the *Financial Times*, and the weekly *Agra Europe* (the weekly *Economist* gives views rather than news). The Commission's information services are inadequate; the US Department of Agriculture is much better organised.

The Uruguay Round provoked a spate of analysis. An important study was published in 1987 by the OECD under the title *National Policies and Agricultural Trade*: this included estimates of PSEs and CSEs (see previous chapter). Successive annual "Monitoring and Outlook" reports update these calculations and report in great detail on policy changes. See also the sources mentioned under item 1 above.

10. EC and GATT. The Member States and not the Community itself are "Contracting Parties" to the GATT, but they are represented by the Commission, acting on the basis of Council mandates and in consultation with a special committee of representatives of Member States known as the "113 Committee" (by reference to the relevant article of the Treaty of Rome). Difficulties with this procedure have appeared at various stages in the Uruguay Round. Ultimately, although the Commission can sign a GATT agreement, it must be approved by the Council.
Normally, Trade Ministers in the Foreign Affairs Council are responsible in this field. In the Uruguay Round context, however, it has proved impossible to exclude the Agriculture Ministers, and joint sessions have been held at crucial stages.

11. The Cairns Group. The fourteen members are Argentina, Australia, Brazil, Canada, Chile, Colombia, Indonesia, Malaysia, New Zealand, Philippines, Singapore, Thailand and Uruguay—plus Hungary as the only European member.

12. Trade statistics. Eurostat trade statistics are available in various published series and on "micro-fiches": these are difficult to consult, and do not provide the latest data. "On-line" consultation of the data-base is also possible, and there are magnetic tapes, diskettes and ROM disks: these however are expensive solutions for academic research. Here, Table 13.1 has been derived from the Commission's *Agricultural Situation in the Community*, various years (Tables 3.6.10–11 in recent issues); Table 13.2 and Figure 13.1 are obtained from tables prepared for internal Commission use and from the ROM disk.
Eurostat trade data are presented either according to the Standard International Trade Classification (SITC) or, since 1988, the EC's "Combined Nomenclature" (NC)—which is also the basis of the common tariff. In the former case (used here for Table 13.1) the definition of "agricultural products" covers a wide range of foodstuffs and raw materials, including such items as timber and rubber. Under the NC—used for Table 13.2 and Figure 13.1—chapters 1–24 do not include these raw materials: they do normally include fishery products, but these have been excluded from Table 13.2.
In Table 13.1, the distinction between the original unit of account (UA) and the ECU can be ignored. The inclusion of Greece in "EC 10" from 1973 on, although Greece did not actually join till 1981, does not significantly affect the outcome.

CHAPTER 14

DECISION-MAKING IN AGRICULTURAL POLICY

As previous chapters have shown, governments in practically all the developed market economies have intervened extensively in agricultural product markets and in trade. Price support and protection have provoked surplus production, raised food prices to consumers and caused heavy budgetary expenditure; they have also penalised traditional agricultural exporters and provoked damaging trade conflicts.

Farming is one of the most-assisted sectors of the economy: yet the farm population accounts for only a few per cent of the total. The general consumer interest, or indeed wider economic interests including those of manufacturing industry, play a relatively small role in agricultural policy-making, especially when trade issues are involved. This paradoxical situation needs explanation, which will be attempted below.

It should be observed that while up to now the discussion in this book has been confined as far as possible to verifiable facts, it enters here an area where subjective judgement is inevitable, and where there is an implicit "normative" assumption to the effect that policy "reform" is desirable.

(a) The political science approach

Political scientists have given increased attention to developments in agricultural policy. They tend to seek explanations in terms of "decision-making paradigms" (see sources mentioned in Appendix, item 1). Thus:

"Rational choice models" assume a national authority whose aim is the public good, with complete information and with the power to make and implement policy decisions. Rather like the economist's concept of the "optimum", this is an unlikely situation, but serves as a point of reference.

"Public choice theory" is a not-very-clear term for the rather obvious point that policy-making involves many individuals pursuing their own ends. Although in public they will affirm goals related to the common interest, in reality politicians are interested in power and aim at being elected and re-elected; officials aim to promote their careers; individuals with common interests combine to protect these interests; and so on. The persons with the power to initiate reforms will do so only if this is consistent with their personal aims. This view may be over-cynical—some individuals do aim at the public good, and in the EC context, "European spirit" does exist—but it does often help to interpret the actions of politicians and others in responsibility.

The "organisational process" paradigm stresses that "government" or "the nation" are not monolithic bodies but constellations of loosely-allied organisations, each with its own goals. This too impedes radical change, an obstacle expressed by saying that "the best predictor of what an organisation does today is what it does yesterday". Only a major crisis is likely to overcome this inbuilt inertia. This has indeed been the experience with CAP reform and with the Uruguay Round negotiations.

The "government politics" paradigm focuses on the bargaining process as between the different actors (individuals or organisations). Each must think not only about his own goals but also about what is needed to "win" in the bargaining game. To this end, coalitions may be formed, provided each participant expects thereby to get a better result than through separate action. The bargaining process takes time (particularly if the rules require unanimity for the final decision): compromise is inevitable, and the final agreement is likely to be a "package" with something for everyone. This undoubtedly corresponds to EC "marathons" and to the US legislative process, as will be seen below.

(b) Agricultural policy-making in the EC

i) The Commission

Under the Treaty of Rome (Article 43), the Commission has the sole right of *proposal*: the Council of Ministers cannot formally consider any suggestion that has not come from the Commission. This gives the Commission considerable influence.

A key role is played by the member of the Commission responsible for agriculture. The first Commissioner for Agriculture, Sicco Mansholt, after completing the initial task of setting up the common market organisations, made the largely unsuccessful attempt already described to create more rational farm structures. During most of the 1970s, the responsible Commissioner was Pierre Lardinois (a former Minister of Agriculture in the Netherlands): his period in office was marked by the over-generous price increases described in Chapter 9, which probably aggravated many of the subsequent problems. His Danish successor, Finn Olav Gundelach, had no previous connections with agriculture (he had dealt with trade issues in GATT): during his tenure, the Commission began to stress the need for a "prudent", then for a "restrictive" price policy. After his sudden death in 1981, he was succeeded by another former Agriculture Minister (also a Dane), Poul Dalsager, and for a while the Commission's attitude appeared less restrictive, although milk quotas were inaugurated towards the end of his period.

Budget problems continued to mount and could no longer be ignored by any Agriculture Commissioner. Moreover, Frans Andriessen, who held the post in 1985–88, was a former Dutch Minister of Finance: he proposed the major "stabiliser" reforms which were adopted in 1988. The President of the Commission, Jacques Delors, was also a key player in the 1988 reform: given his main goal of promoting further "integration", though the "Single Market" and then through the "European Union" concepts, he was acutely aware of the need to reduce the budgetary burden of CAP price support.

Further initiatives, which led to the "MacSharry" plan, appear to have been taken by Delors and by some senior French officials in the Commission, aiming to put the Community in a stronger negotiating position in the Uruguay Round. (The French government did not share this view, and in the end accepted the reform with great reluctance.) Ray MacSharry, Commissioner for Agriculture in 1989–92, had been a Finance Minister and then Agriculture Minister in Ireland: he was presumably not unsympathetic to the farmers' cause nor to the Irish interest in the CAP, but realising no doubt that without further reform the CAP was in danger of collapse, he carried the reform process through to a conclusion. (The outcome, as already noted, was not bad for Ireland.)

The EC–US negotiations on the problem of oilseeds and the Uruguay Round pin-pointed issues of personalities as well as national interests. At a crucial stage in November 1992, MacSharry refused to continue negotiating with the Americans, accusing Delors of intervening on behalf of French interests. The conflict was nevertheless resolved within the Commission: MacSharry resumed the negotiation, and Delors supported the agreement reached, despite the very adverse French reaction.

The Agricultural Directorate-General (DG VI) appears large, yet its resources for economic analysis are limited, especially by comparison with those of the US Department of Agriculture. Its reputation of being farmer-oriented is not entirely justified. Undoubtedly, the representatives of major farmers' organisations can always get a hearing from key officials. But DG VI experts play a vital role in preparing reform proposals, and in steering them through the initial stages of discussion in Council working parties and committees. DG VI officials, together with officials from DG I (External Relations), also represent the Community in GATT agricultural negotiations, up to the highest level where Commissioners are involved.

Most DG VI officials are fully occupied in administering the complex CAP programmes. Many decisions are taken through the Management Committee procedure (already mentioned in Chapter 9), where national Ministries are represented but where the Commission generally gets its way. The 1988 reform of the Structural Funds also gave the Commission increased responsibility for implementing rural development policy: here too a Management Committee is involved (the "Committee on Agricultural Structures and Rural Development", or STAR after its French title).

There are a number of Advisory Committees which the Commission can consult, where producer, trade and consumer groups are represented. These are generally regarded as being ineffective.

ii) The European Parliament (EP)

Although the EP has been progressively granted greater powers, in the case of agricultural policy its role remains limited to giving the Council its "Opinion" on Commission proposals: an Opinion which the Council must have in its possession before it can legally act, but which it can—and often does—ignore.

For many years, farming interests were able to dominate the Parliament through its Agriculture Committee, where Opinions are drafted. EP members with a strong interest in the sector seek appointment to this Committee. During the 1970s, the EP as a whole generally supported the rise in support prices. This situation has changed, as the EP too cannot ignore the budgetary implications; also because the accession of Spain and Portugal increased the number of members with an interest in keeping down the costs of price support in order to free resources for structural and regional measures.

iii) The Council of Ministers

While the Commission is in principle independent, the Member States are represented in the Council; the Presidency is held by each Member State in turn, in six-monthly rotation. Commission proposals are first considered in committees (for CAP matters, in the "Special Committee for Agriculture") and in various working parties. The Ministerial-level Council has the power of decision.

The Treaty of Rome required only a "qualified majority" to approve a Commission proposal on agricultural policy, and unanimity to amend it. But for many years, following the "Luxembourg compromise" of 1966, unanimity was sought in practice. This text (see Appendix, item 6) was a political solution to a crisis provoked by President de Gaulle of France, in opposition to an extension of the powers of Community institutions. France contended that where a Member State considered that "very important interests" were at stake, discussion should continue until unanimity was reached. The other Member States disagreed; but work was resumed. Although it did not actually modify the provisions of the Treaty, observance of the Luxembourg compromise led to "marathon" sessions in the Agriculture Council: it also obliged the Commission (or Council President) to construct "packages" offering something to every Minister, and was largely responsible for both the inflationary tendency and the growing complexity of the CAP, with numerous derogations and special concessions (including various "agri-monetary" arrangements as well as hastily-devised structural measures).

The Single European Act of 1986, though it did not change the formal procedures as regards agricultural policy, did introduce a different climate by introducing majority voting more widely in other sectors. Moreover, the inefficiency of the unanimity practice had to be recognised, especially after the accession of Spain and Portugal in 1986 raised the number of Member States to twelve. Increasingly, important decisions began to be taken by majority vote. With the drive towards "European Union" which took shape in the "Maastricht" Treaty, the "Luxembourg compromise" appeared virtually defunct. It was however resurrected by the French right-wing parties during the referendum campaign in the summer of 1992 over ratification of the Maastricht Treaty, and—more surprisingly—in November 1992 by the mainly Socialist government on the "Uruguay Round" issue.

There is, in principle, only one "Council": the "Agriculture Council" has the same authority as the "Foreign Affairs Council" or any other. Joint sessions are rare. It is sometimes suggested by outside observers that involving Budget Ministers in CAP discussions would moderate inflationary tendencies: but two Ministers from the same country will not oppose each other in EC meetings, and if disagreements exist, they have to be sorted out within each national government.

The Uruguay Round issues strained the decision-making procedures almost to breaking-point. As already noted, the Commission negotiates on behalf of the Community, although the final decision lies with the Council ("qualified majority" applies in this context also). The Treaty of Rome provided that the Commission should act "in consultation" with a special committee appointed by the Council (known as the "113 Committee", after the relevant Article of the Treaty). Inevitably, the Commission seeks the widest possible mandate.

On the Uruguay Round, the Member States had conflicting interests; the Agriculture Council as well as the Foreign Affairs Council became involved. At crucial stages, the mandate was unclear; as has already been observed, the outcome of the Commission's negotiation with the US was contested by France.

There has been a growing tendency to refer major policy issues to the "European Council", consisting of "Heads of State and Government" (see Appendix, item 7). As has already been seen in previous chapters, the session of the European Council in Edinburgh in December 1992, under British presidency, had to resolve a complex array of problems including Danish ratification of the Maastricht Treaty and the Community's finances in the coming years.

iv) Producer and consumer representation at the EC level

The various national farmers' organisations are grouped in the *Comité des Organisations des Producteurs Agricoles* (COPA). For many years, this body exerted considerable influence. It had easy access, in particular, to Pierre Lardinois during his time as Commissioner. It continues to submit to the Council its views on major proposals: these can be quoted by farm-oriented Ministers to support their case.

With growing surplus and budget problems, COPA's power has declined. It also has increasing difficulty in reaching agreement among its own members, given the diversity of farm organisations from all twelve Member States. Unlike the US situation (see later section), commodity groups have not so far emerged as powerful lobbies.

The food industry is represented in Brussels by the Confederation of the Food and Drink Industries of the EC (CIAA); there are also numerous European-level associations of particular food and feed sectors. An important task of these bodies is to gather information on EC activities. They do not exert significant influence on agricultural policy-making, but make more impact on food legislation.

However, the margarine industry, dominated by the Dutch-based multi-national Unilever, has successfully opposed the introduction of a tax on vegetable oils, which from time to time has been under discussion as a means of alleviating the butter market and, to some extent, the olive oil market.

There is no organisation comparable to COPA on the consumer side. Opinions on agricultural and especially on food policy are submitted by the *Bureau Européen des Unions des Consommateurs*: the BEUC, however, is simply an umbrella body grouping various voluntary consumer organisations (such as *Which?* in the UK or similar consumer magazines in other countries) and has no representative status.

Another Community institution, the Economic and Social Committee, has in principle the task of representing the interests of "the various categories of economic and social activity", including farmers and "representatives of the general public" (Article 193 of the Rome Treaty), and is formally consulted by the Council. Its opinions, however, carry very little weight.

v) National interests

It is not possible in a short space to analyse all aspects of agricultural policy-making in each EC Member State: the discussion here will concentrate on those forces which appear most relevant in the context of CAP reform and trade liberalisation.

An important factor determining the national interest of each Member State is its net position under the EC budget. Figure 14.1 shows budget contributions and receipts. Germany and the UK (the latter in spite of its "rebate"—see below) are the biggest net contributors, but France, Italy and Belgium are also net contributors. Large net benefits are obtained by Ireland, Denmark, the Netherlands and Greece, thanks to big receipts for agricultural market support under FEOGA "Guarantee". It is notable that Spain receives hardly any more FEOGA Guarantee money than Greece, although it is a much larger country: Greece gets large payments for fruit and vegetables, dried fruit, tobacco and cotton.

Receipts from the structural funds include money from FEOGA Guidance, the Regional Fund and the Social Fund. They account for a relatively large share of total receipts in the Southern European countries (as has been seen in Chapter 10, this type of expenditure is expanding). Only part of this goes to rural areas.

The **United Kingdom** has been the most constant advocate of reforming the CAP in the direction of lower prices, and of trade liberalisation. This is consistent

Figure 14.1—Member States' share of EC budget, 1990

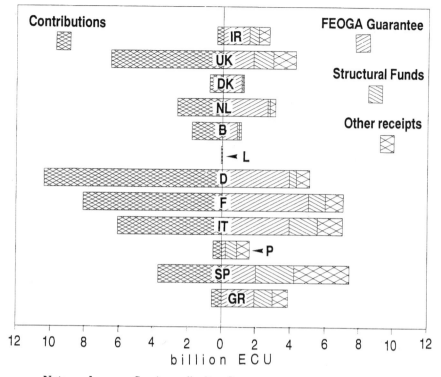

Notes and source: See Appendix, item 8.

with the UK's tradition of maintaining low food prices and obtaining food from the cheapest sources around the world: the UK accepted the CAP very reluctantly, as the necessary price of gaining entry to the EC. But the budgetary issue has also been a very important consideration. With a relatively high proportion of food imports still coming from third countries, the UK contributes a relatively large amount in import levies to the EC budget: on the other hand, having a small farm sector, it receives a relatively small share of FEOGA payments. This issue has been a constant source of friction. A "financial mechanism" to reduce the UK budgetary burden was first agreed in 1974, and Margaret Thatcher obtained firmer concessions in 1984: at the Edinburgh "Summit" in December 1992, John Major succeeded—with much less acrimony—in having this "rebate" prolonged under the budgetary arrangements for 1993–99 (cf. Appendix to Chapter 9, item 5). It was understood by the other leaders that without this concession, ratification of the Maastricht Treaty by the British Parliament would be in doubt.

At the same time, the interests of British farmers have been supported by most Ministers of Agriculture (the only significant exception being under the Labour Minister John Silkin in 1976–79). Despite the reduced size of the farm population, the farming interest has been ably defended by the National Farmers' Union (NFU). Its influence appears to lie not so much in the number of votes it can muster, which is limited, as in the links at all levels between farm leaders and Conservative politicians. The NFU has also managed to retain much public sympathy, particularly in recent years by largely espousing the "green" causes relating to agriculture and the environment.

An increase in domestic food output helps to improve Britain's net balance with the EC budget. Hence, in negotiations in the Agriculture Council, British Ministers of Agriculture have fought for the best deal possible for their farmers. Depreciation of the pound, before its entry into the Exchange Rate Mechanism (see Chapter 7), permitted increases in farm prices expressed in pounds even when common prices in ECU were being frozen: the pound's forced departure from the ERM in September 1992 and its sharp fall in value provided renewed scope for increases in support prices, despite the "MacSharry" reforms.

Denmark and the **Netherlands** have strong agricultural interests: as efficient producers and exporters, access to markets both in the EC and in third countries is vital. They need not oppose reductions in support prices or trade liberalisation, but it is also important for them to preserve the CAP, from which they derive big financial benefits. They consistently object to national aids which distort competition within the EC, and have always pressed for rapid elimination of monetary compensatory amounts. Environmental concerns have caused these countries to adopt the most stringent controls in the EC over the use of agrochemicals and the disposal of animal manure: they will continue to demand that similar controls should be introduced by other Member States.

For **Ireland** too, agricultural exports are vital: accession to the EC in 1973 widened its outlets beyond its traditional market in the UK. But much of Ireland's output of dairy products and beef has gone into EC intervention, and Ireland has opposed any dilution of the support system. In 1984 the Irish Prime Minister made a major issue of Ireland's need for favourable treatment under the milk quota system. The "MacSharry" reform is likely to give a net *increase* in agricultural income, because of the increased premiums for cattle.

Belgium and **Luxembourg**, despite the small share of agriculture in the economy, have usually taken pro-farmer attitudes in CAP negotiations. Their farm unions have strong influence over their Ministries of Agriculture: in Belgium, the Flemish **Boerenbond**, which has widespread commercial activities, maintains close links with the Flemish Christian Democrat party (*Christelijke Volkspartij* or CVP) which is usually the largest coalition partner and has almost always supplied the Minister of Agriculture. But the primary objective for these countries—as for the Netherlands—is to maintain the pace of European integration (which started with the Belgium–Luxembourg Economic Union and Benelux): thus in the end these countries will not oppose a compromise package on agriculture.

Italian agriculture includes a wide range of conditions, covering relatively well-structured and competitive farms in the North but small and backward holdings in difficult natural conditions in the Mezzogiorno. In the late 1970s, Italy was able to obtain more favourable treatment for Mediterranean products in general, as well as increased funds for various programmes to improve farm structures and rural infrastructure. Italy continues to demand favourable treatment for its wine, durum wheat, fruit and vegetables. Political instability reduces Italy's impact on EC policy-making.

Each of the Southern European countries has its own special interests where particular commodities are concerned (Greece, for example, fights for its cotton and tobacco sectors). But **Greece, Portugal, Spain** and to some extent **Italy** share a common objective: that of obtaining more EC finance for their development, including rural development—an aim diplomatically enshrined under the expression "cohesion" in both the Single European Act and the Maastricht Treaty. Besides insistence on increasing the allocations for the structural Funds, this aim can also mean that these countries—up to a point—may accept measures to reduce the support costs for "Northern" products, to release funds for their own purposes.

With its successive enlargements, the EC has thus acquired an internal North-South dimension, which significantly influences its policy-making in all fields, especially as the four Southern European members can constitute a "blocking minority" in the Council (see Appendix, item 6).

The attitudes of the countries so far mentioned to matters of CAP reform and trade liberalisation is fairly constant and predictable. This is not the case for the two remaining Member States, and the positions they finally adopt are crucial.

vi) Germany

The greatest paradox in agricultural policy has been Germany: a highly-industrialised country, with a strong interest in export markets for its manufactures, where agriculture accounts for only a few per cent of national income and of active population, yet where farmers have remained highly supported. German Agriculture Ministers constantly resisted price cuts under the CAP, and when reductions could not be avoided, insisted on compensation either from EC or from national funds.

There are economic reasons for this situation: in several *Länder*—including Bavaria—many farms are small, and costs of production are high. However, most households living on small farms have other sources of income as well.

Political factors are more important. The *Deutscher Bauernverband* (DBV) is a powerful body. Like farm unions in other countries, it has built up political acceptance by associating the role of agriculture with the social values of stability and continuity. As most farmers are Catholic (except in parts of the North), it has strong links with the Christian-Democrat party (*Christliche Demokratische Union*—CDU) and its Bavarian wing, the *Christliche Soziale Union* (CSU). There has also been continuous interaction between the DBV and the Ministry of Agriculture at all levels (cf. Appendix, item 4).

Since 1969, there have been only two Ministers of Agriculture, Josef Ertl and Ignaz Kiechle: both from Bavaria, and both farmers themselves. Their ability to override other government Ministers stemmed from coalition politics. Ertl was a prominent member of the Liberal party (*Freie Demokratische Partei*—FDP), in coalition first with the Socialists (SPD) in 1969-82. Although most farmers vote CDU-CSU, there are those in the North and in Bavaria who support the FDP: Ertl could bring in a marginal but crucial farm vote in his area. In the CDU-CSU coalition in power since 1982 (with FDP support), Kiechle, as one of the CSU leaders, likewise played a key role, aided by Chancellor Kohl's personal commitment to a section of the electorate that is traditionally loyal to his party. The strength of this commitment was underlined in the EC Agriculture Council in 1985 when Kiechle, with Kohl's support, vetoed a cut in cereal prices—the only occasion Germany has invoked the "Luxembourg compromise", and this at a time when Germany was promoting a general move to majority voting in the context of the Single European Act.

The re-unification of Germany creates a significantly different situation, with important implications for agricultural policy. It is not yet clear what will happen to the huge collectives (*Landwirtschaftliche Produktionsgenossenschaften* or LPG) of the former DDR, but it is most unlikely that they will all be broken up into small family farms: many will remain as large commercial or co-operative enterprises. It was thus significant that, in the negotiations on the "MacSharry Plan", Kiechle did not support the Commission's proposal for "degressivity" in the compensatory payments, as he would certainly have done in the past.

In these negotiations, the initial German aim was to limit price cuts and to rely also on supply controls (including set-aside), and to obtain full and lasting compensation for price cuts. After the agreement in May 1992, the Ministry of Agriculture issued a statement (see Appendix, item 4) stressing that Kiechle had opposed the price cuts as long as possible, but in the end had agreed in view of other elements in the package which corresponded to German demands. In particular, the compensation for cereal growers was claimed to be lasting and reliable ("*dauerhaft und verlässlich* "), and independent of the size of farm; effective protection against cereal imports would be maintained; with set-aside now a condition of obtaining the compensatory payments, there was assurance that it would be applied in all Member States; but the exemption from this requirement of "small producers" (output less than 92 tonnes) would cover more than 80% of German holdings (most of those in southern Germany). For beef too, there would be compensation for the price cuts through increased premiums.

In relation to the Uruguay Round, there were conflicting aims. While the agricultural interest opposed concessions by the EC, business interests were strongly in favour of a successful conclusion of the Round. The latter attitude was reflected in statements by the Ministers of Trade and of Economics. For Chancellor Kohl, however, a key consideration remained the close alliance with France in the pursuit of European integration. Nevertheless, in the crisis over these issues arising at the end of 1992, Germany's increased self-confidence following reunification, as well as its obvious economic interests, appeared for the first time to cause it to part company from the French government. The latter's talk of "vetoing" an outcome based on the US–EC agreement provoked no echo in Bonn, and while the French government appeared to encourage farmers' demonstrations, the German government tried to discourage them.

vii) France

With the biggest agricultural sector in the EC and a strong interest in developing agricultural exports (*vocation agricole*), France has always attached great importance to the "principles" of the CAP (cf. Chapter 9): until the mid–1980s, successive French governments opposed even the mention of CAP "reform".

Internally, there has been intense debate over the goals of agricultural policy. French agriculture has undergone traumatic structural and technological change; France also contains regions with great diversity in terms of natural conditions and farm structures. The large, highly-mechanised arable farms of the Paris basin have little in common with the small peasant farms of the western, south-western and mountain regions. The "productivist" approach of the former has clashed with the "ruralist" philosophy defending the latter.

This conflict has been reflected in farmer representation. The largest farm organisation is the *Fédération nationale des syndicats des exploitants agricoles* (FNSEA): this has branches throughout the country, and has had difficulty in maintaining its unity. The tendency of most of its leadership has been conservative, though there is also a reformist element issuing from the young farmers' movement, the *Centre national des jeunes agriculteurs* (CNJA).

On the political left of this "mainstream" body, various organisations representing peasant farmers have contested both government policy and the hegemony of the FNSEA/CNJA over farmer representation; in 1987 some unity was achieved between these groups through the creation of the *Confédération paysanne*. Right-wing organisations, in particular the *Fédération française de l'agriculture*, though less significant, also pose a potential threat to the mainstream movement.

Vying for their clientèle, these various organisations cannot afford to seem conciliatory towards the government. Any French government is faced with a dilemma: should it attempt to co-operate with the various farm movements, or seek some understanding with the FNSEA/CNJA which commands the largest number of supporters? In the Socialist government which came to power in 1981, the first Minister of Agriculture, Edith Cresson, found to her cost that it was unwise to antagonise the mainstream movement; her successor, Michel Rocard, had to mend his fences before he could push through the 1984 milk quota decision. But even with tacit support from the FNSEA/CNJA, measures which displease the peasant movements are always liable to cause violent demonstrations. There is no significant consumer movement to set against the farmers, and business interests usually remain muted.

Faced with the "MacSharry Plan" for CAP reform, the French government was thus in a difficult position. It had gradually been forced to accept the need to deal with surpluses: acceptance of the milk quota system in 1984 was the first sign of this. The realisation that, with the southern enlargement of the EC, France had become a net contributor to the budget, may have played some role in government circles, though it was not raised in public discussion. The initial MacSharry proposal to discriminate in the compensatory payments in favour of small producers went to the heart of the productivist-ruralist controversy. The government finally accepted the compromise agreement in which the degressive element in the compensatory payments was removed, but the "small producer" exemption from the set-aside requirement covers many French farmers.

Widespread demonstrations in opposition to the 1992 CAP reform were organised by a recently-formed *Coordination rurale* movement; many FNSEA and CNJA members participated. The government made various tax concessions. The Prime Minister, Pierre Bérégovoy, also received delegates from the *Confédération paysanne*—an important gesture—and promised to grant one of their main demands: representation on various bodies through which agricultural policy is managed and funds distributed. The Minister of Agriculture associated with the CAP reform, Louis Mermaz, was replaced by Jean-Pierre Soisson, who took a much tougher line.

The government had insisted that the CAP reform decisions had been taken for internal EC reasons, and not because of the GATT Uruguay Round. It immediately denounced the bilateral agreement negotiated by the EC Commission with the US in November 1992. Farm organisations organised large-scale demonstrations, with a strongly anti-American flavour. The Prime Minister, Pierre Bérégovoy, threatened to "veto" the outcome—but was careful to associate this with the final stages (*"la fin des fins"*) of the negotiation. There were some signs that public opinion was becoming less sympathetic to the farmers, and business leadership (the *patronat*) expressed concern at the consequences of blocking a Uruguay Round agreement: still, the government maintained a hardline attitude, declaring the US–EC deal incompatible with the CAP reform programme, denouncing the formal EC submission to GATT and attacking personally the Commissioners concerned (MacSharry and Andriessen—the latter now responsible for trade).

These tactics served at least to justify demands for "compensation", although precisely what would be required to satisfy France remained unclear. In December 1992, at the Edinburgh "Summit", President Mitterrand obtained some leeway in the "guideline" for CAP expenditure (cf. Chapter 9, Appendix item 5), and in the Agriculture Council, France obtained concessions on the suckler cow premium and aids for durum wheat. But with parliamentary elections looming in March 1993, the basic concern was clearly political. Neither the Socialist-led government, nor the centre-right opposition, which was expected to win, could afford to antagonise the farming community.

(c) The United States

US agricultural policy is mainly based on Farm Acts each covering a four- or five-year period: Chapter 12 has discussed in particular the Acts of 1985 (the FSA) and 1990 (the FACT). Draft legislation is prepared by the Executive, mainly in the US Department of Agriculture (USDA) and, after approval by the President, submitted to Congress. In both the Senate and the House of Representatives, a long series of hearings takes place in various committees. Besides their Agriculture Committees, the House has a number of commodity sub-committees which play an important role; the Budget Committees are also involved. The bills drafted by the Agriculture Committees are debated in the full House and Senate; differences between the two versions are reconciled by a "conference" consisting of the Agriculture Committee chairmen and members of their committees whom they select. If the President then signs the bill, it becomes law. He can veto it, in which case a two-thirds majority in each House is necessary to override the Presidential veto. The whole process typically takes about a year to complete.

The outcome represents a series of compromises between different interest groups. Within the Executive, the Agricultural Stabilization and Conservation Service (ASCS), which administers the commodity programmes, exercises strong influence. At all levels—state and county as well as federal—the ASCS has close links with commodity groups, which provide information and support for USDA programmes in return for protection of their interests. Still, the Executive's proposal to Congress bears the stamp of the politically-appointed Secretary for Agriculture: hence the strong market orientation of the draft 1985 and 1990 bills presented by the Reagan and Bush administrations.

The congressional committees tend to be composed largely of members representing States or districts where agriculture is important; and in the House commodity sub-committees, the members overwhelmingly represent the districts where the commodities in question are produced. Service on the relevant committee gives a politician the opportunity to deliver benefits to his potential electors. The tendency, inevitably, is to protect vested interests and minimise changes.

The legislative process gives many opportunities for "lobbies" to exert their influence. The general farmers' organisations—in particular the American Farm Bureau, the National Farmers Union and the Grange—have lost power to the commodity groups, forming with the Congress and the USDA what has been described as a "triangle of power". Still, conflict between the commodity interests, and the emergence of new concerns related to the environment and food quality, have somewhat eroded the influence of the commodity groups. There is also a well-organised consumer lobby in Washington, which testifies before the House and Senate Agriculture Committees during farm bill hearings. Agribusiness concerns exert a more discreet influence on Congressmen and government officials, but can be effective on particular issues.

While Congressmen from farming areas can hope to gain votes by supporting commodity programmes, those from non-farm districts gain little by opposing farm-oriented legislation. Still, with the decline in the number of farming constituencies, the remaining farm-based Congressmen need support from the urban elements. One result has been agreement on increased funding for the Food Stamp Program (already discussed in Chapter 12): here, there is a clear political "trade-off"between the interest-groups.

This legislative process has in the past led to generous treatment for American farmers. But as in the EC, the budgetary excesses resulting from high price supports have imposed increasingly severe constraints. The Gramm-Rudman-Hollings Act of 1987 required across-the-board government spending cuts, and led to cuts in target prices additional to those required by the 1985 FSA. Reference has already been made in Chapter 12 to the Omnibus Budget Reconciliation Act (OBRA) of 1990, which imposed changes in the programmes for arable crops and milk so as to achieve budget savings exceeding $13 billion in 1991–95.

This context explains US aggressivity on agricultural trade matters. The EC is seen first as having largely excluded US produce from its domestic market, and then as having eroded other US export outlets through its own subsidised exports. The growth of subsidised oilseed production in the EC has been a particularly sensitive issue, especially in view of the political strength of the American Soybean Association. In the "Uruguay Round" negotiations, the US had to come a long way from its original "zero option" on price supports and protection: the US–EC agreement of November 1992 involved major concessions by both sides, and was motivated by the recognition that failure to agree on agriculture would not only lead to a damaging trade war over the oilseeds issue but would prevent any overall GATT agreement.

(d) Agricultural policy and the democratic process

The political strength of the farming community is not measured simply by the number of votes it can muster in nation-wide elections. There are of course marginal rural constituencies where the farming vote can decide the outcome, and there may even be enough of such constituencies to influence the overall outcome of an election and the composition of a government, particularly in the case of coalitions, as has been seen in the case of Germany.

As a rule, more subtle forces are at work. One such, noted in several of the countries just discussed, is the interaction between farm representatives on the one hand, and officials or politicians on the other. The latter usually find it easier to work with the farming interest than against it. Farm organisations can provide useful information and may have a role in implementing policy measures: in return, they expect the authorities to take their interests into account. Such interaction may occur particularly when farm and government representatives feel they are the same kind of people, with similar educational and class backgrounds: the United Kingdom and probably Germany are examples of this.

The farming interest can be more easily promoted in so far as there is public sympathy for their cause. On the whole, this seems still to be the case. Among the urban population, there remains a sentimental and partly irrational attachment to the "rural life". Governments—even left-wing ones—often see the farming community as a bulwark of social stability (this is the case even more in Switzerland than in the countries discussed in this chapter). Even the Socialist government in France has been unable to bypass the mainstream, largely conservative farm organisations.

These are all factors militating against radical reform of agricultural policies, and in particular against cuts in support prices. Such action is bound to be acutely unpopular with producers: on the other hand, as the benefits to consumers and/or taxpayers are diffuse, it is unlikely to gain much support on that side.

In these circumstances, significant change is unlikely to occur unless a major crisis makes this inevitable. It has been seen that such a crisis has occurred in both the EC and the USA as a result of overproduction, the build-up of stocks and the consequent growth of budgetary expenditure. This development has widened the issues and brought other players into the ring. In the case of the EC, further economic and political integration required a limit on CAP spending, imposed after negotiations at the highest political level, that of the European Council. In the US, the budgetary authorities in the Executive and in Congress have insisted on cuts in expenditure on commodity programmes.

Other public concerns are playing an increasing role. There are consumer demands for better food quality, calling in question modern intensive production methods: thus the use of chemicals in plant production, of hormones in animal production, have come under closer scrutiny. Such issues are lined to the broad concern with the rural environment: with water and air pollution from agrochemicals and livestock manure, and with preservation of the countryside and its fauna and flora.

There remains the issue of agricultural trade. Attacks by exporting countries on protectionist importers, however justified in economic terms, are often politically naïve and may be counterproductive, stirring up nationalistic reactions. In this field too, when major issues are at stake, as in the Uruguay Round, it seems unfortunately difficult to reach a conclusion without a crisis in which numerous interest-groups become involved.

In conclusion, the democratic process seems unlikely to produce the most rational or "optimum" result in economic terms. Still, sub-optimal or "second-best" outcomes seem generally acceptable to public opinion: the agriculture and food systems of the developed market economies do, after all, provide ample food at prices which most people can afford. In agricultural policy, as in other respects, democratic decision-making does not necessarily produce the best results, but it still seems greatly preferable to any other system.

APPENDIX

1. EC policy-making. The discussion here is largely based on the author's own experience. The works mentioned below have also been taken into account.

The most useful general work is by W. Moyer and T.E. Josling, *Agricultural Policy Reform: Politics and Process in the EC and USA* (Harvester-Wheatsheaf, New York & London, 1990). Another important contribution was a compendium of studies by M. Petit and others, *Agricultural Policy Formation in the European Community: the Birth of Milk Quotas and CAP Reform* (Elsevier, Amsterdam etc., 1987): this contains chapters on several EC countries. More specialised articles include G. Schmitt, "Warum die Agrarpolitik ist, wie sie ist, und nicht wie se sein sollte", *Agrarwirtschaft* 33(5) 1984 (pp.129–136); S.M. Senior-Nello, "An application of public choice theory to the question of CAP reform", *European Review of Agricultural Economics* 11, 1985 (pp.261-283); L.A. Winters, "The political economy of the agricultural policy of industrial countries", *European Review of Agricultural Economics* 14, 1987 (pp.285-304).

E. Neville-Rolfe's *The Politics of Agriculture in the European Community*, (Policy Studies Institute, London, 1984) is out-of-date as regards policy discussion but contains useful background on the UK, Germany, France and Italy.

A doctoral thesis by O.W. Gray, *Pressure groups and their influence on agricultural policy and its reform in the European Community* (University of Bath, England, 1990), deals particularly with activities of the food industries in relation to EC policy.

2. EC Member States. Here too, much of the discussion derives from the author's own experience, together with a variety of sources including current reports by the serious press and specialised agencies, especially *Agra Europe*.

3. France. Among works in English, see John Keeler *The Politics of Neocorporatism in France: Farmers, the State and agricultural policy-making in the Fifth Republic* (OUP, 1987); also Mark Cleary, *Peasants, Politicians and Producers: the organisation of agriculture in France since 1918* (CUP, 1989).

Les Agriculteurs et la Politique is a large volume containing numerous papers edited by P. Coulomb and others (Fondation Nationale des Sciences Politiques, Paris, 1990): the main papers have been translated and edited by the present author in *Farmers and Politics in France* (Arkleton Trust, Enstone, England, 1991).

A useful set of papers by several contributors, recognising the inevitability of continuing adjustment in farm output and employment, is contained in "La mutation de l'agriculture", *Economie et Statistique* 254–5, mai-juin 1992 (INSEE, Paris).

Le Monde is a valuable source on French political developments; on trade issues it shares the anti-American bias characteristic of most French attitudes.

4. Germany. The background has been very thoroughly analysed by G. Hendriks in *Germany and European Integration: The Common Agricultural Policy—An Area of Conflict* (Berg, Oxford: 1991). As regards the effects of re-unification, those studies that have so far appeared must be regarded as preliminary: more will no doubt follow, with more material to go on.

German objectives as regards the "MacSharry Plan" and the agricultural issues in the Uruguay Round were set out in a government statement presented by Agriculture Minister Kiechle to the *Bundestag* on 9th October 1991 (*Amtsblad*, 12. Wahlperiode–46. Sitzung; also in the Ministry's *Agrarbericht* 1992). The Ministry of Agriculture statement following conclusion of the CAP reform negotiations was reproduced in the German-language *Agra Europe* of 1 June 1992.

5. The United States. The Moyer–Josling work mentioned above gives an excellent account of policy processes and indicates numerous additional sources. However, it predates the important 1990 FACT. Some sources mentioned in the Appendix to Chapter 12 are also relevant.

6. Majority voting in the EC and the "Luxembourg compromise". According to Article 43 of the Treaty of Rome, Commission proposals on agricultural policy can be adopted by the Council by "qualified majority". In the Community of Twelve, the distribution of votes is:

* 10 votes each for Germany, France, Italy and the UK;
* 8 votes for Spain;
* 5 votes each for Belgium, Netherlands, Greece and Portugal;
* 3 votes each for Denmark and Ireland;
* 2 votes for Luxembourg.

Total 76: 54 votes constitute the qualified majority. A "blocking minority" can thus be formed by countries totalling 23 votes.

The "Luxembourg compromise" has been widely misunderstood. It was imposed—in contradiction to the Treaty—by President de Gaulle of France in 1966. It was agreed by the Six that when "very important issues" were at stake, the Council would endeavour to reach solutions which could be adopted by all members. France added its own declaration, stating that in such cases discussion must continue until unanimous agreement was reached. The others did not accept this view: the Benelux countries in particular never formally invoked a "vital national interest". In the enlarged Community, however, the UK, Ireland, Denmark and later Greece explicitly made use of this procedure: less openly, most Member States would indicate cases where they had special difficulty, and in such cases there was general reluctance among Ministers to vote down a colleague; most Presidents in such circumstances would not take a vote. If necessary, France would side with a delegation that had formally stated a vital interest, whatever the French views on substance.

7. The European Council. This was not provided for by the Treaty of Rome. As the practice of "summit" meetings developed, the Single European Act provided a formal basis by stating (Article 2) that "The European Council shall bring together the Heads of State or of Government of the Member States and the President of the Commission of the European Communities... [It] shall meet at least twice a year." (The reference to "Heads of State" was necessary to accommodate the French President, who has responsibility for foreign affairs: otherwise, the participants are Prime Ministers or equivalent.)

In practice, the European Council meets three times a year. It cannot itself formally adopt Community Acts, but its conclusions are subsequently acted upon by the relevant Council of Ministers.

8. Figure 14.1. Contributions to the budget totalled 41.4 billion ECU, individual country receipts 37.3 billion, the difference consisting of payments not allocated by Member State (administration, overseas aid, etc.). (The total budget was 46.9 billion ECU, with the addition of a surplus from the previous year.) The rebate to the UK is taken into account. "Other" receipts include repayment of expenditure for the depreciation of agricultural stocks and for the disposal of butter surpluses; in the cases of Portugal and Spain, they also include refunds of part of their VAT-based budget contributions (a temporary concession which ended in 1991) and of part of their share in financing the UK rebate.

Source: Court of Auditors, "Annual Report concerning the financial year 1990", *Official Journal* C324 of 13.12.91 (Vol. II: Annex tables 5b and 11b).

PART C

CONCLUSION

CHAPTER 15

IMPLICATIONS FOR TRANSITION FROM SOCIALISED AGRICULTURE

Parts A and B of this book have sought to analyse the strengths and weaknesses of the food and agriculture systems in the developed market economies. This final chapter will consider what conclusions may be drawn for the Central and Eastern Europe countries (CEECs), which are currently emerging from decades of central planning, State trading and mainly collectivised agriculture, and as a result are undergoing drastic adjustments.

In many respects, the problems of the CEECs are unparalleled: there is little experience in the West that can be simply drawn upon, few models that can just be transposed. Moreover, the political and economic context as well as the situation of the agri-food systems differ from country to country: each must find the most appropriate solutions.

The following sections, therefore, will not attempt to prescribe precise remedies, but only to set out some broad guidelines where Western experience has some relevance. It will concentrate on matters which concern all or most of the formerly centrally-planned countries. (The same issues have arisen in the former DDR, but in this case the solutions are to a large extent imposed by its absorption in the economy of the Federal Republic and, subject to certain adjustments, in the market mechanisms of the CAP.)

(a) Prices, markets and trade

In the CEECs, prices at various stages of the production and distribution chain, instead of being fixed by official decree as formerly, are being freed, though they are still subject to restraint in some cases. As official price-fixing generally kept food prices to consumers artificially low, the initial effect of this liberalisation is to raise consumer prices, sometimes very sharply.

Distribution channels, formerly in State ownership, remain largely unreformed—this will be discussed in section (c) below. Supplies are erratic; and the lack of experience with price formation in a free market system often causes prices in food shops to be set in an arbitrary fashion. In conditions of shortage, opportunities for profiteering abound.

Following price liberalisation, queues for scarce supplies may be reduced or disappear, but the higher prices can have severe consequences, especially for low-income consumers.

Imports, which could in principle help to meet food needs and keep down prices, are limited by shortages of foreign exchange. Food aid from the West can make at best a marginal and temporary impact, and may, unless carefully targeted, discourage local production.

In the early stages of economic reform, average incomes and consumer purchasing-power are liable to fall. As a result, the opposite problem of apparent oversupply is liable to arise for some commodities. CEECs which formerly exported agricultural produce to the USSR—especially Hungary and Poland—have practically lost this outlet as a result of the inability of Russia and other newly-independent States to finance imports, and as a result of the collapse of the trading system in the Council for Mutual Economic Co-operation.

In the CMEA, comparative advantage played little part in the allocation of productive tasks and in the evolution of trade. Prices bore no relationship to those of trade in the rest of the world. With the "transferable rouble", export earnings within the CMEA could not be used to finance hard-currency imports. Much trade was conducted on a barter basis. The integration of this whole region into the world trading system cannot be achieved overnight.

Some of these problems should be temporary, related to the initial stages of transition and to the general economic situation. Controlling inflation, stabilising the external value of the currency, liberalising foreign trade, restoring an economic and political climate favourable to recovery: all these are crucial conditions for reform of the agri-food sector as of all other sectors. The experience since the collapse of the former regimes has demonstrated the importance—and difficulty—of proper "sequencing": should economic reform be implemented all at once, with the risk of social hardship and upheaval, or gradually, with the risk of impetus being lost or even of the whole process being diverted? In this respect, the CEECs have followed different strategies.

This is not the place to discuss these macro-economic and political issues more fully, but the significance of interaction between economic sectors cannot be underestimated. While the agri-food sector needs general economic stability, the success of economic recovery depends on the provision of adequate food supplies.

Some guidance for the move to a market economy in the agri-food sector can be derived from the economic principles outlined in Part A of this book. The significance of the "*marginalist*" approach to supply and demand theory has been explained, and its implications for efficient allocation of resources.

It is not suggested that farmers, businessmen or government decision-makers in the West consciously base their actions on this particular approach. The theory, indeed, does not require this: it implies that, so long as market forces are permitted to operate in a competitive economy, the profit motive will bring about the result which the theory anticipates (Adam Smith's "invisible hand").

This leads to the concept of the "*economic optimum*", most precisely defined in the so-called "Pareto optimum": a hypothetical situation in which there is no change that will make someone better off without making someone else worse off. The technical definition has been set out in Chapter 5 and will not be repeated here. For practical purposes, it is sufficient to say that an economy should approximate to the optimum when all its component firms (or farms) employ resources and determine their output on a least-cost basis, and when buyers have full freedom of choice, without restriction of competition and without public interference in the pricing system.

Although this optimum cannot be measured in practice, and although in a dynamic economy it is constantly shifting with technological change, the concept can serve as a guideline. Supply and demand analysis based on the "marginalist" approach can identify existing distortions and indicate the direction and extent of the price adjustments needed to achieve more efficient allocation of productive resources. The "elasticity" concepts outlined in Part A are a useful tool, helping to estimate the effects of such adjustments.

While public intervention in markets always carries the risk of distortion, certain types of intervention are held to be justified by the theory of welfare economics. These relate especially to *"externalities"*, where the actions of firms or individuals give rise to costs or benefits for others: taxes or subsidies are then needed to restore a situation closer to the optimum. They also relate to *"market imperfections"*, when firms produce less and at a higher price than would be the case in the theoretical situation of "perfect competition": this indicates the need for public control to prevent restrictive practices and the emergence of monopolies.

Further, the economic optimum says nothing about *equity*. Social and political considerations may require a redistribution of benefits. A complex area of welfare economics is then involved. The general preference of economists is for redistribution to be achieved as far as possible through the systems of taxation and social security, and as little as possible through interference with the market mechanism. Thus, if price liberalisation seems likely to have very adverse effects on low-income consumers, income supplements to those in need are preferable to generalised food subsidies. If a general welfare safety-net is lacking, welfare food programmes, such as the US "Food Stamp" programme, can be considered. In any case, schemes such as subsidised school meals help to ensure adequate nutrition for a vulnerable sector of the population.

Part B of this book has demonstrated that, in agricultural policy, the Western market economies have departed from economic principles, and have encountered serious problems as a result. It has been pointed out that, while market stabilisation may be a justifiable aim, with buffer stocks and limited price support, such action can all too easily develop into market-distorting intervention. The aim of *stabilisation* becomes confused with that of *farm income support*—for which there may also be justification on equity grounds. The result has been overproduction, high budgetary costs, misallocation of productive resources and trade conflicts. But once established, support and protection are difficult to remove. The economist's preferred solution to farm income problems—direct income payments—has proved difficult to implement on a large scale.

The CEECs need to secure their food production, and price guarantees to farmers must play a role. In the transitional phase, consumer subsidies may need to be maintained. But with relatively weak economies and in some cases still a high dependency on agriculture, could not easily afford the economic and budgetary costs of high price support. If they raise food costs to consumers, they will raise their industrial production costs and erode their competitiveness. With public debts that are already large, there are urgent calls on their limited budgets for improving infrastructure, such as energy, transport and telecommunications. Several of the CEECs, moreover, have too much of their labour force in agriculture and need to promote a shift to other sectors, both to raise labour productivity in farming and to assist development elsewhere.

For those CEECs which aim to become members of the European Community, the choices in agricultural price policy are to some extent dictated by the need to adapt to the market organisation of the Common Agricultural Policy. As has been seen in Chapter 9, the CAP itself is changing, in the direction of lower market prices but with compensation to existing holdings (which will presumably not be available to new Member States); agreement under the GATT Uruguay Round will reinforce this tendency and possibly involve further liberalisation of imports and limitation of subsidised exports.

Finally, the prospects for agriculture in the CEECs, several of which have considerable export potential, are very dependent on market outlets. The agreements with the European Community, pending eventual membership in some cases, offer progressively improving access. Developments in the countries which have emerged from the break-up of the USSR also remain crucial for the other countries of the region; other export markets, particularly the Middle East, are gaining in importance.

(b) Farm structures and tenure

A second set of issues relates to the use and ownership of land and other farm assets. The collective farms and State farms which have occupied most of the farmland in the countries concerned (except Poland and parts of the former Yugoslavia, where many small private holdings remain), were in most cases inefficient, especially because of excessive size and lack of incentive to efficient management as well as to workers.

There is general agreement that the collectives and State farms must be privatised (except perhaps for those engaged in non-profit-making research and experimentation). There is less agreement as to what should be done with them. Should the land, and the other assets (buildings and equipment), be divided up among the former workers, or can some form of voluntary co-operation in production be maintained? In the latter case, what are the appropriate legal forms? What about the rights of those who owned the land *before* collectivisation? What ways can be found to distinguish between the *use* of the land and its *ownership*, so that the restoration of property rights does not lead to a fragmented farm structure with holdings too small to be viable? Does tenancy, as it is known in the West, provide an answer, or do other arrangements have to be devised? Can co-operatives continue to play a role in providing inputs to private farms, in hiring out machinery, in marketing?

In these respects, the solutions being worked out vary from country to country. Inevitably, conflicts of interest arise, and the process is a difficult one. Equity considerations, together with political realities, may dictate that land ownership should be restored to former owners. This is likely to result in an extremely fragmented structure, with consequential low efficiency and insufficient incomes—a problem with which Western European countries are confronted in some regions, partly as a result of land reforms in this century. The CEECs can avoid this problem by accompanying land redistribution with the creation and encouragement of land markets and a wide variety of forms of operation and tenure.

The West has been able to raise food output partly because it has given farmers the incentive to do so—in fact, too much incentive—through price support. As indicated above, the CEECs need to be cautious in this respect.

But the success in raising food output in the West is also attributable to the personal involvement of farmers, their families and to some extent farm workers. Economic considerations alone are not a sufficient explanation: a deep personal attachment to land, whether owned or tenanted, is a fundamental feature of Western agriculture. This strong sense of identity, and the control it provides over the management of the farm enterprise, gives the motivation to care for the land and to extract the best results from it. This motivation is precisely what has been lacking in socialised agriculture.

With their income dependent on their own efforts, private farmers have had the incentive to become as productive as possible, and the means to do so. They have been free to take their own planning decisions as to what to produce and how to produce it, and have achieved increased output with much less labour, substituting capital in various forms: more machinery, better buildings, better livestock, land improvements through drainage or irrigation, better use of fertiliser and other agro-chemicals. They have also been able to take the daily management decisions on which farming success also depends, such as when precisely to sow, cultivate and harvest—on-the-spot decisions, often dependent on the weather; in livestock farming they can give their animals individual attention. Many farmers have become increasingly skilled too in marketing their produce: adapting their produce to demand, and choosing the right time and place to sell.

Such skills have been developed, in some cases, through full-time education in agricultural colleges, often through participation in short-term training courses. They have been reinforced through the work of public advisory services, and of private consulting agencies: increasingly, management as well as technical knowledge is promoted through these channels.

The credit essential for farming operations is available through a variety of channels, including (as in the UK and the US) the general banking system, and in many other countries credit co-operatives, mostly of the "Raiffeisen" type (see Chapter 1). Local credit co-operatives invariably now form part of a nation-wide network. There are now few if any credit institutions specialising exclusively in agricultural operations: funds have to be sought outside agriculture, and some of the credit co- operatives which began in agriculture are now major national banks, in particular the *Rabobank* in the Netherlands and the *Crédit Agricole* in France.

Co-operation in marketing is also very important for some commodities, to an extent varying between countries. The contribution made by co-operative marketing to the development of livestock farming in Denmark has been particularly mentioned.

Thus the institutional framework plays an essential role. In the CEECs, new institutions have to be built practically from scratch.

As regards land tenure, it has been pointed out that most farms in Western Europe are owner-occupied. This is generally what farmers prefer: it gives them a feeling of security, and since land can be offered as collateral, it also makes it easier to get credit. There are countries—Ireland has been mentioned—where tenancy has a particularly bad reputation as a result of a past history of exploitation by landlords.

Objectively, however, tenancy has advantages. In the United Kingdom, for a long time, it played a constructive role, with landlords providing and maintaining buildings, farm roads and other fixed assets. In many countries, farms have expanded from an owner-occupied base by renting additional land. But it has proved difficult to maintain a balance of interests between landlords and tenants. The former need the assurance of an adequate return, and the possibility, in certain circumstances, of getting their land back: otherwise they have no interest in letting out land and the supply of it will dry up. Tenants need security—i.e. a sufficiently long lease; they need protection against excessive rent increases; at the end of a lease, they want compensation for improvements they have made or financed. In Chapter 1, it was suggested that Belgian tenancy law, particularly with improvements made in 1988, is a possible example in this field (Belgium has the higher percentage of land in tenancy of any West European country).

Other forms of tenure can be envisaged. It is doubtful whether any Western models can be simply transposed—they are usually too rooted in tradition. Still, Chapter 1 has also referred to some alternative forms, including company farms, partnerships and group farming. Among the latter, the GAEC in France appear the most successful recent development: from small beginnings in 1966, they have come to occupy about 11% of the farmland. Although they usually begin as just a father-son association, they can expand to take in other members (the legal maximum is ten). The members of a GAEC put together their land and capital, and share in the work. Other legal forms in France provide for non-active members to provide land (the GFA) or working capital (the EARL).

Such enterprises will only succeed if the individuals concerned take the initiative. But appropriate legal forms are also required.

(c) Agribusiness

Yet another urgent task is the creation of an efficient agribusiness sector. In the absence of competition within the country, and protected by import controls against any competition from abroad, State-owned food processing enterprises, like many other industrial activities, had little incentive to be efficient. They were wasteful, overmanned, lacking in innovation; their produce was often of poor quality and lacked variety; hygiene standards were often inadequate. The distribution system too was wasteful; prices fixed by central authority bore no relation to costs; supplies to State food shops were erratic; special distribution channels to factories and offices created further distortions; all along the chain, opportunities for favouritism and corruption were rife.

Demonopolisation is essential; the freedom to buy and sell on domestic and foreign markets are key elements permitting competition to operate and ensuring that costs are reduced. But in the CEECs, while the former agro-industrial complexes have broken down, the finance and managerial know-how needed to build a competitive agribusiness sector are lacking. In this vacuum, those who maintain some control can make quick profits at the public expense.

Since processing and distribution may account for a greater part of consumer expenditure on food than the farm-gate value, efficiency at these stages is vital. In the West, the dynamism of agribusiness has been a major factor in the success of the entire food system. Chapter 3 has suggested that, despite numerous mergers, competition—including international competition—remains a sufficiently powerful force to restrain restrictive practices and to keep down prices, both "upstream" from the farm sector (the supply of farm inputs such as machinery, fertiliser and seeds) and "downstream" (the marketing and processing of food from the farm gate to the consumer).

Public action is however needed to preserve competition against restrictive practices and monopolistic tendencies. This seems particularly important in the CEECs, as their industries, including the agribusiness sector, are vulnerable to take-over by large Western companies.

Efficient and transparent marketing is essential at all stages in the food chain. Solutions appropriate to each case need to be found. Reference has been made in Chapter 3 to some Western experience, in particular the case of France, where market channels have been substantially reformed in recent years. Many different elements need to be combined to permit efficient marketing: these include physical characteristics, such as transport, means of access and suitable buildings so that perishable produce can be moved quickly; grading and sorting of produce so that buyers know what they are getting; a communications network enabling market information to circulate quickly. The auction system enables supply and demand to be matched in an efficient and transparent way: the "Dutch auction" has been mentioned as suitable for fruit and vegetables in particular, permitting many lots to pass through the market in a short space of time.

*　　*　　*

The CEECs can learn from the experience of the Western market economies. They can avoid the pitfalls of excessive price support and protection; they can avoid creating a multitude of small, non-viable farms. On the other hand, observing the features responsible for the success of the Western agri-food system in the supply of ample food at affordable prices, they can through appropriate legislation and policies establish the conditions for the development of efficient and productive structures of production, marketing, processing and distribution. This is indeed vital for the success of their entire economic and political transformation.

ABBREVIATIONS AND ACRONYMS
(these may be used in the indexes which follow)

ACP—African, Caribbean and Pacific
AMS—Aggregate Measure of Support
ANSGAEC—Association Nationale des Sociétés et Groupements pour
l'Exploitation en Commun (France)
AWB—Australian Wheat Board
BEUC—Bureau Européen des Unions de Consommateurs
CAP—Common Agricultural Policy
CCC—Commodity Credit Corporation (US)
CEECs—Central and Eastern European countries
CFCE—Centre Français de Commerce Extérieur
CMEA—Council for Mutual Economic Assistance
CMO—Common Market Organisation
CNJA—Centre National des Jeunes Agriculteurs (France)
COGECA—Comité Général de la Coopération Agricole (EC)
COPA—Comité des Producteurs Agricoles (EC)
CRP—Conservation Reserve Program (US)
CSE—Consumer Subsidy Equivalent
CSFR—Czech and Slovak Federal Republic
CSF—Community Support Framework (EC)
CWB—Canadian Wheat Board
DBV—Deutscher Bauernverband
DDR—Deutsche Demokratische Republik
EAGGF—European Agricultural Guidance and Guarantee Fund (FEOGA in
French)
EARL—Exploitation Agricole à Responsabilité Limitée (France)
EC—European Community
ECU—European Currency Unit
EEA—European Economic Area
EEC—European Economic Community
EFTA—European Free Trade Association
EMS—European Monetary System
EP—European Parliament
ERM—Exchange Rate Mechanism (EC)
ESA—Environmentally Sensitive Area (EC)
ESU—European Size Unit
EUROSTAT—Statistical Office of the European Communities
FACT—Food, Agriculture, Conservation and Trade Act (US)
FADN—Farm Accountancy Data Network (RICA in French)
FEDESA—Fédération Européenne de la Santé Animale
FEFAC—Fédération Européenne des Fabricants des Aliments Composés
FEFANA—Fédération Européenne des Fabricants d'Adjuvants pour la
Nutrition Animale

FEOGA—Fonds Européen d'Orientation et de Garantie Agricoles
FNSEA—Fédération National des Syndicats d'Exploitants Agricoles (France)
FNSP—Fondation Nationale des Sciences Politiques (France)
FSA—Food Security Act (US)
GAEC—Groupement Agricole d'Exploitation en Commun (France)
GATT—General Agreement on Tariffs and Trade
GDP—Gross Domestic Product
GFA—Groupement Foncier Agricole (France)
GNP—Gross National Product
GSP—General System of Preferences
IAM—Institut Agronomique Méditerranéen (Montpellier)
IEEP—Institute for European Environmental Policy
IFA—International Fertilizer Industry Association
IIA—International Institute of Agriculture
INRA—Institut National de la Recherche Agronomique (France)
INSEE—Institut National de la Statistique et des Etudes Economiques
    (France)
LPG—Landwirtschaftliche Produktionsgenossenschaft (DDR)
MCA—Monetary Compensatory Amount (EC)
MGQ—Maximum Guaranteed Quanity (EC)
MMB—Milk Marketing Board (UK)
MMC—Monopolies and Mergers Commission (UK)
NAFTA—North American Free Trade Agreement
NFS—National Food Survey (UK)
NFU—National Farmers' Union (UK)
OBRA—Omnibus Budget Reconciliation Act (US)
OECD—Organisation for Economic Cooperation and Development
OEEC—Organisation for European Economic Cooperation
OJ—Official Journal (EC)
ONIC—Office National Interprofessionnel des Céréales (France)
PPP—Purchasing Power Parity
PSE—Producer Subsidy Equivalent
RICA—Réseau Intercommunautaire de Comptabilité Agricole (FADN in
    English)
SITC—Standard International Trade Classification
USDA—United States Department of Agriculture
VAT—Value-Added Tax
WWF—World Wildlife Fund
WRP—Wetlands Reserve Program (US)

INDEX OF AUTHORS

GENERAL INDEX

COMMON AGRICULTURAL POLICY